MATRIX THEORY

Prentice-Hall
Series in Applied Mathematics

MATRIX THEORY

Joel N. Franklin

PROFESSOR OF APPLIED MATHEMATICS
CALIFORNIA INSTITUTE OF TECHNOLOGY

Prentice-Hall, Inc., Englewood Cliffs, New Jersey

© 1968 by
PRENTICE-HALL, INC.
Englewood Cliffs, N.J.

Current Printing (last digit):

10 9 8

Library of Congress Catalog Card Number: 68-16345
Printed in the United States of America

PRENTICE-HALL INTERNATIONAL, INC., *London*
PRENTICE-HALL OF AUSTRALIA, PTY., LTD., *Sydney*
PRENTICE-HALL OF CANADA, LTD., *Toronto*
PRENTICE-HALL OF INDIA PRIVATE LTD., *New Delhi*
PRENTICE-HALL OF JAPAN, INC., *Tokyo*

PREFACE

The widespread applicability of high-speed digital computers has made it necessary for every modern engineer, mathematician, or scientist to have a knowledge of matrix theory. The connection between digital computation and matrices is almost obvious. Matrices represent *linear* transformations from a *finite* set of numbers to another finite set of numbers. Since many important problems are *linear*, and since digital computers with a finite memory manipulate only *finite* sets of numbers, the solution of linear problems by digital computation usually involves matrices.

This book developed from a course on matrix theory which I have given at Caltech since 1957. The course has been attended by graduate students, seniors, and juniors majoring in mathematics, economics, science, or engineering. The course was originally designed to be a preparation for courses in numerical analysis; but as the attendance increased through the years, I modified the syllabus to make it as useful as possible for the many different purposes of the students. In many fields—mathematical economics, quantum physics, geophysics, electrical network synthesis, crystallography, and structural engineering, to name a few—it has become increasingly popular to formulate and to solve problems in terms of matrices.

Ten years ago there were few texts on matrices; now there are many texts, with different points of view. This text is meant to meet many different needs. Because the book is mathematically rigorous, it can be used by students of pure and applied mathematics. Because it is oriented towards applications, it can be used by students of engineering, science, and the social sciences. Because it contains the basic preparation in matrix theory required for numerical analysis, it can be used by students whose main interest is their future use of computers.

The book begins with a concise presentation of the theory of determinants. There follows a presentation of classical linear algebra, and then there is an optional chapter on the use of matrices to solve systems of linear differential equations. Next is a presentation of the most commonly used diagonalizations or triangularizations of Hermitian and non-Hermitian matrices. The following chapter presents a proof of the difficult and important matrix theorem of Jordan. Then there is a chapter on the variational principles and perturbation theory of matrices, which are used in applications and in numerical analysis. The book ends with a long chapter on matrix numerical analysis. This last chapter is an introduction to the subject of linear computations, which is discussed in depth in the advanced treatises of Householder, Varga, Wilkinson, and others.

The book presents certain topics which are relatively new in basic texts on matrix theory. There are sections on vector and matrix norms, on the condition-number of a matrix, on positive and irreducible matrices, on the numerical identification of stable matrices, and on the QR method for computing eigenvalues.

A course on matrix theory lasting between one and two academic quarters could be based on selections from the first six chapters. A full-year course could cover the entire book.

The book assumes very little mathematical preparation. Except for the single section on the continuous dependence of eigenvalues on matrices, the book assumes only a knowledge of elementary algebra and calculus. The book begins with the most elementary results about determinants, and it proceeds gradually to cover the basic preparation in matrix theory which is necessary for every modern mathematician, engineer, or scientist.

I wish to thank Dr. George Forsythe and Dr. Richard Dean for reading parts of the manuscript and for suggesting the inclusion of certain special topics.

JOEL N. FRANKLIN

Pasadena, California

CONTENTS

NOTATION USED
IN THIS BOOK

Some authors denote vectors by boldface $(\mathbf{x}, \mathbf{y}, \mathbf{z})$, but we shall simply denote them by using lower-case English letters (x, y, z). If we wish to designate the components of a vector, x, we shall use subscripts; thus, $x_1, \ldots, x_n$ designates the components of x. Superscripts will be used to designate different vectors; thus, x^1, x^2, x^3 designates three vectors, and if there appears to be any chance of confusion with the powers of a scalar, we shall enclose the superscripts in parentheses—e.g., $x^{(1)}, x^{(2)}, x^{(3)}$. Thus, $x_1^{(2)}, \ldots, x_n^{(2)}$ designates the n components of the vector $x^{(2)}$, whereas $x_1^2, \ldots, x_n^2$ designates the squares of the n components of a vector x.

Matrices will be denoted by capital letters (A, B, C). Subscripts may be used to designate different matrices—e.g., $A_1, A_2, A_3, \ldots$ —but A, A^2, A^3 will designate different powers of the same square matrix, A. Thus,

$$A^2 = A \cdot A, \qquad A^3 = A \cdot A \cdot A, \qquad A^4 = A \cdot A \cdot A \cdot A, \ldots$$

A lower case Greek letter—e.g., λ, α, γ—will always designate an ordinary real or complex number. A Greek letter will never be used to designate a vector or a matrix. We will also occasionally use subscripted English letters—e.g., $c_1, \ldots, c_n$—to designate real or complex numbers. Subscripted English letters will *never* be used to designate vectors; thus, z_3 cannot designate a vector, although it may be used to designate the third component of a vector z.

For the columns of a matrix A we will often use the notation $a^{(1)}, \ldots, a^{(n)}$ or simply $a^1, \ldots, a^n$. For the components of a matrix A we will write a_{ij}. Sometimes we shall write

$$A = (a_{ij}) \qquad i = 1, \ldots, m$$
$$j = 1, \ldots, n$$

to indicate that A is the matrix

$$A = \begin{bmatrix} a_{11} & a_{12} & \cdots & a_{1n} \\ a_{21} & a_{22} & \cdots & a_{2n} \\ \cdot & \cdot & \cdots & \cdot \\ a_{m1} & a_{m2} & \cdots & a_{mn} \end{bmatrix}$$

If A has the same number, n, of rows and columns, we may write

$$A = (a_{ij}) \qquad i, j = 1, \ldots, n$$

The rows of a matrix are horizontal; the columns are vertical. Thus,

$$[a_{31}, \ldots, a_{3n}]$$

may be the third row of a matrix, whereas

$$\begin{bmatrix} a_{17} \\ \cdot \\ \cdot \\ \cdot \\ a_{m7} \end{bmatrix}$$

may be the seventh column. Since a column vector takes much space to print, we will sometimes refer to it by the prefix "col." Thus, the preceding vector may be written as col $(a_{17}, \ldots, a_{m7})$.

The superscripted letter e has a particular meaning throughout the book. The vector e^j is a column-vector with its jth component equal to 1 and with all other components equal to 0. Thus, if there are five components,

$$e^1 = \begin{bmatrix} 1 \\ 0 \\ 0 \\ 0 \\ 0 \end{bmatrix}, \quad e^2 = \begin{bmatrix} 0 \\ 1 \\ 0 \\ 0 \\ 0 \end{bmatrix}, \quad e^3 = \begin{bmatrix} 0 \\ 0 \\ 1 \\ 0 \\ 0 \end{bmatrix}, \quad e^4 = \begin{bmatrix} 0 \\ 0 \\ 0 \\ 1 \\ 0 \end{bmatrix}, \quad e^5 = \begin{bmatrix} 0 \\ 0 \\ 0 \\ 0 \\ 1 \end{bmatrix}$$

1 DETERMINANTS

1.1 INTRODUCTION

Suppose that we wish to solve the equations

$$2x_1 + 7x_2 = 4$$
$$3x_1 + 8x_2 = 5$$

(1)

To solve for x_1 we multiply the first equation by 8, multiply the second equation by 7, and subtract the resulting equations. This procedure gives

$$[(8 \cdot 2) - (7 \cdot 3)]x_1 = (8 \cdot 4) - (7 \cdot 5)$$

Thus, $x_1 = -3/-5 = \frac{3}{5}$. To find x_2, multiply the second equation by 2, the first equation by 3, and subtract. The result is

$$[(8 \cdot 2) - (7 \cdot 3)]x_2 = (2 \cdot 5) - (3 \cdot 4)$$

Thus $x_2 = -2/-5 = \frac{2}{5}$. To generalize these equations, write

$$a_{11}x_1 + a_{12}x_2 = b_1$$
$$a_{21}x_1 + a_{22}x_2 = b_2$$

In the example (1)

$$a_{11} = 2, \quad a_{12} = 7, \quad b_1 = 4$$
$$a_{21} = 3, \quad a_{22} = 8, \quad b_2 = 5$$

1

Solving for x_1 and x_2, we find

$$
\begin{aligned}
(a_{11}a_{22} - a_{12}a_{21})x_1 &= b_1 a_{22} - b_2 a_{12} \\
(a_{11}a_{22} - a_{12}a_{21})x_2 &= a_{11}b_2 - a_{21}b_1
\end{aligned}
\tag{2}
$$

If we introduce the notation

$$
ab - cd = \begin{vmatrix} a & d \\ c & b \end{vmatrix}
\tag{3}
$$

formula (2) yields

$$
x_1 = \frac{\begin{vmatrix} b_1 & a_{12} \\ b_2 & a_{22} \end{vmatrix}}{\begin{vmatrix} a_{11} & a_{12} \\ a_{21} & a_{22} \end{vmatrix}} = \frac{b_1 a_{22} - b_2 a_{12}}{a_{11}a_{22} - a_{21}a_{12}}
$$

$$
x_2 = \frac{\begin{vmatrix} a_{11} & b_1 \\ a_{21} & b_2 \end{vmatrix}}{\begin{vmatrix} a_{11} & a_{12} \\ a_{21} & a_{22} \end{vmatrix}} = \frac{a_{11}b_2 - a_{21}b_1}{a_{11}a_{22} - a_{21}a_{12}}
\tag{4}
$$

if the denominator in each fraction is not zero.

A rectangular collection of numbers is a matrix. Thus,

$$
\begin{bmatrix} a_{11} & a_{12} \\ a_{21} & a_{22} \end{bmatrix} \quad \text{and} \quad \begin{bmatrix} a_{11} & a_{12} & b_1 \\ a_{21} & a_{22} & b_2 \end{bmatrix}
\tag{5}
$$

are matrices. So is the number 17—a single number is a 1×1 matrix. Systems of linear equations are completely specified by the matrices containing their coefficients and by their right-hand sides. *A vector is a matrix with only one column or only one row.* Thus

$$
[a_{21}a_{22}] \quad \text{and} \quad \begin{bmatrix} x_1 \\ x_2 \end{bmatrix}
\tag{6}
$$

are vectors. The first is a *row vector*; the second, a *column vector*.

A determinant is a single number computed from a square matrix. We speak of "the determinant of a matrix," and in the next section, we shall define the determinant of an $n \times n$ matrix. For $n = 2$ we define

$$
\det \begin{bmatrix} a & d \\ c & b \end{bmatrix} = ab - cd = \begin{vmatrix} a & d \\ c & b \end{vmatrix}
\tag{7}
$$

For example, the collection of four coefficients

$$\begin{bmatrix} 2 & 7 \\ 3 & 8 \end{bmatrix}$$

from equations (1) is a *matrix* with a *determinant* that is the single number

$$\begin{vmatrix} 2 & 7 \\ 3 & 8 \end{vmatrix} = 16 - 21 = -5$$

As we saw in (4), determinants appear in the solution of linear equations.

1.2 THE DEFINITION OF A DETERMINANT

We wish to generalize our solution of two equations in two unknowns to n equations in n unknowns. For $n = 3$ write

$$a_{11}x_1 + a_{12}x_2 + a_{13}x_3 = b_1$$
$$a_{21}x_1 + a_{22}x_2 + a_{23}x_3 = b_2 \qquad (1)$$
$$a_{31}x_1 + a_{32}x_2 + a_{33}x_3 = b_3$$

If x_2 and x_3 are eliminated, we can obtain by a long computation the formula

$$\Delta x_1 = \Delta_1 \qquad (2)$$

where

$$\Delta = a_{11}a_{22}a_{33} + a_{13}a_{21}a_{32} + a_{12}a_{23}a_{31}$$
$$-a_{11}a_{23}a_{32} - a_{12}a_{21}a_{33} - a_{13}a_{22}a_{31} \qquad (3)$$

and where Δ_1 is found by substituting b_1, b_2, b_3, respectively, for a_{11}, a_{21}, a_{31} in the expression for Δ. A second enormous computation would yield

$$\Delta x_2 = \Delta_2 \qquad (4)$$

where Δ_2 is found by substituting b_1, b_2, b_3, respectively, for a_{12}, a_{22}, a_{32} in the expression for Δ. A third computation would give

$$\Delta x_3 = \Delta_3 \qquad (5)$$

where Δ_3 is found by substituting b_1, b_2, b_3, respectively, for a_{13}, a_{23}, a_{33}. In a later section these results will be proved and generalized. Here we only wish to motivate the definition of the determinant.

Every term in the expression for Δ has the form $a_{1j}a_{2k}a_{3l}$ where j, k, l is a permutation of 1, 2, 3. With each term there is a sign $\pm 1 = s(j, k, l)$, which we call the *sign of the permutation* j, k, l. Thus

$$s(1, 2, 3) = 1, \qquad s(3, 1, 2) = 1, \qquad s(2, 3, 1) = 1$$
$$s(1, 3, 2) = -1, \qquad s(2, 1, 3) = -1, \qquad s(3, 2, 1) = -1 \tag{6}$$

Evidently,

$$s(j, k, l) = 1 \qquad \text{if } (k - j)(l - j)(l - k) > 0$$
$$s(j, k, l) = -1 \qquad \text{if } (k - j)(l - j)(l - k) < 0 \tag{7}$$

Now (3) takes the form

$$\Delta = \sum_{(j, k, l)} s(j, k, l) a_{1j} a_{2k} a_{3l} \tag{8}$$

where the summation extends over all six permutations j, k, l.

For an $n \times n$ matrix $(a_{ij})(i, j = 1, \ldots, n)$ we define the determinant Δ as the sum of $n!$ terms

$$\Delta = \sum_{(j_1, \ldots, j_n)} s(j_1, \ldots, j_n) a_{1j_1} a_{2j_2} \ldots a_{nj_n} \tag{9}$$

The summation extends over all $n!$ permutations $j_1, \ldots, j_n$ of $1, \ldots, n$. The sign $s(j_1, \ldots, j_n)$ is defined as

$$s(j_1, \ldots, j_n) = \text{sign} \prod_{1 \leq p < q \leq n} (j_q - j_p) \tag{10}$$

In other words, $s = 1$ if the product of all $j_q - j_p$ for $q > p$ is positive; $s = -1$ if the product is negative.

For example, the determinant of a 5×5 matrix has 120 terms. One of the terms is $-a_{13}a_{25}a_{31}a_{42}a_{54}$. The minus sign appears because

$$s(3, 5, 1, 2, 4) = \text{sign} (5 - 3) \cdot (1 - 3)(1 - 5) \cdot (2 - 3)(2 - 5)(2 - 1) \cdot$$
$$(4 - 3)(4 - 5)(4 - 1)(4 - 2)$$
$$= (1) \cdot (-1)(-1) \cdot (-1)(-1)(1) \cdot (1)(-1)(1)(1) = -1$$

It should be emphasized that so far we have proved nothing. We merely have a definition (9) which we hope will be useful. For $n = 2$, the definition gives

$$\Delta = a_{11}a_{22} - a_{12}a_{21}$$

which is consistent with the definition given in the preceding section. For $n = 1$, we define $\Delta = a_{11}$, $\underline{s}(1) = 1$.

PROBLEMS

1. Verify formula (7) for the six permutations in formula (6).

2. In the expansion (9) of the determinant of a 7×7 matrix there will be a term $\pm a_{17}a_{26}a_{35}a_{44}a_{53}a_{62}a_{71}$. Is the sign plus or is it minus?

3. Consider the equations

$$x_1 - x_2 + x_3 = 2$$
$$2x_1 + x_2 - x_3 = 0$$
$$3x_1 + 2x_2 - x_3 = 4$$

Evaluate the determinants $\Delta, \Delta_1, \Delta_2, \Delta_3$ and solve for x_1, x_2, x_3 by formulas (2), (4), and (5).

1.3 PROPERTIES OF DETERMINANTS

The definitions (9) and (10) in the last section show that, to study determinants, we must study permutations.

Theorem 1. *If two numbers in the permutation* $j_1, \ldots, j_n$ *are interchanged, the sign of the permutation is reversed.* For example,

$$s(5, 1, 3, 2, 4) = -s(5, 4, 3, 2, 1)$$

Proof. Suppose that the two numbers are adjacent, say k and l, in the permutation $j_1, \ldots, k, l, \ldots, j_n$. When k and l are interchanged, the product $\prod (j_s - j_r)$ for $s > r$ is unchanged except that the single term $l - k$ becomes $k - l$. Therefore, the sign is reversed.

If k and l are not adjacent, let them be separated by m numbers. Move k to the right by m successive interchanges of adjacent numbers so that k is just to the left of l. Now move l to the left by $m + 1$ successive interchanges of adjacent numbers. The effect of these interchanges is simply to interchange k and l in the original permutation. Since the sign is reversed an odd number of times, namely $m + m + 1$ times, the sign is reversed when k and l are interchanged.

Theorem 2. *Let the permutation* $j_1, \ldots, j_n$ *be formed from* $1, 2, \ldots, n$ *by* t *successive interchanges of pairs of numbers. Then* $s(j_1, \ldots, j_n) = (-1)^t$.

Proof. According to the last theorem, the sign of the permutation $1, 2, \ldots, n$ is reversed t times as the permutation $j_1, \ldots, j_n$ is formed. The result follows because $s(1, 2, \ldots, n) = 1$. For example,

$$s(4, 3, 2, 1) = -s(1, 3, 2, 4) = s(1, 2, 3, 4) = +1$$

If t is even, the permutation $j_1, \ldots, j_n$ is called an *even permutation*; if t is odd, j is called an *odd permutation*. Since the sign of a permutation is uniquely defined, a permutation cannot be both even and odd. *The number of even permutations equals the number of odd permutations* $= n!/2$ if $n > 1$, since the even permutations $j_1, j_2, \ldots, j_n$ may be put into a one-to-one correspondence with the odd permutations by the single interchange of j_1 and j_2.

The *transpose of a matrix* is formed by interchanging corresponding rows and columns. Thus, if $A = (a_{ij})$, the component b_{ij} of A^T equals a_{ji}. For example,

$$\begin{bmatrix} 1 & 2 & 3 \\ 4 & 5 & 6 \end{bmatrix}^T = \begin{bmatrix} 1 & 4 \\ 2 & 5 \\ 3 & 6 \end{bmatrix}$$

Another example is

$$\begin{bmatrix} a_{11} & a_{12} \\ a_{21} & a_{22} \end{bmatrix}^T = \begin{bmatrix} a_{11} & a_{21} \\ a_{12} & a_{22} \end{bmatrix}$$

Theorem 3. *If* A *is a square matrix,* det A $=$ det A^T.

Proof. Let $B = (b_{ij}) = A^T = (a_{ji})$. By definition

$$\det B = \sum_{(j)} s(j) b_{1j_1} b_{2j_2} \ldots b_{nj_n}$$

where the summation extends over all $n!$ permutations, $j = j_1, \ldots, j_n$. Since $b_{ij} = a_{ji}$,

$$\det B = \sum_{(j)} s(j) a_{j_11} a_{j_22} \ldots a_{j_nn} \tag{1}$$

By rearranging the terms, we may write

$$a_{j_11} a_{j_22} \ldots a_{j_nn} = a_{1i_1} a_{2i_2} \ldots a_{ni_n} \tag{2}$$

For example, $a_{31} a_{12} a_{23} = a_{12} a_{23} a_{31}$. The rearrangement (2) establishes a one-to-one correspondence between permutations j and permutations i. Therefore, as j goes through all $n!$ permutations in the summation (1), i goes through all permutations. If a rearrangement from the left-hand side of (2) can be accomplished by t interchanges of pairs of a's, then the right-hand side can be rearranged by t interchanges to produce the left-hand side. Thus,

$$j_1, \ldots, j_n \rightarrow 1, \ldots, n \text{ by } t \text{ interchanges} \tag{3}$$

implies that

$$1, \ldots, n \leftarrow i_1, \ldots, i_n \text{ by } t \text{ interchanges}$$

Therefore, $s(j) = (-1)^t = s(i)$, and

$$\det B = \sum_{(i)} s(i) a_{1i_1} a_{2i_2} \ldots a_{ni_n} = \det A \qquad (4)$$

Theorem 4. *If two rows of a square matrix* A *are interchanged, the sign of the determinant is reversed. Or, if two columns are interchanged, the sign is reversed. For example,*

$$- \begin{vmatrix} 3 & 4 \\ 1 & 2 \end{vmatrix} = \begin{vmatrix} 1 & 2 \\ 3 & 4 \end{vmatrix} = - \begin{vmatrix} 2 & 1 \\ 4 & 3 \end{vmatrix}$$

Proof. Suppose that rows r and s are interchanged in the matrix A to produce a matrix B. Then

$$b_{rj} = a_{sj}, \qquad b_{sj} = a_{rj}, \qquad b_{ij} = a_{ij} \text{ if } i \neq r \text{ or } s \qquad (5)$$

By definition,

$$\det B = \sum_{(j)} s(j) b_{1j_1} \ldots b_{rj_r} \ldots b_{sj_s} \ldots b_{nj_n} \qquad (6)$$

Let k be the permutation produced from j by interchanging j_r and j_s. This interchange establishes a one-to-one correspondence between permutations j and k. The sign $s(k) = -s(j)$. Interchanging b_{rj_r} with b_{sj_s} gives

$$b_{1j_1} \ldots b_{rj_r} \ldots b_{sj_s} \ldots b_{nj_n} = a_{1k_1} \ldots a_{rk_r} \ldots a_{sk_s} \ldots a_{nk_n}$$

Therefore,

$$\det B = \sum_{(k)} - s(k) a_{1k_1} \ldots a_{rk_r} \ldots a_{sk_s} \ldots a_{nk_n} = -\det A$$

To establish the column-analog, we use Theorem 4. Let C be produced by interchanging two columns in A. Then C^T is produced by interchanging two rows in A^T. Therefore,

$$\det C = \det C^T = -\det A^T = -\det A \qquad (7)$$

Corollary. *If two rows, or two columns, of a square matrix are identical, the determinant is zero.*

Proof. If the two identical rows or columns are interchanged, the matrix is unaltered, but the determinant must change sign. Therefore, the determinant equals minus itself, and is thus equal to zero.

Theorem 5. *If a row or a column of a square matrix is multiplied by a constant, c, the determinant is multiplied by* c. For example,

$$\begin{vmatrix} .1 & 2 \\ .3 & 4 \end{vmatrix} = \frac{1}{10} \begin{vmatrix} 1 & 2 \\ 3 & 4 \end{vmatrix} = \begin{vmatrix} 1 & 2 \\ .3 & .4 \end{vmatrix}$$

Proof. Each term $a_{1j_1} \ldots a_{nj_n}$ in the expansion of det A contains exactly one component from each row. Therefore, if any one row is multiplied by c, the determinant is multiplied by c. Each term $a_{1j_1} \ldots a_{nj_n}$ contains exactly one term from each column. Therefore, if a column is multiplied by c, the determinant is multiplied by c.

Theorem 6. *If a multiple of one row (column) is subtracted from another row (column) of a matrix, the determinant is unchanged.* For example,

$$\begin{vmatrix} 1 & 2 \\ 0 & -2 \end{vmatrix} = \begin{vmatrix} 1 & 2 \\ 3 & 4 \end{vmatrix} = \begin{vmatrix} 1 & 0 \\ 3 & -2 \end{vmatrix}$$

Proof. By the transpose theorem, Theorem 3, we only need to prove the row part of Theorem 6. Let λ times row r be subtracted from row s. Then a_{sj_s} is replaced by $a_{sj_s} - \lambda a_{rj_s}$. For definiteness, assume that $r < s$. The new matrix has the determinant

$$\sum s(j) a_{1j_1} \ldots a_{rj_r} \ldots (a_{sj_s} - \lambda a_{rj_s}) \ldots a_{nj_n}$$
$$= \sum s(j) a_{1j_1} \ldots a_{rj_r} \ldots a_{sj_s} \ldots a_{nj_n}$$
$$- \lambda \sum s(j) a_{1j_1} \ldots a_{rj_r} \ldots a_{rj_s} \ldots a_{nj_n}$$

The first sum equals det A. The second sum is zero because it is the expansion of a determinant with identical rows r and s. This completes the proof.

Theorem 6 is used to evaluate determinants by reducing them to triangular form. For example,

$$\begin{vmatrix} 1 & 1 & 1 \\ 1 & 2 & 2 \\ 1 & 2 & 3 \end{vmatrix} = \begin{vmatrix} 1 & 1 & 1 \\ 0 & 1 & 1 \\ 0 & 1 & 2 \end{vmatrix} = \begin{vmatrix} 1 & 1 & 1 \\ 0 & 1 & 1 \\ 0 & 0 & 1 \end{vmatrix}$$

The last determinant equals 1 because of the following result:

Theorem 7. *If* $a_{ij} = 0$ *for* $i > j$, *then* det $A = a_{11} a_{22} \ldots a_{nn}$.

Proof. A term $s(j)a_{1j_1} \ldots a_{nj_n}$ in the expansion of det A can be nonzero only if $1 \leqslant j_1, 2 \leqslant j_2, \ldots, n \leqslant j_n$. But the only permutation j that satisfies all of these inequalities is $j = 1, 2, \ldots, n$. Therefore, det A equals the single term $a_{11}a_{22} \ldots a_{nn}$.

Theorem 8. *If* $a_{ij} = 0$ *for* $i < j$, *then* det $A = a_{11}a_{22} \ldots a_{nn}$.

Proof. det $A = $ det $A^T = a_{11}a_{22} \ldots a_{nn}$.

PROBLEMS

1. By applying Theorems 4 and 6, show that

$$\begin{vmatrix} 1 & 4 & 7 \\ 2 & 5 & 8 \\ 3 & 6 & 9 \end{vmatrix} = 0$$

2. Let A have the form

$$A = \begin{bmatrix} a_{11} & a_{12} & a_{13} & a_{14} & a_{15} \\ a_{21} & a_{22} & a_{23} & a_{24} & a_{25} \\ 0 & 0 & a_{33} & a_{34} & a_{35} \\ 0 & 0 & a_{43} & a_{44} & a_{45} \\ 0 & 0 & a_{53} & a_{54} & a_{55} \end{bmatrix} = \begin{bmatrix} A_1 & \ldots \\ \bigcirc & A_2 \end{bmatrix}$$

Show that

$$\det A = \begin{vmatrix} a_{11} & a_{12} \\ a_{21} & a_{22} \end{vmatrix} \cdot \begin{vmatrix} a_{33} & a_{34} & a_{35} \\ a_{43} & a_{44} & a_{45} \\ a_{53} & a_{54} & a_{55} \end{vmatrix} = \det A_1 \cdot \det A_2$$

Use an argument similar to the proof of Theorem 7.

3. Generalize the result of Problem 2. Let A be a *block*-triangular matrix

$$A = \begin{bmatrix} A_1 & \cdot & \ldots & \cdot \\ \bigcirc & A_2 & \ldots & \cdot \\ \cdot & \cdot & \ldots & \cdot \\ \bigcirc & \bigcirc & \ldots & A_p \end{bmatrix}$$

Show that

$$\det A = \det A_1 \cdot \det A_2 \cdots \det A_p$$

Can you prove this result by induction from the result of Problem 2?

4. Is it possible to rearrange the letters of the alphabet $a, b, \ldots, z$ in reverse order $z, y, \ldots, a$ by exactly 100 successive interchanges of pairs of letters?

1.4   ROW AND COLUMN EXPANSIONS

If A is a square matrix, we may regard det A as a function of the elements $a_{11}, a_{12}, \ldots, a_{1n}$ in the first row. Each term $a_{1j_1} a_{2j_2} \ldots a_{nj_n}$ contains exactly one element, a_{1j_1}, from the first row. Therefore, we may write the determinant as a linear combination

$$\det A = c_{11} a_{11} + c_{12} a_{12} + \cdots + c_{1n} a_{1n} \tag{1}$$

From the definition of det A we observe that

$$c_{1k} = \sum_k s(j) a_{2j_2} a_{3j_3} \ldots a_{nj_n} \tag{2}$$

where the summation $\sum_k$ is extended over all $(n-1)!$ permutations $j = j_1, j_2, \ldots, j_n$ with $j_1 = k$. Note that

$$s(j) = s(k, j_2, j_3, \ldots j_n) = (-1)^{k-1} s(j_2, j_3, \ldots, j_n) \tag{3}$$

where

$$s(j_2, j_3, \ldots, j_n) \equiv \text{sign} \prod_{p>q \geqslant 2} (j_p - j_q)$$

since the numbers $1, 2, \ldots, k-1$ appear to the right of k in the permutation $j = k, j_2, \ldots, j_n$. Therefore,

$$c_{1k} = (-1)^{k-1} \sum s(j_2, \ldots, j_n) a_{2j_2} a_{3j_3} \ldots a_{nj_n} \tag{4}$$

where the summation extends over all the $(n-1)!$ permutations $j_2, \ldots, j_n$ of the $n-1$ numbers $1, \ldots, k-1, k+1, \ldots, n$. Thus,

$$c_{1k} = (-1)^{k-1} \det A_{1k} \tag{5}$$

where A_{1k} is the $(n-1) \times (n-1)$ matrix formed by eliminating row 1 and column k from A.

Formulas (1) and (5) give the *expansion of* det A *by the first row*. For example,

$$\begin{vmatrix} 4 & 5 & 7 \\ -2 & 1 & 0 \\ 3 & 8 & 7 \end{vmatrix} = 4 \begin{vmatrix} 1 & 0 \\ 8 & 7 \end{vmatrix} - 5 \begin{vmatrix} -2 & 0 \\ 3 & 7 \end{vmatrix} + 7 \begin{vmatrix} -2 & 1 \\ 3 & 8 \end{vmatrix} \tag{6}$$

Suppose that we wish to expand the determinant (6) by the third row. We bring the third row to the top, without disturbing the order of the other rows, by interchanging rows 3 and 2 and then interchanging rows 2 and 1.

$$\begin{vmatrix} 4 & 5 & 7 \\ -2 & 1 & 0 \\ 3 & 8 & 7 \end{vmatrix} = - \begin{vmatrix} 4 & 5 & 7 \\ 3 & 8 & 7 \\ -2 & 1 & 0 \end{vmatrix} = (-1)^2 \begin{vmatrix} 3 & 8 & 7 \\ 4 & 5 & 7 \\ -2 & 1 & 0 \end{vmatrix} \tag{7}$$

We now expand by the first row to obtain

$$\begin{vmatrix} 4 & 5 & 7 \\ -2 & 1 & 0 \\ 3 & 8 & 7 \end{vmatrix} = 3 \cdot (-1)^0 \begin{vmatrix} 5 & 7 \\ 1 & 0 \end{vmatrix} + 8 \cdot (-1)^1 \begin{vmatrix} 4 & 7 \\ -2 & 0 \end{vmatrix} + 7 \cdot (-1)^2 \begin{vmatrix} 4 & 5 \\ -2 & 1 \end{vmatrix} \tag{8}$$

This illustrates the general result:

Theorem 1. *Let* $A = (a_{ij})$ *be an* $n \times n$ *matrix, where* $n \geqslant 2$. *Let* A_{ij} *be the* $(n-1) \times (n-1)$ *matrix formed by deleting row* i *and column* j *from* A. *Defining the cofactors*

$$c_{ij} \equiv (-1)^{i+j} \det A_{ij} \qquad (i,j = 1, \ldots, n) \tag{9}$$

we then have the expansion by row i:

$$\det A = c_{i1}a_{i1} + c_{i2}a_{i2} + \cdots + c_{in}a_{in} \tag{10}$$

and we have the expansion by column j:

$$\det A = c_{1j}a_{1j} + c_{2j}a_{2j} + \cdots + c_{nj}a_{nj} \tag{11}$$

Proof. We have already proved (9) for $i = 1$ in formulas (1) and (5). For $i > 1$ bring row i to the top by $i - 1$ successive interchanges of pairs of rows: i and $i - 1$, $i - 1$ and $i - 2, \ldots, 2$ and 1. Call the resulting matrix B. Because of the $i - 1$ interchanges,

$$\det A = (-1)^{i-1} \det B \tag{12}$$

Expand $\det B$ by its first row.

$$\det B = b_{11} \det B_{11} - b_{12} \det B_{12} + \cdots + (-)^{n-1} b_{1n} \det B_{1n} \tag{13}$$

Since $b_{1j} = a_{ij}$ and $B_{1j} = A_{ij}$, we have

$$\det B = a_{i1} \det A_{i1} - a_{i2} \det A_{i2} + \cdots + (-)^{n-1} a_{in} \det A_{in}$$

Therefore, by (12),

$$\det A = (-)^{i-1} \det B = \sum_{j=1}^{n} a_{ij}(-1)^{i-1}(-1)^{j-1} \det A_{ij}$$

This establishes the row expansion (10).

To establish the column expansion (11), let $R = A^T$. Expand R by row j:

$$\det R = \sum_{k=1}^{n} (-)^{j+k} r_{jk} \det R_{jk}$$

But $r_{jk} = a_{kj}$ and $R_{jk} = A_{kj}^T$. For example, if $n = 3$,

$$R_{13} = \begin{bmatrix} r_{21} & r_{22} \\ r_{31} & r_{32} \end{bmatrix} = \begin{bmatrix} a_{12} & a_{22} \\ a_{13} & a_{23} \end{bmatrix} = \begin{bmatrix} a_{12} & a_{13} \\ a_{22} & a_{23} \end{bmatrix}^T = A_{31}^T$$

Therefore, since $\det A = \det A^T$,

$$\det A = \det R = \sum_{k=1}^{n} (-)^{j+k} a_{kj} \det A_{kj}$$

This is the expansion by column j.

As an example of a row expansion, we shall evaluate *Vandermonde's determinant*:

$$V_n(x_1, \ldots, x_n) = \begin{vmatrix} 1 & x_1 & x_1^2 & \cdots & x_1^{n-1} \\ 1 & x_2 & x_2^2 & \cdots & x_2^{n-1} \\ . & . & . & \cdots & . \\ 1 & x_n & x_n^2 & \cdots & x_n^{n-1} \end{vmatrix} \tag{14}$$

If $x_i = x_j$ for some $i \neq j$, the determinant equals 0. Suppose that $x_1, \ldots, x_n$ are distinct. We regard V_n as a function of the variable $x \equiv x_n$, and we regard $x_1, \ldots, x_{n-1}$ as constants. Now V_n is a polynomial of degree $n-1$ in x, and V_n has the distinct roots $x = x_1, x = x_2, \ldots, x = x_{n-1}$. Therefore,

$$V_n = \alpha(x - x_1)(x - x_2) \ldots (x - x_{n-1}) \tag{15}$$

where α is independent of x. But α is the coefficient of $x^{n-1} \equiv x_n^{n-1}$. Expanding the determinant (14) by its last row, we see that α is the cofactor belonging to x_n^{n-1}. But this cofactor is the lower-order Vandermonde determinant,

$$\alpha = V_{n-1}(x_1, \ldots, x_{n-1}) \tag{16}$$

Direct computation for $n = 2$ gives

$$V_2(x_1, x_2) = x_2 - x_1$$

Now (15) gives

$$V_3 = V_2(x_1, x_2) \cdot (x - x_1)(x - x_2)$$
$$= (x_2 - x_1) \cdot (x_3 - x_1)(x_3 - x_2)$$

We conjecture

$$V_n(x_1, \ldots, x_n) = \prod_{i>j} (x_i - x_j) \qquad (17)$$

But if

$$V_{n-1}(x_1, \ldots, x_{n-1}) = \prod_{\substack{i>j \\ i \leqslant n-1}} (x_i - x_j)$$

then (15) gives

$$V_n(x_1, \ldots, x_n) = \left[\prod_{\substack{i>j \\ i \leqslant n-1}} (x_i - x_j) \right] \cdot \prod_{n>j}(x_n - x_j)$$

which establishes (17) by induction. The identity (17) is correct even if the x_i are not distinct because in that case both sides are zero.

PROBLEMS

1. Evaluate

$$\Delta = \begin{vmatrix} 1 & -2 & 3 \\ 2 & 0 & -1 \\ 7 & -5 & 2 \end{vmatrix}$$

by the three row expansions and by the three column expansions.

2. By certain simplifications, evaluate

$$\begin{vmatrix} 1 & 4 & 9 & 16 \\ 4 & 9 & 16 & 25 \\ 9 & 16 & 25 & 36 \\ 16 & 25 & 36 & 49 \end{vmatrix}$$

3. Give a simple expression for

$$\begin{vmatrix} a & a & a & a \\ a & b & b & b \\ a & b & c & c \\ a & b & c & d \end{vmatrix}$$

4. Give a simple expression for

$$\begin{vmatrix} 1 & a & a^2 & a^4 \\ 1 & b & b^2 & b^4 \\ 1 & c & c^2 & c^4 \\ 1 & d & d^2 & d^4 \end{vmatrix}$$

Note that this determinant, as a function of a, is a quartic polynomial with roots b, c, and d; and the coefficient of a^3 is zero.

1.5 VECTORS AND MATRICES

A set of m linear equations in n unknowns

$$\sum_{j=1}^{n} a_{ij}x_j = y_i \qquad (i = 1, \ldots, m) \tag{1}$$

may be represented in a compact form

$$Ax = y \tag{2}$$

Here A is the *matrix*

$$A = \begin{bmatrix} a_{11} & a_{12} & \cdots & a_{1n} \\ a_{21} & a_{22} & \cdots & a_{2n} \\ \cdot & \cdot & \cdots & \cdot \\ a_{m1} & a_{m2} & \cdots & a_{mn} \end{bmatrix}$$

and x and y are the *column vectors*

$$x = \begin{bmatrix} x_1 \\ \cdot \\ \cdot \\ \cdot \\ x_n \end{bmatrix}, \qquad y = \begin{bmatrix} y_1 \\ \cdot \\ \cdot \\ \cdot \\ y_m \end{bmatrix}$$

If A is fixed while x is allowed to vary over all column vectors with n components, the equation $Ax = y$ gives a *mapping* from the "space" X of all n-component vectors x into the "space" Y of all m-component vectors y. When we solve the linear equations (1) we find those "points" x in X which are mapped into a given "point" y in Y by the matrix A.

A mapping $Ax = y$ might be followed by another mapping, $By = z$, from Y into the space Z of p-component column-vectors z. Let B be the matrix

$$B = \begin{bmatrix} b_{11} & b_{12} & \cdots & b_{1m} \\ b_{21} & b_{22} & \cdots & b_{2m} \\ \cdot & \cdot & \cdots & \cdot \\ b_{p1} & b_{p2} & \cdots & b_{pm} \end{bmatrix}$$

The successive mappings $Ax = y$, $By = z$ map X into Z. Explicitly,

$$\sum_{j=1}^{n} a_{ij}x_j = y_i \quad (i = 1, \ldots, m), \qquad \sum_{j=1}^{m} b_{ij}y_j = z_i \quad (i = 1, \ldots, p) \tag{3}$$

yield

$$\sum_{k=1}^{m} b_{ik}\left(\sum_{j=1}^{n} a_{kj}x_j \right) = z_i \qquad (i = 1, \ldots, p) \tag{4}$$

or, equivalently,

$$\sum_{j=1}^{n} \left(\sum_{k=1}^{m} b_{ik} a_{kj} \right) x_j = z_i \qquad (i = 1, \ldots, p) \tag{5}$$

Therefore, the successive mappings $Ax = y$, $By = z$ yield a mapping $Cx = z$, where C is the $p \times n$ matrix

$$(c_{ij}) = \left(\sum_{k=1}^{m} b_{ik} a_{kj} \right) \qquad (i = 1, \ldots, p; j = 1, \ldots, n) \tag{6}$$

In this case we write

$$B(Ax) = (BA)x = Cx = z \tag{7}$$

The product BA *of the matrices* B *and* A *is defined as the matrix* C *with the components* (6).

Two matrices are called equal if their corresponding components are equal. As a rule, $BA \neq AB$. The product is not even defined unless the number of columns of the matrix on the left equals the number of rows of the matrix on the right. Thus, if

$$A = \begin{bmatrix} 1 & 2 & 3 \\ 4 & 5 & 6 \end{bmatrix} \quad \text{and} \quad B = \begin{bmatrix} 1 & 2 \\ 3 & 4 \end{bmatrix}$$

we have

$$BA = \begin{bmatrix} 9 & 12 & 15 \\ 19 & 26 & 33 \end{bmatrix}$$

but AB is undefined. If

$$A = \begin{bmatrix} 1 & 0 \\ 0 & 2 \end{bmatrix} \quad \text{and} \quad B = \begin{bmatrix} 1 & 2 \\ 3 & 4 \end{bmatrix}$$

we have

$$AB = \begin{bmatrix} 1 & 2 \\ 6 & 8 \end{bmatrix} \neq BA = \begin{bmatrix} 1 & 4 \\ 3 & 8 \end{bmatrix} \tag{8}$$

The inequality $AB \neq BA$ means that the transformation AB coming from B followed by A, is different from the transformation BA coming from A followed by B.

If $Ax = y$, $By = z$, and $Dz = w$ we may write

$$w = (DB)y = [(DB)A]x$$

or

$$w = Dz = D[(BA)x] = [D(BA)]x$$

Thus, the product of three matrices may be taken in either order:

$$DBA = (DB)A = D(BA) \tag{9}$$

The i, j component of DBA is the double sum

$$\sum_k \sum_l d_{ik} b_{kl} a_{lj}$$

The inequality $AB \neq BA$ states that *matrix multiplication is not commutative*. The equality $(DB)A = D(BA)$ states that *matrix multiplication is associative*.

Sometimes it is convenient to multiply every component of a vector x or a matrix A by the same number α. We then write

$$\alpha x = \alpha \begin{bmatrix} x_1 \\ \cdot \\ \cdot \\ \cdot \\ x_n \end{bmatrix} = \begin{bmatrix} \alpha x_1 \\ \cdot \\ \cdot \\ \cdot \\ \alpha x_n \end{bmatrix}$$

$$\alpha A = \alpha(a_{ij}) = (\alpha a_{ij}) \qquad (i = 1, \ldots, m; j = 1, \ldots, n)$$

Obviously, multiplication of a matrix or vector by a number is commutative. Thus, $\alpha ABx = A(\alpha B)x = AB(\alpha x)$.

PROBLEMS

1. Let A and B be the matrices

$$A = \begin{bmatrix} 1 \\ 2 \end{bmatrix}, \qquad B = [3, 4]$$

Form the products AB and BA.

2. Let

$$y_1 = 3x_1 + 2x_2$$
$$y_2 = x_1 + x_2$$

and let

$$z_1 = y_1 - 2y_2$$
$$z_2 = -y_1 + 3y_2$$

Express z_1 and z_2 in terms of x_1 and x_2. If $y = Ax$ and $z = By$, what is the product BA?

3. If $y = Ax$ for all x, and if $z = By$ for all y, we have shown that $z = Cx$ for all x, where C is defined in (6). Could there be another matrix, C', with this property? Suppose that $z = Cx = C'x$ for *all* x; show that $C = C'$. [Hint: Let x, successively, be the unit vectors column $(1, 0, \ldots, 0)$, column $(0, 1, 0, \ldots)$, $\ldots$, column $(0, 0, \ldots, 1)$.]

4. If $y = Ax$ can be solved for x in terms of y by a formula $x = A'y$, we call A' an *inverse* of A, and we write $A' = A^{-1}$. Compute an inverse A^{-1} for

$$A = \begin{bmatrix} 3 & 2 \\ 1 & 1 \end{bmatrix}$$

5. If A^{-1} is an inverse of A, and if B^{-1} is an inverse of B, what is an inverse for BA expressed as a matrix product?

6. Let A be an $m \times n$ matrix. Let $y = Ax$ for all x. Define the *row*-vectors $x' = (x_1, \ldots, x_n)$ and $y' = (y_1, \ldots, y_m)$, where x and y are the column-vectors with the same components. How can you construct an $n \times m$ matrix, A', such that $y' = x'A'$ for all x'? If

$$A = \begin{bmatrix} 1 & 2 & 3 \\ 4 & 5 & 6 \end{bmatrix}$$

what is A'?

7. Define A' as in the last problem. Express $(AB)'$ in terms of A' and B'

1.6 THE INVERSE MATRIX

Let a system of n equations in n unknowns be written in matrix-vector form: $Ax = b$. Define the $\text{n} \times \text{n}$ *identity matrix*

$$I = \begin{bmatrix} 1 & 0 & \cdots & 0 \\ 0 & 1 & \cdots & 0 \\ . & . & \cdots & . \\ 0 & 0 & \cdots & 1 \end{bmatrix} \tag{1}$$

as the matrix with ones on the main diagonal and zeros off the main diagonal. We can solve $Ax = b$ if we can find an $n \times n$ matrix B such that $AB = I$. A solution is $x = Bb$ because $Ax = A(Bb) = (AB)b = Ib = b$.

Theorem 1. *Let* A *be an* $\text{n} \times \text{n}$ *matrix, with* $\text{n} > 1$. *Let* A_{ij} *be the* $(\text{n} - 1) \times (\text{n} - 1)$ *matrix formed by deleting row* i *and column* j *from* A. *Define the cofactor matrix*

$$\text{cof } A = C = [(-1)^{i+j} \det A_{ij}] \qquad (i, j = 1, \ldots, n) \tag{2}$$

Let $\Delta = \det A$. *Then*

$$AC^T = C^T A = \Delta I \tag{3}$$

If $\Delta \neq 0$, *then* A *has an inverse matrix* $\text{B} = \Delta^{-1} \text{C}^{\text{T}}$ *satisfying*

$$AB = BA = I \tag{4}$$

EXAMPLE 1. Let

$$A = \begin{bmatrix} 1 & 2 \\ 3 & 6 \end{bmatrix}$$

Then

$$C = \begin{bmatrix} 6 & -3 \\ -2 & 1 \end{bmatrix}, \qquad C^T = \begin{bmatrix} 6 & -2 \\ -3 & 1 \end{bmatrix}, \qquad \Delta = 0$$

$$AC^T = C^T A = \begin{bmatrix} 0 & 0 \\ 0 & 0 \end{bmatrix} = \Delta \cdot \begin{bmatrix} 1 & 0 \\ 0 & 1 \end{bmatrix}$$

In this example, $\det A = 0$. We will show later that $\det A = 0$ implies that no matrix B exists such that either $AB = I$ or $BA = I$.

EXAMPLE 2. Let

$$A = \begin{bmatrix} 1 & 2 \\ 3 & 4 \end{bmatrix}$$

Then

$$C = \begin{bmatrix} 4 & -3 \\ -2 & 1 \end{bmatrix}, \quad C^T = \begin{bmatrix} 4 & -2 \\ -3 & 1 \end{bmatrix}, \quad \Delta = -2$$

$$AC^T = C^T A = \begin{bmatrix} -2 & 0 \\ 0 & -2 \end{bmatrix} = \Delta \begin{bmatrix} 1 & 0 \\ 0 & 1 \end{bmatrix}$$

Since $\Delta \neq 0$, we have

$$B = \Delta^{-1} C^T = \begin{bmatrix} -2 & 1 \\ 1.5 & -.5 \end{bmatrix}, \quad AB = BA = I = \begin{bmatrix} 1 & 0 \\ 0 & 1 \end{bmatrix}$$

Proof of Theorem 1. Since (4) follows by dividing (3) by the number Δ, we only need to prove (3). Let $D = AC^T$, $E = C^T A$. We wish to show that

$$d_{ij} = e_{ij} = \Delta \delta_{ij} \qquad (5)$$

where

$$\delta_{ij} = 1 \quad \text{if } i = j, \qquad \delta_{ij} = 0 \quad \text{if } i \neq j \qquad (6)$$

The symbol δ_{ij} defines the *Kronecker delta*; it is a useful abbreviation.

If $C = (c_{ij})$, then

$$d_{ii} = \sum_{k=1}^{n} a_{ik} c_{ik} \qquad (i = 1, \ldots, n)$$

But this is the sum (10) in Section 1.4 in the row-expansion theorem. Therefore, $d_{ii} = \Delta$ $(i = 1, \ldots, n)$. Similarly,

$$e_{ii} = \sum_{k=1}^{n} c_{ki} a_{ki} = \Delta \qquad (i = 1, \ldots, n)$$

by the column expansion (11) in Section 1.4. This proves (5) for $i = j$.

For $i \neq j$, we have

$$d_{ij} = \sum_{k=1}^{n} a_{ik} c_{jk} \qquad (7)$$

If a_{ik} were replaced by a_{jk} in (7), the sum would be the expansion of $\det A$ by row j. Let A' be the matrix formed by replacing row j of A by row i.

Thus, A' has identical rows i and j. Further, $c'_{jk} = c_{jk}$ because the cofactors of elements in row j are unaffected by modifications of row j. Expanding $\det A'$ by row j, we find

$$\det A' = \sum_{k=1}^{n} a'_{jk} c'_{jk} = \sum_{k=1}^{n} a_{ik} c_{jk} = d_{ij}$$

But $\det A' = 0$ because A' has two equal rows. Therefore, $d_{ij} = 0$ if $i \neq j$. Similarly,

$$e_{ij} = \sum_{k=1}^{n} c_{ki} a_{kj} \qquad (i \neq j)$$

is the expansion by column i of the determinant of the matrix A'' formed from A by replacing column i by column j. Since A'' has two equal columns, $\det A'' = e_{ij} = 0$. This completes the proof of the theorem.

Theorem 2. (Cramer's rule) *Let* $A = (a_{ij})$ *be an* $n \times n$ *matrix. Let* $\Delta = \det A \neq 0$. *Then the equations*

$$\sum_{j=1}^{n} a_{ij} x_j = b_i \qquad (i = 1, \ldots, n) \tag{8}$$

have the unique solution

$$x_j = \frac{\Delta j}{\Delta} \qquad (j = 1, \ldots, n) \tag{9}$$

where Δ_j *is the determinant of the matrix formed by replacing the jth column of* A *by the vector* b.

EXAMPLE. For $n = 2$ this rule states

$$x_1 = \frac{\begin{vmatrix} b_1 & a_{12} \\ b_2 & a_{22} \end{vmatrix}}{\begin{vmatrix} a_{11} & a_{12} \\ a_{21} & a_{22} \end{vmatrix}}, \qquad x_2 = \frac{\begin{vmatrix} a_{11} & b_1 \\ a_{21} & b_2 \end{vmatrix}}{\begin{vmatrix} a_{11} & a_{12} \\ a_{21} & a_{22} \end{vmatrix}}$$

Proof. Let the cofactor matrix C and the inverse matrix B be defined as in Theorem 1. The matrix form of (8) is $Ax = b$. Letting $x = Bb$, we see that $x = Bb$ is a solution because $AB = I$. Multiplying $Ax = b$ on the left by B, we see that $x = Bb$ is the only possible solution because $BA = I$. The jth component of $x = Bb$ is

$$x_j = \Delta^{-1} \sum_{i=1}^{n} c_{ij} b_i \tag{10}$$

But the sum in (10) is just the expansion of Δ_j by column j. Therefore, $x_j = \Delta^{-1} \Delta_j$.

PROBLEMS

1. Define

$$A = \begin{bmatrix} 1 & 2 \\ 3 & 7 \end{bmatrix} \quad \text{and} \quad B = \begin{bmatrix} 1 & 3 \\ 2 & 7 \end{bmatrix}$$

Compute A^{-1} and B^{-1}. Compute $(A + B)^{-1}$.

2. Solve

$$\begin{bmatrix} 1 & 2 \\ 3 & 7 \end{bmatrix} \begin{bmatrix} x_1 \\ x_2 \end{bmatrix} = \begin{bmatrix} 4 \\ 9 \end{bmatrix}$$

by multiplying the equation by the inverse matrix.

3. Solve the equation in the last problem by Cramer's rule.

4. Solve

$$\begin{bmatrix} 1 & 3 & 1 \\ 2 & 2 & 1 \\ 3 & 1 & 0 \end{bmatrix} \begin{bmatrix} x_1 \\ x_2 \\ x_3 \end{bmatrix} = \begin{bmatrix} 1 \\ 0 \\ 2 \end{bmatrix}$$

by Cramer's rule.

5. If $\det A \neq 0$, show that $(A^T)^{-1} = (A^{-1})^T$.

6.* Let A be an $n \times n$ matrix. Let $A^2 = A \cdot A$, $A^3 = A \cdot A \cdot A$, etc. Let λ be a complex number. Suppose that the series of matrices

$$S = I + \lambda A + \lambda^2 A^2 + \lambda^3 A^3 + \cdots$$

converges, i.e., that each of the n^2 components is a convergent series of complex numbers. Show that $S = (I - \lambda A)^{-1}$. Find a series for $(I - \lambda A)^{-2}$.

7. Let A be an $n \times n$ *triangular* matrix, with $a_{ij} = 0$ for $j > i$. Assuming all $a_{ii} \neq 0$, prove that A^{-1} is also a triangular matrix.

1.7 THE DETERMINANT OF A MATRIX PRODUCT

To show that the inverse of A exists and is unique *only* if $\det A \neq 0$ we shall use the following theorem:

Theorem 1. *Let* A *and* B *be* n × n *matrices. Then*

$$\det (AB) = (\det A)(\det B) \tag{1}$$

EXAMPLE. Let

$$A = \begin{bmatrix} 1 & 2 \\ 3 & 4 \end{bmatrix}, \qquad B = \begin{bmatrix} 2 & 3 \\ 4 & 1 \end{bmatrix}$$

Then $\det A = -2$, $\det B = -10$, so $(\det A)(\det B) = 20$. But

$$AB = \begin{bmatrix} 10 & 5 \\ 22 & 13 \end{bmatrix}, \qquad \det(AB) = 130 - 110 = 20$$

Proof of the Theorem. Let $P = AB$. We will show that $\det P = (\det A)(\det B)$. By definition,

$$\det P = \sum_{(j)} s(j) p_{1j_1} p_{2j_2} \ldots p_{nj_n} \tag{2}$$

But

$$p_{1j_1} = \sum_{k_1=1}^{n} a_{1k_1} b_{k_1 j_1}, \qquad p_{2j_2} = \sum_{k_2=1}^{n} a_{2k_2} b_{k_2 j_2} \ldots \tag{3}$$

Therefore,

$$\det P = \sum_{k_1=1}^{n} \ldots \sum_{k_n=1}^{n} a_{1k_1} \ldots a_{nk_n} \sum_{(j)} s(j) b_{k_1 j_1} \ldots b_{k_n j_n} \tag{4}$$

But the last sum equals a determinant:

$$\sum_{(j)} s(j) b_{k_1 j_1} \ldots b_{k_n j_n} = \begin{vmatrix} b_{k_1 1} & b_{k_1 2} & \cdots & b_{k_1 n} \\ b_{k_2 1} & b_{k_2 2} & \cdots & b_{k_2 n} \\ \cdot & \cdot & \cdots & \cdot \\ b_{k_n 1} & b_{k_n 2} & \cdots & b_{k_n n} \end{vmatrix} \tag{5}$$

This determinant is zero if $k_\alpha = k_\beta$ for any $\alpha \neq \beta$, for then it is the determinant of a matrix with identical rows α and β. In other words, the determinant (5) is zero unless $k_1, k_2, \ldots, k_n = $ a permutation, k, of the numbers $1, 2, \ldots, n$. Therefore, in the summation (4) we may eliminate all of the n^n combinations $k_1, \ldots, k_n$ except the $n!$ permutations k. Therefore,

$$\det P = \sum_{(k)} a_{1k_1} \ldots a_{nk_n} \sum_{(j)} s(j) b_{k_1 j_1} \ldots b_{k_n j_n} \tag{6}$$

The determinant (5) can be reduced to $\pm \det B$ if $k_1, \ldots, k_n$ is a permutation. Let k be reduced to $1, \ldots, n$ by t interchanges of pairs of numbers. If the corresponding pairs of rows are interchanged in (5), we find

$$\sum_{(j)} s(j) b_{k_1 j_1} \ldots b_{k_n j_n} = (-1)^t \det B \tag{7}$$

But $(-1)^t = s(k)$, the sign of the permutation k. Now (6) becomes

$$\det P = \sum_{(k)} a_{1k_1} \ldots a_{nk_n} s(k) \det B = (\det A)(\det B) \tag{8}$$

Theorem 2. *Let* A *be an* n × n *matrix. If det* A = 0, *then for some* b *the equation* Ax = b *has no solution* x. *Equivalently, if the equation* Ax = b *is solvable for every* b, *then det* A ≠ 0.

Proof. Let $e^1, e^2, \ldots, e^n$ be the columns of I:

$$e^1 = \begin{bmatrix} 1 \\ 0 \\ \cdot \\ \cdot \\ \cdot \\ 0 \end{bmatrix}, \quad e^2 = \begin{bmatrix} 0 \\ 1 \\ \cdot \\ \cdot \\ \cdot \\ 0 \end{bmatrix}, \quad \ldots, e^n = \begin{bmatrix} 0 \\ 0 \\ \cdot \\ \cdot \\ \cdot \\ 1 \end{bmatrix} \tag{9}$$

If every equation $Ax = b$ is solvable, then in particular the equations $Ax = e^1, \ldots, Ax = e^n$ have solutions $x = x^1, \ldots, x = x^n$. Let X be the $n \times n$ matrix with columns $x^1, \ldots, x^n$ (each x^j is an n-component column vector). Then

$$AX = A[x^1, \ldots, x^n] = [Ax^1, \ldots, Ax^n] = [e^1, \ldots, e^n] = I \tag{10}$$

Then, by Theorem 1,

$$1 = \det I = \det(AX) = (\det A)(\det X)$$

Therefore, the factor det A must be nonzero.

Theorem 3. *If* det A = 0, *no matrix* B *can be found for which either* AB = I *or* BA = I.

Proof. $I = AB$ implies $1 = \det(AB) = (\det A)(\det B)$, so that $\det A \neq 0$. Similarly, $I = BA$ implies $\det A \neq 0$.

Theorem 4. *If det* A = Δ ≠ 0, *define*

$$A^{-1} = \Delta^{-1}(\operatorname{cof} A)^T \tag{11}$$

Then AB = I *if and only if* B = A⁻¹. *Similarly,* BA = I *if and only if* B = A⁻¹. *Every equation* Ax = b *has the unique solution* x = A⁻¹b.

Proof. In the last section we proved that $A^{-1}A = AA^{-1} = I$. Conversely, suppose $AB = I$ for some matrix B. Multiply both sides by A^{-1} on the left; then

$$A^{-1}(AB) = A^{-1}(I) \quad \text{or} \quad IB = A^{-1} \quad \text{or} \quad B = A^{-1}$$

If $BA = I$, multiply both sides by A^{-1} on the right; then

$$(BA)A^{-1} = (I)A^{-1}, \quad \text{or} \quad BI = A^{-1}, \quad \text{or} \quad B = A^{-1}$$

A square matrix A is called *singular* if det $A = 0$; it is called *nonsingular* if det $A \neq 0$.

PROBLEMS

1. For the matrices

$$A = \begin{bmatrix} a & b \\ c & d \end{bmatrix}, \qquad B = \begin{bmatrix} \alpha & \beta \\ \gamma & \delta \end{bmatrix}$$

verify the identity det $(AB) = (\det A)(\det B)$.

2. The function $\phi(A) = \det A$ satisfies the relation $\phi(AB) = \phi(BA)$ even if $AB \neq BA$. Show that another function that satisfies this relation, is $\phi(A) = \text{trace } A \equiv \sum a_{ii}$.

3. Let A be a 3×2 matrix. Show that there is some vector $b = \text{col } (\beta_1, \beta_2, \beta_3)$ for which the equation $Ax = b$ is unsolvable. (Hint: Form a square matrix A' by adjoining a column of zeros to A, and note that the equation $Ax = b$ is equivalent to an equation $A'x' = b$, where det $A' = 0$.)

4. Generalize the preceding result. Let A be an $m \times n$ matrix with $m > n$. Show that some equation $Ax = b$ is unsolvable.

5. Assume that $m > n$. Let A be an $m \times n$ matrix, and let B be an $n \times m$ matrix. Show that det $(AB) = 0$ by proving that some equation $ABy = b$ has no solution. Use the result of Problem 4.

6.*Assume that $m < n$. Let A be an $m \times n$ matrix, and let B be an $n \times m$ matrix. Let $\alpha(k_1, k_2, \ldots, k_m)$ be the determinant formed from *columns* $k_1, k_2, \ldots, k_m$ of A. Let $\beta(k_1, k_2, \ldots, k_m)$ be the determinant formed from *rows* $k_1, k_2, \ldots, k_m$ of B. Using the method in the proof of Theorem 1, show that

$$\det (AB) = \sum_{k_1 < k_2 < \cdots < k_m} \alpha(k_1, \ldots, k_m)\, \beta(k_1, \ldots, k_m)$$

If $m = 2$ and $n = 3$, this identity becomes det $(AB) =$

$$\begin{vmatrix} a_{11} & a_{12} \\ a_{21} & a_{22} \end{vmatrix} \begin{vmatrix} b_{11} & b_{12} \\ b_{21} & b_{22} \end{vmatrix} + \begin{vmatrix} a_{11} & a_{13} \\ a_{21} & a_{23} \end{vmatrix} \begin{vmatrix} b_{11} & b_{12} \\ b_{31} & b_{32} \end{vmatrix} + \begin{vmatrix} a_{12} & a_{13} \\ a_{22} & a_{23} \end{vmatrix} \begin{vmatrix} b_{21} & b_{22} \\ b_{31} & b_{32} \end{vmatrix}$$

$$= \alpha(1, 2)\beta(1, 2) + \alpha(1, 3)\beta(1, 3) + \alpha(2, 3)\beta(2, 3)$$

1.8 THE DERIVATIVE OF A DETERMINANT

For certain problems in analysis we require the derivative $\Delta'(\lambda)$ of a determinant $\Delta(\lambda) = \det A(\lambda) = \det [a_{ij}(\lambda)]$.

Theorem 1. *Let* $a_{ij}(\lambda)$ *be differentiable functions of* $\lambda(i, j = 1, \ldots, n)$. *Then*

$$\left(\frac{d}{d\lambda}\right)\Delta(\lambda) = \sum_{k=1}^{n} \Delta_k(\lambda) \tag{1}$$

where $\Delta(\lambda) = \det [a_{ij}(\lambda)]$, *and where* $\Delta_k(\lambda)$ *is the determinant formed by replacing the kth row* $a_{kj}(\lambda)$ $(j = 1, \ldots, n)$ *by the row of derivatives* $a'_{kj}(\lambda)$ $(j = 1, \ldots, n)$.

EXAMPLE 1.

$$\frac{d}{d\lambda} \begin{vmatrix} \sin \lambda, & e^{-\lambda} \\ \lambda^2, & \log \lambda \end{vmatrix} = \begin{vmatrix} \cos \lambda, & -e^{-\lambda} \\ \lambda^2, & \log \lambda \end{vmatrix} + \begin{vmatrix} \sin \lambda, & e^{-\lambda} \\ 2\lambda, & \lambda^{-1} \end{vmatrix}$$

Proof of the Theorem. By definition

$$\Delta(\lambda) = \sum_{(j)} s(j) a_{1j_1} \ldots a_{kj_k} \ldots a_{nj_n} \tag{2}$$

From calculus we know that

$$\frac{d}{d\lambda} (a_{1j_1} \ldots a_{kj_k} \ldots a_{nj_n}) = \sum_{k=1}^{n} a_{1j_1} \ldots a'_{kj_k} \ldots a_{nj_n} \tag{3}$$

Now (2) becomes

$$\frac{d}{d\lambda} \Delta(\lambda) = \sum_{k=1}^{n} \sum_{(j)} s(j) a_{1j_1} \ldots a'_{kj_k} \ldots a_{nj_n} = \sum_{k=1}^{n} \Delta_k(\lambda) \tag{4}$$

EXAMPLE 2. Let $\Delta(\lambda) = \det (\lambda I - B)$, where B is an $n \times n$ matrix of constants $(n > 1)$, for example,

$$\det (\lambda I - B) = \begin{vmatrix} \lambda - b_{11} & -b_{12} & -b_{13} \\ -b_{21} & \lambda - b_{22} & -b_{23} \\ -b_{31} & -b_{32} & \lambda - b_{33} \end{vmatrix}$$

Then

$$\Delta_1(\lambda) = \begin{vmatrix} 1 & 0 & 0 \\ -b_{21} & \lambda - b_{22} & -b_{23} \\ -b_{31} & -b_{32} & \lambda - b_{33} \end{vmatrix}$$

$$= \begin{vmatrix} \lambda - b_{22}, & -b_{23} \\ -b_{32}, & \lambda - b_{33} \end{vmatrix} = \det (\lambda I - B_1)$$

where B_1 is formed from B by deleting row 1 and column 1. Similarly, $\Delta_k(\lambda) = \det (\lambda I - B_k)$, where B_k is formed from B by deleting row k and column k. The identity (1) now states

$$\frac{d}{d\lambda} \det (\lambda I - B) = \sum_{k=1}^{n} \det (\lambda I - B_k) \tag{5}$$

PROBLEMS

1. Differentiate the determinant

$$\begin{vmatrix} e^\lambda & 1 & \log \lambda \\ \cos \lambda & \lambda & \sin \lambda \\ e^{-\lambda} & \lambda^2 & \lambda^3 \end{vmatrix}$$

2. Let $A(\lambda)$ be an $n \times n$ matrix. Let $\delta_k(\lambda)$ be the determinant of the matrix formed by replacing the kth *column* of A by the column of derivatives. Prove that

$$\frac{d}{d\lambda} \det A(\lambda) = \sum_{k=1}^{n} \delta_k(\lambda)$$

3. Let $\phi_1(\lambda)$ and $\phi_2(\lambda)$ be different solutions of the differential equation $\phi''(\lambda) + a(\lambda)\phi'(\lambda) + b(\lambda)\phi(\lambda) = 0$. Define the *Wronskian*

$$\Delta(\lambda) = \begin{vmatrix} \phi_1(\lambda) & \phi_2(\lambda) \\ \phi_1'(\lambda) & \phi_2'(\lambda) \end{vmatrix}$$

Prove that

$$\Delta'(\lambda) = -a(\lambda)\Delta(\lambda)$$

4. Generalize the preceding result for linear differential equations of order n.

5. Let $A(\lambda)$ be a 2×2 matrix. Let $x(\lambda)$ be a vector satisfying the differential equation $x'(\lambda) = A(\lambda)x(\lambda)$, i.e.,

$$x_i'(\lambda) = a_{i1}(\lambda)x_1(\lambda) + a_{i2}(\lambda)x_2(\lambda) \qquad (i = 1, 2)$$

Let $y(\lambda)$ also satisfy $y'(\lambda) = A(\lambda)y(\lambda)$. Form the Wronskian

$$\Delta(\lambda) = \begin{vmatrix} x_1(\lambda) & y_1(\lambda) \\ x_2(\lambda) & y_2(\lambda) \end{vmatrix}$$

Prove that

$$\frac{d}{d\lambda}\Delta(\lambda) = [a_{11}(\lambda) + a_{22}(\lambda)]\Delta(\lambda)$$

6. Generalize the preceding result for the differential equation $x'(\lambda) = A(\lambda)x(\lambda)$, where A is an $n \times n$ matrix whose components are continuous functions of λ. Let $x^{(1)}(\lambda), \ldots, x^{(n)}(\lambda)$ be different solutions. Find a first-order differential equation for the Wronskian. By solving this differential equation, show that either the Wronskian is zero for all λ, or the Wronskian is never zero. This is an important result in the theory of differential equations.

2   THE THEORY OF LINEAR EQUATIONS

2.1   INTRODUCTION

In the last chapter we showed that a system $Ax = b$ of n equations in n unknowns has one and only one solution *if* det $A \neq 0$. If $b \neq 0$, the system is called *inhomogeneous*; if $b = 0$, the system is called *homogeneous*.

We have not discussed systems with more equations than unknowns.
We have not discussed systems with more unknowns than equations.

Most importantly, we have not discussed homogeneous systems $Ax = 0$ where A is an $n \times n$ matrix with det $A = 0$. As we shall see in Chapter 3, *homogeneous linear systems of equations characterize the solutions of linear systems of differential equations with constant coefficients*. Homogeneous systems $Ax = 0$ thus play a fundamental role in engineering and science.

To discuss homogeneous systems and general inhomogeneous systems we need the powerful concepts of *linear vector space* and of *rank*. Although abstract, these concepts are not difficult.

2.2   LINEAR VECTOR SPACES

We want to define a *linear vector space* L *over a field* F *of scalars*. First we shall give four useful instances of *fields* and then the general definition of a *field*.

The *real numbers* constitute a field. These are all the positive and negative numbers and zero, e.g., 0, -1.3, $\sqrt{2}$, $-\pi$.

The *rational numbers* constitute a field. These are zero and the quotients of nonzero integers, e.g., 0, $-4/5$, $194/13$, 65, $-224/95$.

The *complex numbers* $\rho + i\sigma$ (ρ and σ real) constitute a field.

The two *numbers* 0, 1 *operating modulo* 2 constitute a field. Here we define

$$0 + 0 = 0, \quad 0 + 1 = 1, \quad 1 + 1 = 0; \quad 0 \cdot 0 = 0, \quad 0 \cdot 1 = 0, \quad 1 \cdot 1 = 1$$

This field is used in the theory of electronic communication.*

A *field*, F, is defined to be a set of elements for which there are operations $+$ and $\cdot$ defined with these properties:

For every α and β in F, there is an element $\alpha + \beta$ in F. The operation $+$ must satisfy these laws:

(i) $\alpha + \beta = \beta + \alpha$ (commutativity)
(ii) $(\alpha + \beta) + \gamma = \alpha + (\beta + \gamma)$ (associativity)
(iii) There exists a unique element 0 in F such that $\alpha + 0 = \alpha$ for all α in F.
(iv) For every α there is a unique element $-\alpha$ such that $\alpha + (-\alpha) = 0$

For every α and β in F there is an element $\alpha \cdot \beta$ in F. The operation $\cdot$ must satisfy these laws:

(i) $\alpha \cdot \beta = \beta \cdot \alpha$ (commutativity)
(ii) $(\alpha \cdot \beta) \cdot \gamma = \alpha \cdot (\beta \cdot \gamma)$ (associativity)
(iii) There exists a unique element 1 in F such that $\alpha \cdot 1 = \alpha$ for all α in F.
(iv) For every α *except* 0 there is a unique inverse α^{-1} such that $\alpha \cdot \alpha^{-1} = 1$.

The two operations are connected by the distributive law:

(v) $(\alpha + \beta) \cdot \gamma = \alpha \cdot \gamma + \beta \cdot \gamma$

These laws are familiar to the reader for the real numbers, for the rational numbers, and for the complex numbers. But the student unfamiliar with abstract algebra should now painstakingly verify each of these laws for the field consisting of 0, 1 operating modulo 2.

We can now define a *linear vector space* L over a field F. We shall use the terms linear vector space, linear space, and vector space with the same meaning. The elements of the field F are called *scalars* with respect to L. For every two elements, x and y, called "vectors" in L, there is a sum $x + y$ in L. (Vector addition $x + y$ must not be confused with scalar addition $\alpha + \beta$ for elements α, β of the field F.) Vector addition is required to

---

*See *Digital Communication with Space Applications* by S. W. Golomb, L. D. Baumert, M. F. Easterling, J. J. Stiffler, and A. J. Viterbi. Englewood Cliffs, N.J.: Prentice-Hall, Inc., 1964.

satisfy these laws:

    (i) $x + y = y + x$ (commutativity)

    (ii) $(x + y) + z = x + (y + z)$ (associativity)

   (iii) There exists a unique vector **0** in L (not to be confused with the scalar 0) such that $x + \mathbf{0} = x$ for all x in L.

   (iv) For every vector x there is a unique vector $-x$ such that $x + (-x) = \mathbf{0}$

For every α in F and every x in L there is supposed to be a vector αx in L. We require

    (v) $\alpha(\beta x) = (\alpha\beta)x$ (associativity)

         for all scalars α, β and vectors x

   (vi) $1x = x$,

         where 1 is the unit scalar, for all vectors x

  (vii) $\alpha(x + y) = \alpha x + \alpha y$ (distributivity)

         for α in F; x and y in L

 (viii) $(\alpha + \beta)x = \alpha x + \beta x$ (distributivity)

         for α, β in F; x in L

EXAMPLE 1. The set of row vectors

$$a = (\alpha_1, \alpha_2, \alpha_3, \alpha_4, \alpha_5)$$

with *real* components $\alpha_1, \ldots, \alpha_5$ is a linear vector space over the field of *real* numbers. Here we define

$$\alpha a = (\alpha\alpha_1, \ldots, \alpha\alpha_5), \quad a + b = (\alpha_1 + \beta_1, \ldots, \alpha_5 + \beta_5)$$

EXAMPLE 2. The set of row vectors

$$a = (\alpha_1, \alpha_2, \alpha_3, \alpha_4, \alpha_5)$$

with *complex* components $\alpha_1, \ldots, \alpha_5$ is a linear vector space over the field of *complex* numbers.

EXAMPLE 3. Consider the set Q of polynomials

$$x = \alpha_0 + \alpha_1\omega + \alpha_2\omega^2$$

in a *variable* ω, where the coefficients $\alpha_0, \alpha_1, \alpha_2$ lie in any field F, e.g., the field of real numbers. We call the zero element **0** of Q the polynomial with $\alpha_0 = \alpha_1 = \alpha_2 = 0$. Thus, $\omega^2 - 4 \neq \mathbf{0}$ (the zero polynomial) even though we do have $\omega^2 - 4 = 0$ (zero element of the field) when the variable ω is replaced by ± 2. The set Q is a linear vector space if we define

$$(\alpha_0 + \alpha_1\omega + \alpha_2\omega^2) + (\beta_0 + \beta_1\omega + \beta_2\omega^2)$$
$$= (\alpha_0 + \beta_0) + (\alpha_1 + \beta_1)\omega + (\alpha_2 + \beta_2)\omega^2$$

and define

$$\alpha(\alpha_0 + \alpha_1\omega + \alpha_2\omega^2) = (\alpha\alpha_0) + (\alpha\alpha_1)\omega + (\alpha\alpha_2)\omega^2$$

EXAMPLE 4. Let F be the field consisting of 0 and 1 operating modulo 2. Let L be the set of formal power series

$$\alpha_0 + \alpha_1\omega + \alpha_2\omega^2 + \alpha_3\omega^3 + \cdots$$

where $\alpha_0, \alpha_1, \ldots$ lie in F. The set L is a linear vector space under the obvious operations. For example,

$$(1 + \omega^3 + \omega^6 + \omega^9 + \cdots) + (1 + \omega^2 + \omega^4 + \omega^6 + \omega^8 + \omega^{10} + \cdots)$$
$$= \omega^2 + \omega^3 + \omega^4 + \omega^8 + \omega^9 + \omega^{10} + \cdots$$

EXAMPLE 5. Let F be the field of complex numbers. Let $\alpha_0, \alpha_1, \alpha_2$ be in F. Consider the set of polynomials

$$\alpha_0 + \alpha_1\omega + \alpha_2\omega^2 \qquad (\alpha_2 \neq 0)$$

of *exact* degree 2. These polynomials do *not* constitute a linear vector space. Why not?

EXAMPLE 6. Let $\alpha_0, \alpha_1, \ldots, \beta_1, \beta_2, \ldots$ be real. Let $\sum |\alpha_\nu| < \infty$ and $\sum |\beta_\nu| < \infty$. The set of functions of t:

$$x = \alpha_0 + \sum_{\nu=1}^{\infty} (\alpha_\nu \cos \nu t + \beta_\nu \sin \nu t) \qquad (0 \leqslant t < 2\pi)$$

constitutes a linear vector space. What is the element $x(t) = \mathbf{0}$ in this vector space?

EXAMPLE 7. Let N be fixed. Let γ_n be complex numbers ($n = 0, \pm 1, \ldots, \pm N$). The set of functions

$$x = \sum_{n=-N}^{N} \gamma_n e^{int}$$

is a linear vector space over the field of complex numbers.

EXAMPLE 8. Consider all real-valued solutions $x = \phi(t)$ of the linear, homogeneous differential equation

$$\phi^{(4)} + (t^2 + 1)\phi^{(3)} + (\sin t)\phi^{(2)} + e^t\phi' + \phi = 0$$

The zero element $x = \mathbf{0}$ is the trivial solution $\phi(t) \equiv 0$. The set of elements x is a linear vector space over the field of real numbers. Thus, if $\phi_1(t)$ and $\phi_2(t)$ are solutions, another solution is $-7.4\phi_1(t) + \pi\phi_2(t)$.

EXAMPLE 9. Consider the set L of column-vectors

$$x = \begin{bmatrix} x_1 \\ x_2 \end{bmatrix}$$

where x_1 and x_2 are real numbers satisfying the constraint $3x_1 + 4x_2 = 0$. The set L is a linear vector space over the field of real numbers. Note that if x and y both satisfy the constraint, so does the sum $x + y$.

$$3(x_1 + y_1) + 4(x_2 + y_2) = 0$$

Observe the graph of L in Figure 2.1. In a sense which we shall later make precise, the set L is *one*-dimensional. But every member x in L is represented by *two* components, x_1 and x_2. Thus, *the number of parameters used to represent a vector space does NOT necessarily equal the dimension of the space.*

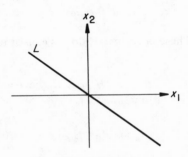

Figure 2.1

EXAMPLE 10. Let A be an $m \times n$ matrix of complex numbers. Let x range over all vectors with n complex components $x_1, \ldots, x_n$. Let L be the set of all vectors y of the form $y = Ax$. Then L is a linear vector space over the field of complex numbers. For example, if

$$A = \begin{bmatrix} 1, & 3 + i, & 8 \\ i, & -1 + 3i, & 8i \end{bmatrix} \tag{9}$$

then L is the set of vectors y of the form

$$
\begin{aligned}
y_1 &= x_1 + (3 + i)x_2 + 8x_3 \\
y_2 &= ix_1 + (-1 + 3i)x_2 + 8ix_3
\end{aligned}
\tag{10}
$$

for some complex x_1, x_2, and x_3. Can you show that L is just the space of vectors $y = \mathrm{col}\,(y_1, y_2)$ satisfying the constraint $y_2 = iy_1$?

EXAMPLE 11. Let A be an $m \times n$ matrix of real numbers. Let L be the set of vectors x with n real components $x_1, \ldots, x_n$ for which $Ax = 0$. The set L is a linear vector space over the real numbers α. Note that $Ax = 0$ and $Ay = 0$ imply that $A(\alpha x + \beta y) = 0$.

EXAMPLE 12. Let A be an $m \times n$ matrix of real numbers, and let b be a column-vector with m real components. Consider the set S of *all* solutions x of the equation $Ax = b$. Unless $b = 0$, the set S is *not* a linear vector space because S does not contain the vector $x = \mathbf{0}$. But suppose that $Ax = b$ has at least one solution, say $x = x^0$. Then for all other solutions x, we have

$$A(x - x^0) = 0 \tag{11}$$

Therefore, x − x⁰ *lies in the linear vector space* L *of all solutions* y *of the homogeneous equation* Ay = 0. For instance, the solutions x of

$$\begin{bmatrix} 1 & 2 & 3 \\ 4 & 5 & 6 \end{bmatrix} \begin{bmatrix} x_1 \\ x_2 \\ x_3 \end{bmatrix} = \begin{bmatrix} 6 \\ 15 \end{bmatrix} \tag{12}$$

are the vectors

$$x = \begin{bmatrix} 1 \\ 1 \\ 1 \end{bmatrix} + \begin{bmatrix} y_1 \\ y_2 \\ y_3 \end{bmatrix} \tag{13}$$

where

$$y_1 + 2y_2 + 3y_3 = 0 \quad \text{and} \quad 4y_1 + 5y_2 + 6y_3 = 0 \tag{14}$$

EXAMPLE 13. Let L be the vector space of column vectors x with real components $x_1, \ldots, x_6$. Let L_1 consist of the vectors in L for which $x_3 - 9x_5 = 0$. Let L_2 consist of the vectors in L_1 for which $x_1 + x_2 + x_6 = 0$. The space L_1 is a *subspace* of L. The space L_2 is a subspace of L_1, and L_2 is also a subspace of L. We also speak of L as a subspace of itself.

In this book we shall study only linear spaces, L, that are subspaces of vectors written in the form

$$x = \begin{bmatrix} x_1 \\ x_2 \\ \cdot \\ \cdot \\ \cdot \\ x_n \end{bmatrix} \tag{15}$$

The only fields that we shall use are the field R of real numbers and the field C of complex numbers. If the components $x_1, \ldots, x_n$ range over all complex numbers, the vectors (15) comprise the vector space $E^n(C)$ over the field C. If the components $x_1, \ldots, x_n$ range over all real numbers, the vectors (15) comprise the vector space $E^n(R)$ over the field R.

When no misunderstanding can occur, we shall simply refer to E^n as *the Euclidean space of n-component column-vectors* x. Properly, E^n should designate *either* $E^n(R)$ *or* $E^n(C)$. If the components $x_1, \ldots, x_n$ are restricted to being real, then the scalars α must also be real, and E^n designates $E^n(R)$. If the components $x_1, \ldots, x_n$ may be complex, then the scalars α are also allowed to be complex, and E^n denotes $E^n(C)$.

The problems illustrate that all "finite-dimensional" vector spaces can be represented, with no loss of information, by coordinate-vectors (15). (The term *finite dimensional* will be defined in Section 2.3). Problem 12 illustrates that linear operations on finite-dimensional vector spaces can always be represented by *matrices*. The study of linear vector spaces defined over fields different from R and C belongs to abstract algebra. The study of linear vector spaces of infinite dimension, illustrated in Examples 4 and 6, belongs to *functional analysis*.

PROBLEMS

1.* Show that there is no number α in the field of rational numbers, for which $\alpha \cdot \alpha = 2$. [Hint: Let $\alpha = p/q$, where p and q are integers with no common divisor. From the equation $p^2 = 2q^2$ deduce that p and q must both be even. Contradiction!)

2. Let V be the set of quantities (x_1, x_2), where x_1 and x_2 are any *complex* numbers. Let F be the field R of *real* numbers. Can V be defined as a linear vector space over R?

3. Let W be the set of quantities (x_1, x_2), where x_1 and x_2 are any *real* numbers. Is W a linear vector space over the field C of complex numbers?

4. Show that the linear space of vectors y satisfying (14) constitutes the line

$$ y = \alpha \begin{bmatrix} 1 \\ -2 \\ 1 \end{bmatrix} \quad (\alpha = \text{any scalar}) $$

5. Let S consist of all solutions of the inhomogeneous differential equation $\phi''(t) + \phi(t) = 1 + t^2$. Is S a linear vector space? One solution of the equation is $x^0 = t^2 - 1$. If $\phi(t)$ is any solution, write $\phi(t) = t^2 - 1 + \psi(t)$. What can you say about the functions $\psi(t)$? (This is an analogy of Example 12.)

6. Show that the set of $m \times n$ matrices A, with components in any field F, is a linear *vector* space over the field F. If F' is a *sub*field of F, are the matrices A a vector space over F'?

Let F be a field. Let X and Y be different linear vector spaces defined over F. We speak of the spaces X and Y as *isomorphic* (having the same form) if there is a one-to-one correspondence $x \sim y$ such that

$$x \sim y \text{ implies } \alpha x \sim \alpha y \qquad \text{for all } \alpha \text{ in } F$$
$$x_1 \sim y_1 \quad \text{and} \quad x_2 \sim y_2 \text{ imply } x_1 + x_2 \sim y_1 + y_2$$

7. Consider the linear space X of all real solutions $\alpha \cos t + \beta \sin t$ of the differential equation $\phi'' + \phi = 0$. Show that X is *isomorphic* to the space Y of real vectors (α, β).

8. Show that the space X of functions

$$x = \sum_{n=-N}^{N} \gamma_n e^{int} \qquad (0 \leqslant t < 2\pi)$$

is isomorphic to the space Y of vectors

$$y = (\gamma_{-N}, \gamma_{-N+1}, \ldots, \gamma_{-1}, \gamma_0, \ldots, \gamma_N)$$

9. Show that the correspondence

$$\alpha_0 + \alpha_1 \omega + \alpha_2 \omega^2 + \alpha_3(\omega^2 - 1) \sim (\alpha_0, \alpha_1, \alpha_2, \alpha_3)$$

is *not* an isomorphism. (Is this correspondence one-to-one?)

10. Show that the correspondence

$$\alpha_0 + \alpha_1 \omega + \alpha_2 \omega^2 \sim (\alpha_0, \alpha_1, \alpha_2)$$

where $\alpha_0, \alpha_1, \alpha_2$ are any real numbers, establishes an isomorphism.

11.* Generalize Problems 7–10 for abstract linear vector spaces X consisting of all linear combinations

$$x = x_1 b^{(1)} + \cdots + x_n b^{(n)}$$

of certain basic vectors $b^{(1)}, \ldots, b^{(n)}$. Assume $x_1, \ldots, x_n$ range over some field F.

12.* Let D be the differential operator operating on polynomials $\phi(\omega) = \alpha_0 + \alpha_1 \omega + \cdots + \alpha_5 \omega^5$ of degree $\leqslant 5$. Thus, $D\phi(\omega) = \alpha_1 + 2\alpha_2 \omega + 3\alpha_3 \omega^2 + 4\alpha_4 \omega^3 + 5\alpha_5 \omega^4$. Show that D is a *linear operator*, satisfying

$$D(\alpha\phi(\omega) + \beta\psi(\omega)) = \alpha D\phi(\omega) + \beta D\psi(\omega)$$

Establish the isomorphism

$$\alpha_0 + \alpha_1 \omega + \cdots + \alpha_5 \omega^5 \sim \text{col}\,(\alpha_0, \alpha_1, \ldots, \alpha_5)$$

of the space X of functions ϕ and the space Y of column vectors $y = \text{col}\,(\alpha_0, \ldots, \alpha_5)$. Show that the linear operator D on X can be *represented* by a 6×6 matrix A operating on Y. In other words, find a 6×6 matrix A such that, if $\phi(\omega) \sim y$, then $D\phi(\omega) \sim Ay$.

2.3 BASIS AND DIMENSION

Let $x^1, \ldots, x^m$ be vectors in a linear space L. These vectors are said to be *linearly independent* if

$$\alpha_1 x^1 + \alpha_2 x^2 + \cdots + \alpha_m x^m = 0 \qquad (1)$$

only when *all* of the scalars $\alpha_1, \ldots, \alpha_m$ are zero. The vectors $x^1, \ldots, x^m$ are called *linearly dependent* when the equation (1) has some solution other than $\alpha_1 = \cdots = \alpha_m = 0$. A sum $\sum \alpha_j x^j$ is called a *linear combination* of the vectors x^j.

EXAMPLE 1. The vectors

$$x^1 = \begin{bmatrix} 1 \\ 2 \end{bmatrix} \quad \text{and} \quad x^2 = \begin{bmatrix} 3 \\ 4 \end{bmatrix}$$

are independent.

Proof. The equation (1) states

$$\alpha_1 + 3\alpha_2 = 0$$
$$2\alpha_1 + 4\alpha_2 = 0$$

The only solution of this system is $\alpha_1 = \alpha_2 = 0$. Why?

EXAMPLE 2. The vectors

$$x^1 = \begin{bmatrix} 1 \\ 2 \end{bmatrix}, \quad x^2 = \begin{bmatrix} 3 \\ 4 \end{bmatrix}, \quad x^3 = \begin{bmatrix} 3 \\ 5 \end{bmatrix}$$

are dependent because

$$3x^1 + x^2 - 2x^3 = 0$$

EXAMPLE 3. The vectors

$$x^1 = \begin{bmatrix} 1 \\ 2 \end{bmatrix}, \quad x^2 = \begin{bmatrix} 3 \\ 4 \end{bmatrix}, \quad x^3 = \begin{bmatrix} 2 \\ 4 \end{bmatrix}$$

are dependent because $2x^1 - x^3 = 0$. Note here that $\alpha_2 = 0$. Dependence does not require that *all* α_j be nonzero in (1).

Lemma 1. *The vectors* $x^1, \ldots, x^m$ *are dependent if and only if one of these vectors is some linear combination of the others.*

Proof. If $x^1, \ldots, x^m$ are dependent, then (1) holds with some scalars $\alpha_1, \ldots, \alpha_m$ that are not all zero. If $\alpha_i \neq 0$, then

$$x^i = \beta_1 x^1 + \cdots + \beta_{i-1} x^{i-1} + \beta_{i+1} x^{i+1} + \cdots + \beta_m x^m \qquad (2)$$

where $\beta_j = -\alpha_j/\alpha_i$ ($j \neq i$). Conversely, an expression (2) of x^i as a linear combination of the other vectors x^j yields an equation of dependence (1) with

$$\alpha_i = 1, \quad \alpha_j = -\beta_j \qquad (\text{for } j \neq i)$$

Note in Example 3 that x^1 is a combination of x^2 and x^3; x^3 is a combination of x^1 and x^2; but x^2 is *not* a combination of x^1 and x^3.

The vectors $y^1, \ldots, y^k$ in L are said to *span* a linear subspace M if every vector x in M is some linear combination of $y^1, \ldots, y^k$.

EXAMPLE 4. The independent vectors

$$y^1 = \begin{bmatrix} 1 \\ 2 \\ 3 \end{bmatrix}, \qquad y^2 = \begin{bmatrix} 4 \\ 5 \\ 6 \end{bmatrix} \tag{3}$$

span a certain plane through the origin in three-space. The *same* plane is spanned by the dependent vectors

$$y^1 = \begin{bmatrix} 1 \\ 2 \\ 3 \end{bmatrix}, \qquad y^2 = \begin{bmatrix} 4 \\ 5 \\ 6 \end{bmatrix}, \qquad y^3 = \begin{bmatrix} 7 \\ 8 \\ 9 \end{bmatrix}, \qquad y^4 = \begin{bmatrix} 10 \\ 11 \\ 12 \end{bmatrix}$$

In fact, all linear combinations

$$\alpha_1 y^1 + \alpha_2 y^2 + \alpha_3 y^3 + \alpha_4 y^4$$

are linear combinations $\beta_1 y^1 + \beta_2 y^2$ or y^1 and y^2 because

$$y^3 = 2y^2 - y^1 \quad \text{and} \quad y^4 = 3y^2 - 2y^1$$

Thus $\alpha_1 y^1 + \cdots + \alpha_4 y^4 = \beta_1 y^1 + \beta_2 y^2$ if we set

$$\beta_1 = \alpha_1 - \alpha_3 - 2\alpha_4, \qquad \beta_2 = \alpha_2 + 2\alpha_3 + 3\alpha_4$$

Vectors $b^1, \ldots, b^m$ are said to be a *basis* for a linear space L if the vectors b^j lie in L, if they are independent, and if they span L.

EXAMPLE 5. In Example 4, the vectors y^1, y^2 are a basis for the plane that they span. The vectors y^1, y^2, y^3, y^4 are not a basis because they are dependent. Another basis for this plane is

$$z^1 = \begin{bmatrix} 1 \\ 1 \\ 1 \end{bmatrix}, \qquad z^2 = \begin{bmatrix} 5 \\ 7 \\ 9 \end{bmatrix}$$

These vectors are a basis for the plane spanned by y^1 and y^2 because z^1 and z^2 are independent and

$$y^1 = \tfrac{1}{2}z^2 - \tfrac{3}{2}z^1, \qquad y^2 = \tfrac{1}{2}z^2 + \tfrac{3}{2}z^1$$

Thus, all vectors $\alpha_1 y^1 + \alpha_2 y^2$ can be expressed in the form $\beta_1 z^1 + \beta_2 z^2$.

In the last example the basis y^1, y^2 and the basis z^1, z^2 both consisted of two vectors. It is intuitively clear that *every* basis must contain exactly two vectors. If this is so, we are justified in saying that *the dimension of the space is the number of vectors in any basis for the space.*

Theorem 1. *Let* $a^1, \ldots, a^r$ *be a basis for a linear vector space,* L. *Let* $b^1, \ldots, b^s$ *be another basis. Then* r = s.

Proof. The proof rests on the following assertion: *If* p *independent vectors* x^i *are linear combinations*

$$x^i = \xi_{i1}y^1 + \xi_{i2}y^2 + \cdots + \xi_{iq}y^q \qquad (i = 1, \ldots, p) \tag{4}$$

of q *vectors* y^j, *then* q $\geqslant$ p. This is obvious if $p = 1$ because $x^1 \neq 0$. If $p > 1$, we proceed by induction. The vector x^p is given by (4) when $i = p$. At least one of the coefficients $\xi_{p1}, \ldots, \xi_{pq}$ is nonzero because $x^p \neq 0$. Without loss of generality, suppose $\xi_{pq} \neq 0$. Then we have

$$y^q = \xi_{pq}^{-1}(x^p - \xi_{p1}y^1 - \cdots - \xi_{p,q-1}y^{q-1}) \tag{5}$$

If (5) is used in (4) when $i = 1, \ldots, p - 1$, we find

$$x^i - \alpha_i x^p = \beta_{i1}y^1 + \cdots + \beta_{i,q-1}y^{q-1} \qquad (i = 1, \ldots, p - 1) \tag{6}$$

where

$$\alpha_i = \xi_{iq}\xi_{pq}^{-1}, \qquad \beta_{ij} = \xi_{ij} - \xi_{iq}\xi_{pq}^{-1}\xi_{pj}$$

But the $p - 1$ vectors, $x^i - \alpha_i x^p$ are independent, since an equation

$$\sum_{i=1}^{p-1} \gamma_i(x^i - \alpha_i x^p) = 0 \qquad \text{(with some } \gamma_i \neq 0\text{)}$$

implies

$$\sum_{i=1}^{p-1} \gamma_i x^i + \gamma x^p = 0 \qquad \text{(where } \gamma = -\sum \alpha_i \gamma_i\text{)}$$

which implies that $x^1, \ldots, x^p$ are dependent. By induction from (6), we conclude that $q - 1 \geqslant p - 1$, and hence $q \geqslant p$.

In our theorem, the r independent vectors a^i are linear combinations of the s vectors b^j; therefore, $s \geqslant r$. Conversely, the s independent vectors b^i are linear combinations of the r vectors a^j; therefore, $r \geqslant s$. In summary, $r = s$.

EXAMPLE 6. The space of polynomials of degree $\leqslant n$ has dimension $n + 1$ because $1, \zeta, \ldots, \zeta^n$ is a basis. By Theorem 1, every other basis also must consist of $n + 1$ polynomials.

EXAMPLE 7. The linear space of polynomials of *every* degree has no finite basis. Therefore, its dimension is not defined.

Theorem 2. *If* n *vectors lie in a linear space* L *of dimension* m $<$ n, *then the* n *vectors are dependent.*

For example, three vectors in the two-dimensional plane are necessarily dependent.

Proof. If n *independent* vectors are linear combinations of basis vectors $b^1, \ldots, b^m$, then $m \geqslant n$, as we showed in the proof of Theorem 1.

Theorem 3. *Every set of* n *independent vectors in an* n-*dimensional linear space, is a basis for the space.*

Proof. Let $a^1, \ldots, a^n$ be independent. Let $b^1, \ldots, b^n$ be a basis. By the last theorem, each set $a^1, \ldots, a^n, b^i$ is dependent. Then there is a linear combination

$$\sum_{j=1}^{n} \alpha_{ij} a^j + \beta_i b^i = 0 \tag{7}$$

with not all coefficients equal to zero. If $\beta_i = 0$, then $\alpha_{i1} = \cdots = \alpha_{in} = 0$ by the independence of the a's. Therefore, $\beta_i \neq 0$, and each b^i can be found as a linear combination of the a's. The a's, therefore, span the whole space. Since they are independent, they are a basis for the whole space.

EXAMPLE 8. For three-dimensional Euclidean space, any three vectors in the space which are not in the same plane are a basis.

PROBLEMS

1. Let A be an $m \times n$ matrix. Show that $Ax = 0$ has a solution $x \neq 0$ if and only if the columns of A are dependent.

2. Let L be the set of vectors x in E^4 for which $x_1 + x_2 + x_3 + x_4 = 0$. Find a basis for L. What is the dimension of L?

3. Let x and y lie in the space $E^n(R)$ of column-vectors with n real components. These vectors are said to be *orthogonal* if $x_1 y_1 + \cdots + x_n y_n = 0$. Let $x^1, \ldots, x^k$ be nonzero vectors in $E^n(R)$. Let every two of these vectors be orthogonal. Show that the vectors $x^1, \ldots, x^k$ are linearly independent.

4. Let L be the linear space of solutions of the differential equation $\phi''(t) + \phi(t) = 0$. Find a basis for this space. What is the dimension of the space?

5. Let L be the linear space of finite trigonometic sums

$$x = x_1 \sin t + x_2 \sin 2t + \cdots + x_k \sin kt \qquad (0 \leqslant t < 2\pi)$$

where $x_1, \ldots, x_k$ are real coefficients. Show that the "vectors" $x^1 = \sin t$, $\ldots, x^k = \sin kt$ constitute a basis for L. To prove independence, use Euler's identity

$$\int_0^{2\pi} \sin rt \sin st \, dt = 0 \qquad (r \neq s; r, s \text{ integers})$$

6. Find a basis for E^n. What is the dimension of E^n?

7. Consider the vector space of $m \times n$ matrices with complex components over the field of complex numbers. What is a basis for this space? What is the dimension?

8. Consider the vector space of $m \times n$ matrices with complex components over the field of *real* numbers. Show that the dimension of this space is $2mn$.

9. Let $a^1, \ldots, a^n$ be dependent vectors in L. Assume that at least one $a^j \neq 0$. Show that there is a linearly independent subset $a^{j_1}, a^{j_2}, \ldots, a^{j_r}$ of which every other a^k is some linear combination. (If $a^1, \ldots, a^n$ are the columns of a matrix A, the integer r is called the *rank* of A).

10. Let the positive integer N be fixed. Let L be the space of real-valued functions $\phi(t)$ defined at the times $t = 0, \pm 1/N, \pm 2/N, \ldots$ and satisfying the condition of periodicity $\phi(t + 1) = \phi(t)$. What is the dimension of L? Give a basis for L.

2.4   SOLVABILITY OF HOMOGENEOUS EQUATIONS

We are now ready to prove the result which, as we shall see later, is the basis for the theory of eigenvalues and eigenvectors.

Theorem 1. *Let* A *be an* $n \times n$ *matrix. Then the equation* $Ax = 0$ *has a solution* $x \neq 0$ *if and only if det* $A = 0$.

Proof. We know already, from Section 1.6, that det $A \neq 0$ implies that A has an inverse A^{-1}. Then $Ax = 0$, multiplied on the left by A^{-1}, yields $x = 0$.

Therefore, we have only to prove that det $A = 0$ implies the existence of a nonzero solution x to the equation $Ax = 0$. Let $a^1, \ldots, a^n$ be the columns of A. Let $x_1, \ldots, x_n$ be the components of x. Then

$$Ax = x_1 a^1 + x_2 a^2 + \cdots + x_n a^n \tag{1}$$

Thus, $Ax = 0$ *has a solution* $x \neq 0$ *if and only if the columns of* A *are dependent.*

The columns $a^1, \ldots, a^n$ lie in the space E^n of column vectors with n components. The dimension of this linear space is n because it has a basis consisting of the n vectors

$$e^1 = \begin{bmatrix} 1 \\ 0 \\ \cdot \\ \cdot \\ \cdot \\ 0 \end{bmatrix}, \quad e^2 = \begin{bmatrix} 0 \\ 1 \\ \cdot \\ \cdot \\ \cdot \\ 0 \end{bmatrix}, \ldots, \quad e^n = \begin{bmatrix} 0 \\ 0 \\ \cdot \\ \cdot \\ \cdot \\ 1 \end{bmatrix} \tag{2}$$

The vectors (2) clearly span E^n. They are independent because a linear combination of the e^i with coefficients c_i is simply the column-vector with components c_i, which is zero only if all $c_i = 0$.

By Theorem 3 of the last section, if the n vectors $a^1, \ldots, a^n$ are independent, they are a basis for the n-dimensional space E^n. Then every vector b in E^n is a linear combination

$$b = y_1 a^1 + y_2 a^2 + \cdots + y_n a^n = Ay$$

In other words, the equation $Ay = b$ is solvable for every b. Then $\det A \neq 0$, by Theorem 2 of Section 1.7. Therefore, $\det A = 0$ implies that the columns a^j are dependent, i.e., that $Ax = 0$ for some $x \neq 0$.

Theorem 2. *If* A *is an* m $\times$ n *matrix with* m $<$ n, *then* Ax $= 0$ *has a solution* x $\neq 0$.

EXAMPLE 1. The two equations in three unknowns

$$x_1 + 2x_2 + 3x_3 = 0,$$
$$x_1 + 9x_2 + 28x_3 = 0$$

must have a solution with not all $x_i = 0$.

Proof. The columns of A are n vectors in the space E^m of dimension $m < n$. Therefore, the columns are dependent, by Theorem 2 of Section 2.3. Thus,

$$Ax = x_1 a^1 + \cdots + x_n a^n = 0$$

for some $x \neq 0$.

If $Ax = 0$ for some $x \neq 0$, it is natural to ask, in some sense, how many solutions there are. If x is a solution $\neq 0$, so is λx for all $\lambda \neq 0$. Can $Ax = 0$ have linearly independent solutions? The set of solutions x to $Ax = 0$ is known as the *null space* of A.

EXAMPLE 2. The null space of

$$A = \begin{bmatrix} 1 & 2 & 3 \\ 2 & 4 & 6 \end{bmatrix} \tag{3}$$

consists of all vectors x of the form

$$x = \begin{bmatrix} -2\alpha & -3\beta \\ \alpha \\ \beta \end{bmatrix} \qquad (\alpha, \beta \text{ arbitrary}) \tag{4}$$

Theorem 3. *The null space of an* m × n *matrix is a linear vector space of dimension* ⩽n.

Proof. If $Ax = 0$ and $Ay = 0$, then $A(\alpha x + \beta y) = 0$. Therefore, the null space is a linear vector space. If the null space contains k independent vectors, then $k \leqslant n$, because these vectors are also independent vectors in the including space E^n, which has dimension n. If $x = 0$ is the only vector in the null space, its dimension is zero. Otherwise, let $k \geqslant 1$ be the largest integer such that the null space contains k independent vectors, say $b^1, \ldots, b^k$. Then these vectors are a basis for the null space because, for any x in the space, we have the dependence

$$\alpha_0 x + \alpha_1 b^1 + \cdots + \alpha_k b^k = 0 \qquad \text{(not all } \alpha_i = 0) \tag{5}$$

Now $\alpha_0 \neq 0$ for $\alpha_0 = 0$ implies that the b's are dependent. Hence, x is a linear combination of the independent vectors b^j. Therefore, the null space has dimension $k \leqslant n$.

In the context of this proof we have proved the obvious but useful result: *If a linear space* L *is included in a linear space* L¹ *of dimension* n, *then* L *has a dimension* ⩽n.

In Example 2 we note that the null space has dimension 2. In fact,

$$b^1 = \begin{bmatrix} -2 \\ 1 \\ 0 \end{bmatrix}, \qquad b^2 = \begin{bmatrix} -3 \\ 0 \\ 1 \end{bmatrix} \tag{6}$$

provide a basis. The matrix A has dependent columns; all three columns of A are multiples of the first column. *We define the rank of a matrix as the dimension of the linear space spanned by its columns.*

EXAMPLE 3. We have

$$\operatorname{rank} \begin{bmatrix} 1 & 2 & 3 \\ 2 & 4 & 6 \end{bmatrix} = 1 \tag{7}$$

because the linear space of all combinations

$$\alpha \begin{bmatrix} 1 \\ 2 \end{bmatrix} + \beta \begin{bmatrix} 2 \\ 4 \end{bmatrix} + \gamma \begin{bmatrix} 3 \\ 6 \end{bmatrix}$$

has col (1, 2) as a basis.

Theorem 4. *The rank of* A *is the largest integer* r ⩾ 0 *such that* A *has* r *independent columns.*

Proof. Let L be the linear space spanned by the columns of A. Suppose that A has r independent columns, for example, $a^1, \ldots, a^r$. If $r = n$, the dimension of L is n.

Suppose $1 \leqslant r < n$. If every $r + 1$ columns of A are dependent, the $r + 1$ vectors $a^1, \ldots, a^r, a^s$ are dependent for any s. Let

$$\alpha_0 a^s + \alpha_1 a^1 + \cdots + \alpha_r a^r = 0 \qquad \text{(not all } \alpha_i = 0) \qquad (8)$$

Then $\alpha_0 \neq 0$ because $a^1, \ldots, a^r$ are independent. Therefore, (8) may be solved for a^s as a linear combination of $a^1, \ldots, a^r$. Since every column of A is a linear combination of $a^1, \ldots, a^r$, all the linear combinations of the columns of A are linear combinations of just the r columns $a^1, \ldots, a^r$. Therefore, these r independent columns are a basis for L. Therefore, the dimension of L is r.

If $r = 0$ is the largest number of independent columns, then A is the zero matrix, and the dimension of L equals zero. This completes the proof. We can now evaluate the dimension of the null space of A in terms of the rank of A.

Theorem 5. *The vectors* x *solving* Ax $= 0$ *comprise a linear space with a dimension which is the number of columns of* A *minus the rank of* A.

EXAMPLE 4. Let A be defined as in the last two examples. The null space has dimension 2, the rank is 1, and the number of columns is 3.

Proof of the Theorem. Let A be an $m \times n$ matrix with rank r. If $r = n$, the columns of A are independent; $x = 0$ is the null space, with dimension $0 = n - r$. If $r = 0$, then $A = O$; the null space is all E^n, with dimension $n = n - r$.

Suppose $1 \leqslant r < n$. Without loss of generality, suppose that the first r columns of A, namely $a^1, \ldots, a^r$, are independent. Let $x^1, \ldots, x^v$ be a basis for the null space. We want to show that $v = n - r$.

If $e^1, e^2, \ldots$ are the unit vectors in E^n, then $a^1 = Ae^1, a^2 = Ae^2, \ldots$. We assert that the $r + v$ vectors $e^1, \ldots, e^r, x^1, \ldots, x^v$ are independent. Suppose

$$\alpha_1 e^1 + \cdots + \alpha_r e^r + \beta_1 x^1 + \cdots + \beta_v x^v = 0 \qquad (9)$$

Since each x^j lies in the null space, we have $Ax^j = 0$. Therefore, multiplication of (9) by A yields

$$\alpha_1 a^1 + \cdots + \alpha_r a^r = 0 \qquad (10)$$

Now the independence of $a^1, \ldots, a^r$ implies all $\alpha_i = 0$. Equation (9) now becomes $\sum \beta_j x^j = 0$, which implies all $\beta_j = 0$, by the independence of the basis vectors x^j.

Having shown that the $r + \nu$ vectors $e^1, \ldots, e^r, x^1, \ldots, x^\nu$ are independent, we now show that they span E^n, hence that they are a basis for E^n, hence that $r + \nu = n$. For any column a^s there is a representation

$$a^s = \alpha_{s1} a^1 + \cdots + \alpha_{sr} a^r \tag{11}$$

because $a^1, \ldots, a^r$ are a basis for the space spanned by the columns of A. Since $a^i = Ae^i$, (11) states that

$$Ax = 0, \quad (\text{where } x = e^s - \alpha_{s1} e^1 - \cdots - \alpha_{sr} e^r) \tag{12}$$

Thus, x is in the null space. Therefore, x is a linear combination of the basis vectors $x^1, \ldots, x^\nu$. Therefore, e^s is a combination of $e^1, \ldots, e^r$ and $x^1, \ldots, x^\nu$. This is true for all the n unit vectors e^s that span E^n. Therefore, $e^1, \ldots, e^r, x^1, \ldots, x^\nu$ span E^n; the proof is done.

EXAMPLE 5. Let A be defined as in the preceding examples. A basis for the null space is given by (6). Now

$$e^1 = \begin{bmatrix} 1 \\ 0 \\ 0 \end{bmatrix}, \quad x^1 = b^1 = \begin{bmatrix} -2 \\ 1 \\ 0 \end{bmatrix}, \quad x^2 = b^2 = \begin{bmatrix} -3 \\ 0 \\ 1 \end{bmatrix} \tag{13}$$

form a basis for E^3.

PROBLEMS

1. Let A be an $n \times n$ matrix. In terms of a determinant, give the necessary and sufficient condition on the scalar λ such that the equation $Ax = \lambda x$ has a solution $x \neq 0$.

2. Let

$$A = \begin{bmatrix} 1 & 4 & 7 \\ 2 & 5 & 8 \\ 3 & 6 & 9 \end{bmatrix}$$

What is the null space of A? What is the rank of A? What is the dimension of the null space? Which sets of columns of A are bases for the space spanned by all of the columns?

3. Answer the questions of Problem 2 for the matrix

$$A = \begin{bmatrix} 0 & 1 & 2 & 4 \\ 0 & 2 & 4 & 5 \\ 0 & 3 & 6 & 6 \end{bmatrix}$$

4. Prove that rank $(A + B) \leqslant$ rank $(A) +$ rank (B)

5. Prove that rank $(AB) \leqslant$ rank B. Prove also that rank $(AB) \leqslant$ rank A, and hence, rank $(AB) \leqslant$ min (rank A, rank B).

6. Let $\bar{A}$ be the matrix $(\bar{a}_{\mu v})$ formed by taking the complex conjugates of the components of A. Show that rank $\bar{A} =$ rank A.

7. Define $A^* = (\bar{A})^T =$ the transpose of $\bar{A}$. In particular, if x is a column-vector, define x^* to be the row-vector formed from the conjugates of the components of x. For any vector y, define $\|y\|^2 = \sum |y_\mu|^2 = y^*y$. Show that $x^*A^* = (Ax)^*$. Hence, show that $A^*Ax = 0$ implies $\|Ax\|^2 = 0$, which implies $Ax = 0$. Deduce that A^*A and A have the *same* null space.

8. From the result of the last problem, and from Theorem 5, deduce that A^*A and A have the same rank. From the result of Problem 5, prove that rank $A \leqslant$ rank A^*. By replacing A by A^* [what is $(A^*)^*$?], prove that rank $A^* \leqslant$ rank A, and hence rank $A =$ rank A^*. From the result of Problem 6, show that rank $A =$ rank (A^T). Deduce that the rank of a matrix A equals the dimension of the linear space spanned by its *rows*.

9. From the result of Problem 7, show that the vectors $a^1, a^2, \ldots, a^n$ in $E^m (m \geqslant n)$ are independent if and only if det $(A^*A) \neq 0$, where A is the $m \times n$ matrix with the columns $a^1, \ldots, a^n$. The determinant of the square matrix A^*A is known as the *Gram determinant*.

2.5   EVALUATION OF RANK BY DETERMINANTS

Given an $m \times n$ matrix A, we wish to find the rank of A by observing the determinants of square submatrices. A *submatrix* is defined as a square matrix formed from certain columns and rows of A.

EXAMPLE 1. The matrix

$$S = \begin{bmatrix} a_{32} & a_{34} & a_{38} \\ a_{52} & a_{54} & a_{58} \\ a_{82} & a_{84} & a_{88} \end{bmatrix} \tag{1}$$

is the submatrix formed from rows $3, 5, 8$ and columns $2, 4, 8$ of the rectangular matrix $A = (a_{ij})$ $(i = 1, \ldots, 14; j = 1, \ldots, 93)$.

We may speak of a submatrix R of a submatrix S.

EXAMPLE 2. S is a submatrix of itself. Other submatrices of the submatrix S defined in (1) are

$$\begin{bmatrix} a_{34} & a_{38} \\ a_{84} & a_{88} \end{bmatrix} \quad \text{and} \quad [a_{52}] \tag{2}$$

EXAMPLE 3. Let

$$A = \begin{bmatrix} 1 & 2 & 3 \\ 2 & 4 & 6 \end{bmatrix} \tag{3}$$

We showed in the last section that rank $A = 1$. Observe that the 2×2 submatrices

$$\begin{bmatrix} 1 & 2 \\ 2 & 4 \end{bmatrix}, \quad \begin{bmatrix} 1 & 3 \\ 2 & 6 \end{bmatrix}, \quad \begin{bmatrix} 2 & 3 \\ 4 & 6 \end{bmatrix} \tag{4}$$

all have zero determinants, but that there is a 1×1 submatrix of A that has a nonzero determinant.

Theorem 1. *Let* A *be an* m × n *matrix. Suppose that* A *has an* r × r *submatrix* S *with* det S $\neq$ 0. *And suppose that every* (r + 1) × (r + 1) *submatrix* T *of which* S *is a submatrix, has* det T = 0. *Then rank* A = r.

EXAMPLE 4. Let

$$A = \begin{bmatrix} 0 & 1 & 0 & 1 & 2 & 0 & 3 \\ 0 & 2 & 0 & 2 & 4 & 0 & 6 \\ 0 & 1 & 0 & 2 & 3 & -1 & 4 \end{bmatrix} \tag{5}$$

The submatrix

$$S = \begin{bmatrix} 1 & 1 \\ 1 & 2 \end{bmatrix} \tag{6}$$

has det $S \neq 0$. But every 3×3 submatrix T including S has det $T = 0$. For example,

$$\begin{vmatrix} 1 & 1 & 2 \\ 2 & 2 & 4 \\ 1 & 2 & 3 \end{vmatrix} = 0, \quad \begin{vmatrix} 1 & 1 & 0 \\ 2 & 2 & 0 \\ 1 & 2 & -1 \end{vmatrix} = 0, \quad \begin{vmatrix} 0 & 1 & 1 \\ 0 & 2 & 2 \\ 0 & 1 & 2 \end{vmatrix} = 0 \tag{7}$$

Theorem 1 now states that rank $A = 2$.

Proof of the Theorem. For definiteness, suppose that S is the $r \times r$ submatrix in the upper left corner of A, i.e.,

$$S = (a_{ij}) \qquad (i, j = 1, \ldots, r) \tag{8}$$

It will be apparent in the proof that this specification involves no loss of generality.

Let $a^1, \ldots, a^r, \ldots, a^n$ be the columns of A. Let $b^1, \ldots, b^r, \ldots, b^n$ be the columns of the $r \times n$ matrix formed from the first r rows of A. Thus, if $r = 2$ and

$$\text{if } A = \begin{bmatrix} 1 & 1 & 1 & 1 \\ 1 & 2 & 3 & 4 \\ 2 & 3 & 4 & 5 \end{bmatrix}, \quad \text{then } B = \begin{bmatrix} 1 & 1 & 1 & 1 \\ 1 & 2 & 3 & 4 \end{bmatrix} \tag{9}$$

We assert that the columns $a^1, \ldots, a^r$ are independent. This is true if the columns $b^1, \ldots, b^r$ are independent because

$$\sum_{j=1}^{r} \alpha_j a^j = 0 \quad \text{implies} \quad \sum_{j=1}^{r} \alpha_j b^j = 0 \tag{10}$$

But the columns $b^1, \ldots, b^r$ form the submatrix S in formula (8). Since $\det S \neq 0$, $Sz = 0$ implies $z = 0$, and the columns of S are independent.

It only remains to show that the independent columns $a^1, \ldots, a^r$ span the other columns of A if $n > r$. Let $s > r$. Since $\det S \neq 0$, b^s is some linear combination of $b^1, \ldots, b^r$:

$$b^s = \beta_1 b^1 + \beta_2 b^2 + \cdots + \beta_r b^r \tag{11}$$

In the example (9), if $s = 4$, formula (11) becomes

$$\begin{bmatrix} 1 \\ 4 \end{bmatrix} = (-2) \begin{bmatrix} 1 \\ 1 \end{bmatrix} + (3) \begin{bmatrix} 1 \\ 2 \end{bmatrix} \tag{12}$$

We now assert that a^s is a linear combination of $a^1, \ldots, a^r$ with the same coefficients:

$$a^s = \beta_1 a^1 + \beta_2 a^2 + \cdots + \beta_r a^r \tag{13}$$

In our example, we assert that

$$\begin{bmatrix} 1 \\ 4 \\ 5 \end{bmatrix} = (-2) \begin{bmatrix} 1 \\ 1 \\ 2 \end{bmatrix} + (3) \begin{bmatrix} 1 \\ 2 \\ 3 \end{bmatrix} \tag{14}$$

Suppose that (13) were false. Then for some lower-row component a_{ts} with $t > r$ we must have inequality:

$$a_{ts} \neq \beta_1 a_{t1} + \beta_2 a_{t2} + \cdots + \beta_r a_{tr} \tag{15}$$

We now form the $(r + 1) \times (r + 1)$ submatrix

$$T = \begin{bmatrix} a_{11} & a_{12} & \cdots & a_{1r} & a_{1s} \\ \cdot & \cdot & \cdots & \cdot & \cdot \\ a_{r1} & a_{r2} & \cdots & a_{rr} & a_{rs} \\ a_{t1} & a_{t2} & \cdots & a_{tr} & a_{ts} \end{bmatrix} = \begin{bmatrix} b^1 & b^2 & \cdots & b^r & b^s \\ a_{t1} & a_{t2} & \cdots & a_{tr} & a_{ts} \end{bmatrix} \tag{16}$$

The given matrix S is the $r \times r$ submatrix formed by deleting the last row and column of T. We will show that (15) implies det $T \neq 0$, contrary to hypothesis.

Formulas (11) and (15) show that the computation of det T may be simplified by subtracting the multiples $\beta_1, \ldots, \beta_r$ of the first r columns of T from the last column of T. The last column of the resulting matrix, T', consists of r zeros followed by the nonzero difference, δ, between the two sides of the inequality (15).

$$T' = \begin{bmatrix} & & & 0 \\ & S & & \cdot \\ & & & \cdot \\ & & & \cdot \\ & & & 0 \\ \hline a_{t1} & \cdots & a_{tr} & \delta \end{bmatrix} \tag{17}$$

Expansion of det T' by the last column gives

$$\det T = \det T' = \delta \det S \neq 0 \tag{18}$$

Since T is an $(r + 1) \times (r + 1)$ submatrix including S, we must have det $T = 0$. The contradiction (18) shows that the inequality (15) does not occur. This completes the proof.

Theorem 1 gives a construction for the rank: Look for any nonzero component a_{pq}. If there is none, rank $A = 0$. Let S_1 be the 1×1 matrix a_{pq}. Look for a 2×2 matrix S_2 including S_1, with det $S_2 \neq 0$. If no such S_2 exists, rank $A = 1$. Proceed until an $r \times r$ matrix S_r is formed including S_{r-1}, such that det $S_r \neq 0$, where r is as large as possible. Then rank $A = r$.

EXAMPLE 5. Let

$$A = \begin{bmatrix} 1 & 1 & 1 & 1 \\ 1 & 2 & 3 & 4 \\ 2 & 3 & 4 & 5 \end{bmatrix}$$

Then we may take

$$S_1 = [5], \qquad S_2 = \begin{bmatrix} 1 & 1 \\ 3 & 5 \end{bmatrix} \tag{19}$$

Now no 3×3 S_3 can be found in A such that S_3 includes S_2 and det $S_3 \neq 0$. Therefore, $r = 2$ is as large as possible. Note that another chain of submatrices, e.g.,

$$S_1 = [1], \qquad S_2 = \begin{bmatrix} 1 & 1 \\ 1 & 2 \end{bmatrix} \tag{20}$$

would also yield $r = 2$. Note also that we need not look at *all* 3×3 submatrices; we need only to look for those that include S_2.

Theorem 2. *The rank of a matrix* A *is the largest integer* r *such that* A *has an* r $\times$ r *submatrix* S_r *with det* $S_r \neq 0$.

Proof. Every $(r + 1) \times (r + 1)$ submatrix T including S_r has det $T = 0$. The result now follows from Theorem 1.

We have defined rank as the dimension of the space spanned by the columns. It is a remarkable fact that the space spanned by the rows has the *same* dimension.

Theorem 3. Rank $A = $ rank A^T.

Proof. Since the submatrices of A^T are the transposes of the submatrices of A, the result follows from Theorem 2.

EXAMPLE 6. The 3×7 matrix in formula (5) has just two independent rows. *Therefore*, it has just two independent columns, and the rank equals 2.

In the problems for Section 2.4 a proof that rank $A = $ rank A^T was outlined which does not use determinants.

PROBLEMS

1. Find the rank of

$$A = \begin{bmatrix} 0 & 0 & 1 & 0 & 5 \\ 0 & -2 & 0 & 0 & 4 \\ 0 & 3 & 0 & 0 & -6 \end{bmatrix}$$

What can you choose for the submatrix S described in Theorem 1?

2. When the submatrix S described in Theorem 1 has been found, how can one find a set of columns of A which form a basis for the space spanned by *all* the columns of A?

3. Prove that the rank of a matrix is not changed if two rows are interchanged, if a row is multiplied by a nonzero scalar, or if a scalar multiple of one row is added to another row.

2.6 THE GENERAL $m \times n$ INHOMOGENEOUS SYSTEM

Theorem 1. *Let* A *be an* m $\times$ n *matrix. Then the* m *equations in* n *unknowns*

$$\sum_{j=1}^{n} a_{ij}x_j = b_i \qquad (i = 1, \ldots, m) \tag{1}$$

have a solution x *if and only if the* m $\times$ (n + 1) *matrix* B *formed by adjoining the extra column* b *to the right of* A*, has rank* B = *rank* A*. If this condition for solvability holds, then the set of all solutions* x *consists of any particular solution* x^0 *plus a linear space of dimension* n $-$ *rank* A*.*

EXAMPLE 1. Consider three equations in two unknowns:

$$\begin{aligned} x_1 + 2x_2 &= b_1 \\ 2x_1 + 4x_2 &= b_2 \\ 3x_1 + 6x_2 &= b_3 \end{aligned} \tag{2}$$

In this example,

$$A = \begin{bmatrix} 1 & 2 \\ 2 & 4 \\ 3 & 6 \end{bmatrix}, \qquad B = \begin{bmatrix} 1 & 2 & b_1 \\ 2 & 4 & b_2 \\ 3 & 6 & b_3 \end{bmatrix} \tag{3}$$

If $b = \text{col}\,(1, 0, 0)$, then (2) has no solution because rank $B = 2 >$ rank $A = 1$. If $b = \text{col}\,(5, 10, 15)$, then rank $B = 1$, and every vector of the form

$$x = \begin{bmatrix} 5 \\ 0 \end{bmatrix} + \alpha \begin{bmatrix} 2 \\ -1 \end{bmatrix} \qquad (\alpha \text{ arbitrary})$$

solves (2).

Proof of the Theorem. Let L_A and L_B be the linear vector spaces spanned, respectively, by the columns of A and by the columns of B. Since L_A is a subset of L_B, we have

$$\dim L_A = \text{rank } A \leqslant \dim L_B = \text{rank } B \tag{4}$$

If rank $A =$ rank $B = r$, then r independent columns of A are a basis for L_A; and they provide a basis for L_B because they are r independent vectors in the linear space L_B of dimension r. In particular, the vector b in L_B is some linear combination of the r independent columns of A:

$$b = \sum x_k a^k \qquad (a^k \text{ in the basis}) \tag{5}$$

Setting $x_j = 0$ when a^j is not in the basis, we have a solution x to the equations (1).

If rank $A <$ rank B, then the subset L_A of L_B cannot be identical to L_B, because then they would have the same dimension. If b lay in L_A, then L_B would equal L_A. Therefore, b lies outside L_A, which means that $Ax = b$ has no solution.

If $Ax = b$ is solvable, let x^0 be any particular solution. Then $A(x - x^0) = 0$. By Theorem 5 of Section 2.4, the vectors y satisfying $Ay = 0$ form a linear space of dimension $n - r$. Thus, the vectors x satisfying $Ax = b$ are those for which $x - x^0 = y$, where y lies in the $(n - r)$-dimensional null space of A.

EXAMPLE 2. Since the square matrix

$$A = \begin{bmatrix} 1 & 2 & 3 \\ 4 & 5 & 6 \\ 7 & 8 & 9 \end{bmatrix}$$

has det $A = 0$, either $Ax = b$ has no solution *or* $Ax = b$ has infinitely many solutions.

For square matrices, our results are summarized in Figure 2.2.

Let A be an $n \times n$ matrix.	
Suppose det $A = \Delta \neq 0$	Suppose det $A = 0$
There is a unique inverse: $$A^{-1} = \frac{1}{\Delta} \operatorname{cof} A^T$$ exists for which $$A^{-1}A = I \quad \text{and} \quad AA^{-1} = I.$$	There is no matrix A^{-1} for which $$A^{-1}A = I \text{ or } AA^{-1} = I.$$
Every equation $Ax = b$ has a solution.	Some equations $Ax = b$ have no solution.
The only solution of $Ax = 0$ is $x = 0$.	There are solutions of $Ax = 0$ with $x \neq 0$.
The solution x to every equation $Ax = b$ is unique.	The solution to $Ax = b$ is never unique. If there is any solution x, then there are other solutions $x^1 \neq x$.
rank $A = n$.	rank $A < n$.
Null space has dimension 0.	Null space, i.e., the space of vectors x for which $Ax = 0$, has dimension $n - \operatorname{rank} A \geqslant 1$.

Figure 2.2

PROBLEMS

1. For which vectors b does the system

$$\begin{bmatrix} 1 & 2 & 3 \\ 4 & 5 & 6 \\ 7 & 8 & 9 \end{bmatrix} x = b$$

have a solution?

2. Let A be an $m \times n$ matrix, and B be an $m \times p$ matrix. Give a necessary and sufficient condition so that the system $AX = B$ will have an $n \times p$ matrix-solution X. If $X°$ is a particular solution, and if rank $A = r$, describe all other solutions.

3. Give all the solutions of the system

$$\begin{bmatrix} 1 & 2 & 3 \\ 4 & 5 & 6 \\ 7 & 8 & 9 \end{bmatrix} X = \begin{bmatrix} 10 & , & 13 \\ 11 & , & 14 \\ 12 & , & 15 \end{bmatrix}$$

4. Give all the solutions of the system

$$[1 \quad 2 \quad 3]x = [4]$$

5. Prove that the system

$$\begin{bmatrix} 1 & 3 \\ 2 & 6 \end{bmatrix} x = \begin{bmatrix} 1 \\ 3 \end{bmatrix}$$

has no solution. Apply Theorem 1.

2.7 LEAST-SQUARES SOLUTION OF UNSOLVABLE SYSTEMS

In applied science it is common to try to explain the behavior of a variable b, insofar as it depends on certain variables $a_1, a_2, \ldots, a_n$, by hypothesizing a *linear* dependence

$$b = x_0 + x_1 a_1 + x_2 a_2 + \cdots + x_n a_n \tag{1}$$

For example, we may hypothesize that the average yearly income, b, of men at age forty depends upon the number of years of education, a_1, and upon I.Q. score, a_2, by some relationship

$$b = x_0 + x_1 a_1 + x_2 a_2 \tag{2}$$

An equation (2) might also be used to describe the rate, b, of a certain chemical reaction as it depends upon temperature, a_1, and upon the concentration, a_2, of a certain catalyst. As a third example, the Dow Jones average price, b, for industrial stocks may be hypothesized to depend on time, t (years), by means of a linear relationship $b = x_0 + x_1 a_1 + \cdots + x_4 a_4$, where

$$a_1 = t, \qquad a_2 = t^2, \qquad a_3 = \cos t, \qquad a_4 = \sin t$$

To determine the unknown coefficients of dependence $x_0, x_1, \ldots, x_n$, many observations are made. For each observation $i = 1, \ldots, m$, numerical data

$$b_i; a_{i1}, a_{i2}, \ldots, a_{in} \tag{3}$$

are recorded. Thus, b_i is the value of b in the ith observation (or experiment); a_{ij} is the value of a_j in the ith experiment. We then try to solve the equations

$$b_i = x_0 + x_1 a_{i1} + x_2 a_{i2} + \cdots + x_n a_{in} \qquad (i = 1, \ldots, m) \tag{4}$$

If the number of observations, m, is greater than the number of unknowns, $1 + n$, the linear system (4) usually has no solution. Nevertheless, one would like to find the *best possible* values $x_0, \ldots, x_n$ for the unsolvable linear system (4).

Of the many senses in which the phrase *best possible* can be defined, the commonest is the sense of *least squares: We pick the numbers* $\mathrm{x}_0, \ldots, \mathrm{x}_n$ *to minimize the sum of the squares of the differences:*

$$\phi \equiv \sum_{i=1}^{m} (b_i - x_0 - x_1 a_{i1} - x_2 a_{i2} - \cdots - x_n a_{in})^2 \tag{5}$$

Differentiation of ϕ with respect to x_j gives the condition:

$$0 = -\frac{1}{2} \frac{\partial \phi}{\partial x_j} = \sum_{i=1}^{m} a_{ij}(b_i - x_0 - x_1 a_{i1} - \cdots - x_n a_{in}) \qquad (j = 0, 1, \ldots, n) \tag{6}$$

where we define $a_{i0} = 1$. The system (6), which is called the *normal equations*, consists of $n + 1$ equations in $n + 1$ unknowns.

To discuss the normal equations, we introduce the vector of data b_i, the matrix of data a_{ij}, and the vector of unknown coefficients x_j.

$$\mathbf{b} = \begin{bmatrix} b_1 \\ b_2 \\ \vdots \\ b_m \end{bmatrix}, \qquad A = \begin{bmatrix} 1 & a_{11} & \cdots & a_{1n} \\ 1 & a_{21} & \cdots & a_{2n} \\ \vdots & \vdots & \cdots & \vdots \\ 1 & a_{m1} & \cdots & a_{mn} \end{bmatrix}, \qquad x = \begin{bmatrix} x_0 \\ x_1 \\ \vdots \\ x_n \end{bmatrix} \tag{7}$$

If y is the column-vector of differences

$$y_i = b_i - x_0 - x_1 a_{i1} - \cdots - x_n a_{in} \qquad (i = 1, \ldots, m)$$

then $y = \mathbf{b} - Ax$. The normal equations (6) now take the form

$$0 = \sum_{i=1}^{m} a_{ij} y_1 \qquad (j = 0, \ldots, n)$$

or, with $A^T =$ the transpose of A,

$$0 = A^T y$$

or

$$0 = A^T(\mathbf{b} - Ax)$$

or

$$\boxed{A^T A x = A^T \mathbf{b}} \tag{8}$$

The system (8) can be solved if the square matrix $A^T A$ has det $(A^T A)$ $\neq 0$. But det $(A^T A) = 0$ implies that there is some solution $z \neq 0$ to the equation $A^T A z = 0$. Multiplication of this equation on the left by the row vector z^T gives

$$z^T A^T A z = 0 \tag{9}$$

But the reader will easily verify the identity

$$z^T A^T = (Az)^T \tag{10}$$

which holds for all matrix-vector products Az. Then (9) states that $w^T w = 0$ if $w = Az$. Then

$$\|w\|^2 \equiv w^T w = w_1^2 + w_2^2 + \cdots + w_m^2 = 0 \tag{11}$$

Since we have tacitly assumed that all numbers in this discussion are real, equation (11) yields $w = Az = 0$. In this case there cannot be a *unique* best possible set of coefficients $x_0, \ldots, x_n$ for the equations (4). In matrix-vector form, these equations are written as $\mathbf{b} = Ax$. But if x is any vector, and if $\phi(x)$ is the sum of squares (5), and if $Az = 0$, then

$$\phi(x) = \phi(x + \lambda z) = \|\mathbf{b} - A(x + \lambda z)\|^2$$

for all scalars λ. *Thus, if the sum of squares ϕ is minimized by a unique vector* x, *then* det $(\mathrm{A}^T \mathrm{A}) \neq 0$, *and the vector* x *is the unique solution of the normal equations* $\mathrm{A}^T \mathrm{A} x = \mathrm{A}^T \mathbf{b}$.

EXAMPLE 1. Let us find the best linear fit

$$b = x_0 + x_1 a_1 + x_2 a_2 \tag{12}$$

where four observations give the data

b	a_1	a_2
1	1	0
2	0	1
0	1	1
−1	2	−1

(13)

Here we have

$$A = \begin{bmatrix} 1 & 1 & 0 \\ 1 & 0 & 1 \\ 1 & 1 & 1 \\ 1 & 2 & -1 \end{bmatrix}, \quad A^T = \begin{bmatrix} 1 & 1 & 1 & 1 \\ 1 & 0 & 1 & 2 \\ 0 & 1 & 1 & -1 \end{bmatrix}, \quad b = \begin{bmatrix} 1 \\ 2 \\ 0 \\ -1 \end{bmatrix}$$

The system $Ax = b$ is unsolvable because b is not a linear combination of the columns of A. (*Proof:* Let B be the 4×4 matrix $[A, b]$. Computation yields det $B = 1 \neq 0$. Therefore, the columns of B are independent.) The normal equations are

$$A^T A x = \begin{bmatrix} 4 & 4 & 1 \\ 4 & 6 & -1 \\ 1 & -1 & 3 \end{bmatrix} \begin{bmatrix} x_0 \\ x_1 \\ x_2 \end{bmatrix} = \begin{bmatrix} 2 \\ -1 \\ 3 \end{bmatrix} = A^T b \tag{14}$$

for which computation yields

$$x_0 = \frac{17}{6}, \quad x_1 = -\frac{13}{6}, \quad x_2 = -\frac{4}{6} \tag{15}$$

Thus, the unique best linear fit (12), in the least-squares sense, to the data (13) is

$$b = \frac{17}{6} - \frac{13}{6}a_1 - \frac{4}{6}a_2$$

The reader will note that this equation does not hold exactly for *any* of the four observations (13).

Even if det $(A^T A) = 0$, *the least-squares problem is still solvable.* We have shown that det $(A^T A) = 0$ implies that the columns of A are dependent. The problem is still to choose x so as to minimize

$$\phi(x) = \| \mathbf{b} - Ax \|^2 \tag{16}$$

If A is the zero matrix, then $Ax = 0$ for all x; and all vectors x minimize ϕ. If $A \neq 0$, let A_1 be a matrix formed by successively eliminating dependent columns until only a set of independent columns remains. For example, if

$$A = \begin{bmatrix} 0 & 1 & 2 & 3 \\ 0 & 2 & 4 & 2 \\ 0 & 3 & 6 & 1 \end{bmatrix}, \quad \text{then } A_1 = \begin{bmatrix} 1 & 3 \\ 2 & 2 \\ 3 & 1 \end{bmatrix} \tag{17}$$

Since every column of A is a linear combination of the columns of A_1, every linear combination, Ay, of the columns of A is some linear combination, A_1w, of the columns of A_1. Therefore, if $Ay = A_1w$,

$$\phi(y) \equiv \| \mathbf{b} - Ay \|^2 = \phi_1(w) \equiv \| \mathbf{b} - A_1 w \|^2 \tag{18}$$

and

$$\min_y \phi(y) = \min_w \phi_1(w)$$

But the columns of A_1 are independent! Therefore, we have

$$\det (A_1^T A_1) \neq 0$$

and the normal equations

$$A_1^T A_1 u = A_1^T \mathbf{b} \tag{19}$$

have a unique solution $u = (A_1^T A_1)^{-1} A_1^T \mathbf{b}$. A vector $y = x$ minimizing $\phi(y)$ is now found by letting $x_j = 0$ if the dependent column a^j was deleted from A, and by letting $x_j = u_k$ if a^j is the kth column of the abridged matrix A_1.

EXAMPLE 2. Let A be the first matrix in (17). Let us minimize

$$\phi(y) = \| \mathbf{b} - Ay \|^2 \quad \text{if } \mathbf{b} = \text{col } (1, 1, 1)$$

If A_1 is the second matrix in (17), the normal equations (19) become

$$A_1^T A_1 u = \begin{bmatrix} 14, & 10 \\ 10, & 14 \end{bmatrix} \begin{bmatrix} u_1 \\ u_2 \end{bmatrix} = A_1^T \mathbf{b} = \begin{bmatrix} 6 \\ 6 \end{bmatrix} \tag{20}$$

These equations have the unique solution $u_1 = \frac{1}{4}$, $u_2 = \frac{1}{4}$. Therefore, $y = x$ minimizes $\phi(y)$ if $x = \text{col } (0, \frac{1}{4}, 0, \frac{1}{4})$.

The careful reader will have observed that we never proved that a solution, x, of the normal equations minimizes the sum of squares, ϕ. The vanishing of the first derivatives, $\partial\phi/\partial x_j$, is a necessary but not a sufficient condition for minimization. Suppose that x is a solution of the normal equations $A^TAx = A^T\mathbf{b}$. If y is any other vector, let $y = x + z$. Then

$$\|Ay - \mathbf{b}\|^2 = \|(Ax - \mathbf{b}) + Az\|^2$$
$$= \|Ax - \mathbf{b}\|^2 + 2(Az)^T(Ax - \mathbf{b}) + \|Az\|^2$$

But

$$(Az)^T(Ax - \mathbf{b}) = z^TA^T(Ax - \mathbf{b}) = z^T(A^TAx - A^T\mathbf{b}) = 0$$

Therefore,

$$\|Ay - \mathbf{b}\|^2 = \|Ax - \mathbf{b}\|^2 + \|Az\|^2 \geqslant \|Ax - \mathbf{b}\|^2 \tag{21}$$

with equality if and only if $Az = 0$.

PROBLEMS

1. Find a least-squares fit $b = x_0 + x_1a_1 + x_2a_2$ for the data

b	a_1	a_2
1	1	0
0	2	0
0	3	0
0	4	1

2. Suppose that we desire a least-squares fit

$$b = x_1a_1 + \cdots + x_na_n$$

where there is no constant term x_0. Show that the normal equations are now $A^TA\alpha = A^T\mathbf{b}$, where $A = (a_{ij})$ $i = 1, \ldots, m; j = 1, \ldots, n$. (There is no initial column of 1's.)

3.* Suppose that we require a least-squares fit

$$b = x_0 + x_1a_1 + \cdots + x_na_n$$

where all numbers may be complex. Redefine the sum of squares $\phi(x)$ appropriately. Develop the normal equations $A^*Ax = A^*\mathbf{b}$, where $A^* = (\bar{A})^T$. In other words, generalize the theory in this section for *complex* data.

4. Suppose that we feel that some observations are more important or reliable than others. Redefine the function to be minimized as

$$\phi(x) = \sum_{i=1}^{m} \sigma_i^{-2}(b_i - x_0 - x_1a_{i1} - x_2a_{i2} - \cdots - x_na_{in})^2$$

Now what are the appropriate normal equations? Assume real data.

5. Find a least-squares fit $b = x_0 + x_1a_1 + x_2a_2 + x_3a_3 + x_4a_4$ for the data

b	a_1	a_2	a_3	a_4
1	1	−3	0	5
0	2	−6	0	10
0	3	−9	0	15
0	4	−12	1	3.1416

Note that $\det(A^T A) = 0$.

**MATRIX ANALYSIS OF
DIFFERENTIAL EQUATIONS**

3.1 INTRODUCTION

Although the theory of matrices is usually taught as a branch of algebra, matrices are a powerful tool in mathematical analysis. From a purely logical standpoint, this chapter is unnecessary to the development of the theory of matrices. Nevertheless, the study of differential equations provides an important motivation for the study of eigenvalues, eigenvectors, and canonical forms.

3.2 SYSTEMS OF LINEAR DIFFERENTIAL EQUATIONS

Consider the single differential equation of fourth order

$$\frac{d^4u}{dt^4} + \frac{e^t\,du}{dt} - tu = \cos \omega t \tag{1}$$

This equation is equivalent to a system of four differential equations of first order. Let

$$x_1 = u, \qquad x_2 = \frac{du}{dt}, \qquad x_3 = \frac{d^2u}{dt^2}, \qquad x_4 = \frac{d^3u}{dt^3} \tag{2}$$

Then we have

$$\frac{dx_1}{dt} = \qquad x_2$$

$$\frac{dx_2}{dt} = \qquad\qquad x_3$$

$$\frac{dx_3}{dt} = \qquad\qquad\qquad x_4 \tag{3}$$

$$\frac{dx_4}{dt} = tx_1 - e^t x_2 \qquad\qquad + \cos \omega t$$

The first three equations come from (2); the last comes from (1). The system (3) can be written with matrices and vectors in the form

$$\frac{dx}{dt} = A(t)x + f(t) \tag{4}$$

where

$$A(t) = \begin{bmatrix} 0 & 1 & 0 & 0 \\ 0 & 0 & 1 & 0 \\ 0 & 0 & 0 & 1 \\ t & -e^t & 0 & 0 \end{bmatrix}, \qquad f(t) = \begin{bmatrix} 0 \\ 0 \\ 0 \\ \cos \omega t \end{bmatrix}$$

Most systems of linear ordinary differential equations are equivalent to first-order systems (4). Consider

$$\frac{d^2u}{dt^2} + (\cos \omega t)\frac{dv}{dt} + u = t$$

$$\frac{dv}{dt} + \frac{du}{dt} + v = e^{\alpha t} \tag{5}$$

The highest derivative of u in (5) is u''; the highest derivative of v is v'. Solve for u'' and v' in terms of the lower-order derivatives:

$$u'' = t - (\cos \omega t)(e^{\alpha t} - u' - v) - u$$

$$v' = e^{\alpha t} - u' - v \tag{6}$$

Set

$$x_1 = u, \qquad x_2 = u', \qquad x_3 = v$$

Then

$$x_1' = x_2$$
$$x_2' = -x_1 + (\cos \omega t)x_2 + (\cos \omega t)x_3 - (\cos \omega t)e^{\alpha t} + t$$
$$x_3' = -x_2 - x_3 + e^{\alpha t}$$

Therefore, (5) is equivalent to the first-order system (4) where

$$A(t) \begin{bmatrix} 0 & 1 & 0 \\ -1 & \cos \omega t & \cos \omega t \\ 0 & -1 & -1 \end{bmatrix}, \qquad f(t) = \begin{bmatrix} 0 \\ t - (\cos \omega t)e^{\alpha t} \\ e^{\alpha t} \end{bmatrix} \tag{7}$$

The general principle is clear: Suppose that we have m differential equations for m unknowns $u_1, \ldots, u_m$. Let the highest-order derivative of u_i in the system be of order $\alpha_i \geqslant 1$. *If the* m × m *matrix of coefficients of these highest-order derivatives has a nonzero determinant, we may solve for the highest-order derivatives in terms of the lower-order derivatives.* We now define

$$x_1 = u_1, \qquad x_2 = u_1', \ldots, \qquad x_{\alpha_1} = u_1^{(\alpha_1 - 1)}$$

$$x_{\alpha_1 + 1} = u_2, \qquad x_{\alpha_1 + 2} = u_2', \ldots, \qquad x_{\alpha_1 + \alpha_2} = u_2^{(\alpha_2 - 1)} \tag{8}$$

$$\cdots\cdots\cdots\cdots\cdots\cdots\cdots\cdots\cdots \qquad x_n = u_m^{(\alpha_m - 1)}$$

where $n = \alpha_1 + \cdots + \alpha_m$. Now the x's may be used to form a first-order system $x' = Ax + f$.

PROBLEMS

1. Write the equation

$$u'' + tu' + u = 0$$

as a first-order system $x' = A(t)x$.

2. Write the system

$$u'' + 3v' + 4u + v = 8t$$
$$u'' - v' + u + v = \cos t$$

in the form $x' = Ax + f(t)$.

3. Can the system

$$u' + 2v' + 3u = 0$$
$$2u' + 4v' + v = \sin t$$

be put into the form $x' = Ax + f(t)$? Does this system have a solution satisfying the initial conditions $u(0) = 1, v(0) = 2$?

4. Let $x'(t) = A(t)x(t) + f(t)$ for $0 \leqslant t \leqslant 1$, with $x(0) = 0$. Let $f(t)$ range in some linear vector space of functions of t. Assuming the existence and uniqueness of the solution $x(t)$, show that the constant vector $x(1)$ depends *linearly* on the function $f(t)$.

5. Let $x'(t) = A(t)x(t)$ for $0 \leqslant t \leqslant 1$. Show that there is a constant matrix M such that $x(1) = Mx(0)$ for all solutions $x(t)$. Letting t vary backwards from 1 to 0, show that M has an inverse. (Assume the existence and uniqueness of the solution of the initial-value problem.)

6.* Assume the notation of Problem 5. Let $X(t)$ be the *matrix* satisfying the initial-value problem $X' = AX$, $X(0) = I$. Show that $M = X(1)$. [Hint: Write $x(t)$ in terms of $X(t)$ and $x(0)$.]

7.* Assume the notation of the last two problems. Assume that $A(t + 1) = A(t)$ for all t. Show that $x' = A(t)x$ has a nonzero solution $x(t)$ with $x(t + 1) \equiv x(t)$ if and only if the matrix $X(1) = M$ satisfies the condition $\det(M - I) = 0$.

3.3 REDUCTION TO THE HOMOGENEOUS SYSTEM

In this section we will show how the inhomogeneous system of linear differential equations $x' = Ax + f$ can be reduced, by matrix analysis, to the homogeneous system $x' = Ax$.

Let e^j be the jth unit vector: $e^j = (\delta_{ij})$ $(i = 1, \ldots, n)$. Let $u^j(t)$ solve the initial-value problem

$$\frac{du^j(t)}{dt} = A(t)u^j(t), \qquad u^j(0) = e^j \tag{1}$$

Let $X(t)$ be the $n \times n$ matrix whose jth column is the vector $u^j(t)$. Then (1), taken for $j = 1, \ldots, n$, is equivalent to the initial-value problem

$$\frac{d}{dt}X(t) = A(t)X(t) \tag{2}$$

$$X(0) = I \tag{3}$$

For simplicity, we shall suppose that all components of $A(t)$ are continuous.

The matrix $X(t)$ may be called the *fundamental solution* of the homogeneous equation (2). *For any initial vector,* $\mathrm{x}(0) = \mathrm{c}$, *the equation* (1) *has the solution* $\mathrm{x(t)} = \mathrm{X(t)c}$. Methods for computing $X(t)$ if A is constant, are given in the next two sections. In this section we shall assume that $X(t)$ is known.

To solve the inhomogeneous equation

$$\frac{dy}{dt} = A(t)y + f(t) \tag{4}$$

introduce a new unknown, $z(t)$, by the equation

$$y(t) = X(t)z(t) \tag{5}$$

Now we assert

$$\frac{dy}{dt} = \frac{dX}{dt}z + X\frac{dz}{dt} \tag{6}$$

This follows from differentiation of the identity $y_i = \sum X_{ij}z_j$.

Setting (6) in the left-hand side of (4), and (5) in the right-hand side of (4), we find

$$\frac{dX}{dt} z + X \frac{dz}{dt} = AXz + f \tag{7}$$

Since $dX/dt = AX$, we may simplify (7) to obtain

$$X(t) \frac{dz}{dt} = f(t) \tag{8}$$

By (3), $X(t)$ has an inverse for $t = 0$. Assume that $X^{-1}(t)$ exists and is continuous; the proof of this assumption is outlined in the Problems for this section. Assume that $f(t)$ is continuous. Then

$$\frac{dz}{dt} = X^{-1}(t)f(t) \tag{9}$$

$$z(t) = z(0) + \int_0^t X^{-1}(\tau)f(\tau)\,d\tau \tag{10}$$

From (5) and (10) we obtain the solution

$$\boxed{y(t) = X(t)y(0) + X(t) \int_0^t X^{-1}(\tau)f(\tau)\,d\tau} \tag{11}$$

Note that $z(0) = y(0)$ by (5).

EXAMPLE 1. We will solve the problem

$$\frac{dy}{dt} = \begin{bmatrix} 0 & 1 \\ -1 & 0 \end{bmatrix} y + \begin{bmatrix} 0 \\ e^{-t^2} \end{bmatrix} \tag{12}$$

We are given that (2) and (3) are satisfied by

$$X(t) = \begin{bmatrix} \cos t & \sin t \\ -\sin t & \cos t \end{bmatrix}$$

Then

$$X^{-1}(\tau) = \begin{bmatrix} \cos \tau & -\sin \tau \\ \sin \tau & \cos \tau \end{bmatrix}$$

By the trigonometrical addition-formulas,

$$X(t)\,X^{-1}(\tau) = \begin{bmatrix} \cos{(t-\tau)} & \sin{(t-\tau)} \\ -\sin{(t-\tau)} & \cos{(t-\tau)} \end{bmatrix} \tag{13}$$

Now by (11)

$$y(t) = X(t)y(0) + \int_0^t \begin{bmatrix} \sin{(t-\tau)} \\ \cos{(t-\tau)} \end{bmatrix} e^{-\tau^2}\,d\tau \tag{14}$$

Observe in (13) the curious identity

$$X(t)\,X^{-1}(\tau) = X(t-\tau) \tag{15}$$

We can show that this is always true if the matrix A is independent of t, as it is in (12). Suppose that

$$\frac{dX(t)}{dt} = AX(t), \qquad X(0) = I \quad (A \text{ constant}) \tag{16}$$

Let $Y(t) = X(t-\tau)$ for fixed τ. Evidently,

$$\frac{dY(t)}{dt} = AY(t), \qquad Y(\tau) = I \quad (\tau \text{ fixed}) \tag{17}$$

But *both* sides of (15) satisfy (17). The identity (15) now follows from the uniqueness of the solution of the initial-value problem (17).

We have just shown that, if A *is independent of* t, *the inhomogeneous equation* y′ = Ay + f(t) *has the solution*

$$\boxed{y(t) = X(t)y(0) + \int_0^t X(t-\tau)f(\tau)\,d\tau} \tag{18}$$

provided X′(t) = AX(t), X(0) = I.

That (18) provides the required solution may be verified independently by direct differentiation of the integral:

$$\frac{d}{dt}\int_0^t X(t-\tau)f(\tau)\,d\tau = X(0)f(t) + \int_0^t X'(t-\tau)f(\tau)\,d\tau$$

$$= f(t) + A\int_0^t X(t-\tau)f(\tau)\,d\tau \tag{19}$$

The equation $y' = Ay + f$ follows from adding (19) to

$$\frac{d}{dt}X(t)y(0) = AX(t)y(0) \tag{20}$$

Similarly, (11) may be verified directly.

PROBLEMS

1. We note that $(t + 1)^3$ and $(t + 1)^{-2}$ solve

$$(t + 1)^2 \phi'' - 6\phi = 0 \qquad (t \geqslant 0)$$

Find the fundamental matrix solution $X(t)$ for the system of equations

$$\phi' = \psi$$
$$\psi' = 6(t + 1)^{-2} \phi$$

Compute the Wronskian $\omega \equiv \det X$ and compute the inverse X^{-1}.

2. Solve the initial-value problem

$$x_1' = x_2 + e^{-t}, \qquad\qquad x_1(0) = 1$$
$$x_2' = 6(t + 1)^{-2} x_1 + \sqrt{t}\,, \qquad x_2(0) = 2$$

3. Define the *Wronskian* determinant

$$\omega(t) = \det [u_i^{(j)}(t)] \qquad (i, j = 1, \ldots, n)$$
$$= \det X(t)$$

where $u^j = u^{(j)}$ solves (1). Applying the rule for differentiation in Section 1.8, show that

$$\frac{d\omega}{dt} = \sum_{i=1}^{n} \omega_i(t)$$

where ω_i is the determinant written by replacing the ith row of the Wronskian ω by the row

$$\left(\sum_{k=1}^{n} a_{ik} u_k^{(1)}, \sum_{k=1}^{n} a_{ik} u_k^{(2)}, \ldots, \sum_{k=1}^{n} a_{ik} u_k^{(n)} \right)$$

4. Write the result of Problem 3 explicitly for the general 2×2 system. Prove that the determinants ω_1 and ω_2 can be simplified to the forms:

$$\omega_1 = a_{11} \omega, \qquad \omega_2 = a_{22} \omega$$

5. For the general $n \times n$ system show that

$$\omega_1 = a_{11} \omega, \qquad \omega_2 = a_{22} \omega, \ldots, \omega_n = a_{nn} \omega$$

6. Show that the Wronskian, itself, satisfies a differential equation. Deduce that the Wronskian equals

$$\omega(0) \cdot \exp \int_0^t [a_{11}(\tau) + \cdots + a_{nn}(\tau)]\, d\tau$$

or simply $\omega(0) \cdot \exp [(\sum a_{kk})t]$ if the a's are constants. Can the Wronskian ever equal zero?

7. If the fundamental matrix $X(t)$, solving (2), exists for $0 \leqslant t < t_1$, prove that the inverse matrix $X^{-1}(t)$ exists and is continuously differentiable for $0 \leqslant t < t_1$.

3.4 SOLUTION BY THE EXPONENTIAL MATRIX

We have reduced systems of linear differential equations to the problem of obtaining the fundamental solution $X(t)$ solving

$$\frac{dX}{dt} = AX, \qquad X(0) = I \tag{1}$$

From now on we shall suppose that A is an $n \times n$ *constant* matrix.

If $n = 1$, we have the familiar solution

$$e^{At} = \sum_{k=0}^{\infty} \frac{1}{k!} A^k t^k \tag{2}$$

But the right-hand side of (2) may have a meaning even if $n > 1$. Let $A^0 = I$ and, if $k \geqslant 1$,

$$A^k = A \cdots A \qquad (k \text{ factors}) \tag{3}$$

Then the partial sums

$$S^{(N)}(t) = \sum_{k=0}^{N} \frac{1}{k!} A^k t^k \tag{4}$$

are well-defined $n \times n$ matrices:

$$S^{(N)}(t) = [s_{ij}^{(N)}(t)] \qquad (i, j = 1, \ldots, n) \tag{5}$$

For $n > 1$ the right-hand side of (2) makes sense if each component partial sum $s_{ij}^{(N)}$ tends to a limit as $N \to \infty$. We then regard (2) as a definition. For $t = 0$, $\exp(At)$ has the value I. Differentiation of (2) term by term yields

$$\begin{aligned}
\frac{d}{dt} e^{At} &= \sum_{k=1}^{\infty} \frac{1}{k!} A^k k t^{k-1} \\
&= A \sum_{k=1}^{\infty} \frac{1}{(k-1)!} A^{k-1} t^{k-1} = A \sum_{m=0}^{\infty} \frac{1}{m!} A^m t^m = A e^{At}
\end{aligned} \tag{6}$$

This procedure is valid if the resulting infinite series of matrices converges uniformly for t in any bounded interval.

Theorem 1. *Let* A *be an* n $\times$ n *matrix. Then the infinite series of matrices*

$$e^{At} \equiv \sum_{k=0}^{\infty} \frac{1}{k!} A^k t^k \tag{7}$$

converges uniformly and absolutely for t *in any bounded interval, and provides the solution* X(t) *to the initial-value problem* X′ = AX, X(0) = I.

Proof. The formal term-by-term differentiation (6) shows that we need only to establish the uniform and absolute convergence in each interval $0 \leqslant t \leqslant t_1$. Define

$$|A| \equiv \max_i \sum_{j=1}^{n} |a_{ij}| \tag{8}$$

Note that $|A| \geqslant |a_{ij}|$ for all i, j. For example, if

$$A = \begin{bmatrix} 14 & -14 \\ 5 & 10 \end{bmatrix}$$

then $|A| = 14 + 14 = 28 > 5 + 10$. If B is another $n \times n$ matrix,

$$\begin{aligned} |AB| &= \max_i \sum_{j=1}^{n} \left| \sum_{k=1}^{n} a_{ik}b_{kj} \right| \\ &\leqslant \max_i \sum_{j=1}^{n} \sum_{k=1}^{n} |a_{ik}||b_{kj}| = \max_i \sum_{k=1}^{n} |a_{ik}| \left(\sum_{j=1}^{n} |b_{kj}| \right) \\ &\leqslant \max_i \sum_{k=1}^{n} |a_{ik}||B| = |A||B| \end{aligned} \tag{9}$$

Therefore, $|A^k| \leqslant |A|^k$, and for every i, j, the i, j component of the matrix $(k!)^{-1}A^k t^k$ has absolute value $\leqslant (k!)^{-1}\alpha^k t^k$, where $\alpha = |A|$. Also, therefore, the i, j component series in (7) is dominated by $\sum (k!)^{-1}\alpha^k t_1^k = \exp \alpha t_1 < \infty$. This completes the proof.

This argument made use of a particular *matrix norm* $|A|$. We will discuss matrix norms at length in Section 6.9.

PROBLEMS

1. Let A be an $n \times n$ matrix. How shall you define the matrix functions $\cos At$ and $\sin At$?

2. If the power series $\sum \alpha_k \zeta^k$ converges (and therefore converges absolutely) for all ζ, and if A is an $n \times n$ matrix, prove the "convergence" of the series $\sum \alpha_k A^k$.

3. Let A be an $n \times n$ constant matrix, with $\det A \neq 0$. Solve the initial-value problem

$$\frac{d^2x(t)}{dt^2} + A^2x(t) = 0, \qquad x(0) = g, \qquad \frac{dx(0)}{dt} = h$$

4. Let A be a matrix which can be written in the *canonical form* $A = B\Lambda B^{-1}$,

where $\Lambda = \operatorname{diag}(\lambda_1, \ldots, \lambda_n)$. (In Chapter 4 we shall prove that most matrices have this property.) Let $\sum \alpha_k \zeta^k$ converge for $|\zeta| < \gamma$ and diverge for $|\zeta| > \gamma$. Prove that $A^k = B\Lambda^k B^{-1}$ for all $k = 0, 1, \ldots$. Under what condition on $\lambda_1, \ldots, \lambda_n$ does the infinite series of matrices $\sum \alpha_k A^k$ converge?

3.5 SOLUTION BY EIGENVALUES AND EIGENVECTORS

For the general initial-value problem $x'(t) = Ax(t)$ we have found the solution $x(t) = X(t)x(0)$, where $X(t) = \exp(At)$. This form of the solution tells us very little. For example, it does not tell us whether the solution tends to zero, oscillates, or becomes unbounded as $t \to \infty$.

Let us look for particular solutions of $x'(t) = Ax(t)$ of the form

$$x(t) = e^{\lambda t}c \qquad (c = \text{const} \neq 0) \tag{1}$$

The differential equation yields

$$\lambda e^{\lambda t}c = Ae^{\lambda t}c$$

Dividing both sides by $e^{\lambda t}$ gives

$$\lambda c = Ac \quad \text{or} \quad (\lambda I - A)c = 0 \quad (c \neq 0) \tag{2}$$

The *characteristic equation* (2) should be interpreted by the question: *For which real or complex numbers λ does the homogeneous equation (2) have a solution* $c \neq 0$?

We have already answered this question in Section 2.4. *The necessary and sufficient condition on λ which allows (2) to have a solution $c \neq 0$ is*

$$\det(\lambda I - A) = 0 \tag{3}$$

EXAMPLE 1. Let

$$A = \begin{bmatrix} -7 & 4 \\ -8 & 1 \end{bmatrix}$$

Equation (3) becomes

$$\begin{vmatrix} \lambda + 7 & -4 \\ 8 & \lambda - 1 \end{vmatrix} = \lambda^2 + 6\lambda + 25 = 0 \tag{4}$$

The roots of this equation are the *eigenvalues*

$$\lambda_1 = -3 + 4i \quad \text{and} \quad \lambda_2 = -3 - 4i \tag{5}$$

The *eigenvector* c^1 belonging to λ_1 is found from equation (2):

$$0 = (\lambda_1 I - A)c^1 = \begin{bmatrix} 4+4i, & -4 \\ 8, & -4+4i \end{bmatrix} \begin{bmatrix} c_1^1 \\ c_2^1 \end{bmatrix} \tag{6}$$

This homogeneous equation has the nonzero solution

$$c^1 = \begin{bmatrix} 1 \\ 1+i \end{bmatrix} \tag{7}$$

Similarly, the equation $0 = (\lambda_2 I - A)c^2$ is solved by the eigenvector $c^2 = \mathrm{col}\,(1, 1-i)$:

$$0 = (\lambda_2 I - A)c^2 = \begin{bmatrix} 4-4i, & -4 \\ 8, & -4-4i \end{bmatrix} \begin{bmatrix} 1 \\ 1-i \end{bmatrix} \tag{8}$$

From the eigenvalues and eigenvectors, we construct the particular solutions $c \exp \lambda t$. These are the *eigensolutions:*

$$x^1(t) = \begin{bmatrix} 1 \\ 1+i \end{bmatrix} e^{(-3+4i)t}, \qquad x^2(t) = \begin{bmatrix} 1 \\ 1-i \end{bmatrix} e^{(-3-4i)t} \tag{9}$$

of the differential equation $x'(t) = Ax(t)$. We now require the initial condition

$$x(0) = \begin{bmatrix} 2 \\ -2 \end{bmatrix} \tag{10}$$

Neither of the two eigensolutions (9) satisfies the required initial condition (10). Therefore, we try to find $x(t)$ as a linear combination:

$$x(t) = \alpha_1 x^1(t) + \alpha_2 x^2(t) \tag{11}$$

For every α_1 and α_2, the linear combination (11) solves the linear, homogeneous differential equation $x' = Ax$. We pick α_1 and α_2 to satisfy the initial condition (10):

$$x(0) = \alpha_1 x^1(0) + \alpha_2 x^2(0) = \alpha_1 c^1 + \alpha_2 c^2$$

$$\begin{bmatrix} 2 \\ -2 \end{bmatrix} = \alpha_1 \begin{bmatrix} 1 \\ 1+i \end{bmatrix} + \alpha_2 \begin{bmatrix} 1 \\ 1-i \end{bmatrix} \tag{12}$$

Observe that the eigenvectors c^1 and c^2 are linearly independent, and are hence a basis for E^2. We can therefore solve for α_1 and α_2:

$$\alpha_1 = 1 + 2i, \qquad \alpha_2 = 1 - 2i$$

The required solution x now takes the form

$$x(t) = (1 + 2i)\begin{bmatrix} 1 \\ 1 + i \end{bmatrix} e^{(-3+4i)t} + (1 - 2i)\begin{bmatrix} 1 \\ 1 - i \end{bmatrix} e^{(-3-4i)t} \qquad (13)$$

or, in real form,

$$x(t) = 2e^{-3t}\begin{bmatrix} \cos 4t & -2\sin 4t \\ -\cos 4t & -3\sin 4t \end{bmatrix} \qquad (14)$$

The expression of $x(t)$ as a linear combination of eigensolutions $c^j \exp(\lambda_j t)$ tells us a great deal about the solution. Let $\lambda_j = \gamma_j + i\omega_j$. Then

$$e^{\lambda_j t} = e^{\gamma_j t}(\cos \omega_j t + i\sin \omega_j t) \qquad (15)$$

The amplitude of the eigensolution $\mathrm{x}^j(t)$ *is growing, staying constant, or decaying depending on whether* $\gamma_j > 0, \gamma_j = 0,$ *or* $\gamma_j < 0$. *The imaginary part* ω_j *gives the angular frequency of the eigensolution oscillation.* In (13) of Example 1, there is a decay of amplitude because $\gamma_1 = \gamma_2 = -3$. There are oscillations with angular frequencies $\omega_1 = 4, \omega_2 = -4$.

In the general case of an $n \times n$ matrix, there are n eigenvalues $\lambda_1, \ldots, \lambda_n$, because, as we shall prove in Section 4.1, the characteristic determinant $\det(\lambda I - A)$ is a polynomial of degree n. There are corresponding eigenvectors $c^1, \ldots, c^n$. We shall see, in the next chapter, that the eigenvectors are usually (but not *always*) linearly independent and, therefore, are a basis for E^n. Given an initial vector, $x(0)$, we can find a representation

$$x(0) = \alpha_1 c^1 + \alpha_2 c^2 + \cdots + \alpha_n c^n \qquad (16)$$

Then the solution of the differential equation $x'(t) = Ax(t)$ with initial state $x(0)$, is a linear combination of eigensolutions:

$$x(t) = \alpha_1 c^1 e^{\lambda_1 t} + \alpha_2 c^2 e^{\lambda_2 t} + \cdots + \alpha_n c^n e^{\lambda_n t} \qquad (17)$$

The growth and the oscillation of the solution are observed from the real and imaginary parts of the eigenvalues.

Even when the eigenvectors $c^1, \ldots, c^n$ are dependent, a solution $x(t)$ is provided by the Jordan canonical form, which is the subject of Chapter 5.

EXAMPLE 2. Let us obtain the fundamental solution $X(t)$ of the differential equation

$$\frac{dx}{dt} = \begin{bmatrix} -7 & 4 \\ -8 & 1 \end{bmatrix} x \qquad (18)$$

The fundamental solution X is characterized by the initial-value problem

$$\frac{dX(t)}{dt} = AX(t), \qquad X(0) = I \tag{19}$$

Let $Y(t)$ be the matrix with columns that are the eigensolutions $x^{(1)}(t)$, $x^{(2)}(t)$, which were constructed in (9). Thus,

$$
\begin{aligned}
Y(t) &= [x^{(1)}(t), x^{(2)}(t)] \\
&= [e^{\lambda_1 t} c^{(1)}, e^{\lambda_2 t} c^{(2)}] \\
&= [c^{(1)}, c^{(2)}] \begin{bmatrix} e^{\lambda_1 t} & 0 \\ 0 & e^{\lambda_2 t} \end{bmatrix} \\
&= \begin{bmatrix} 1, & 1 \\ 1+i, & 1-i \end{bmatrix} \begin{bmatrix} e^{(-3+4i)t}, & 0 \\ 0, & e^{(-3-4i)t} \end{bmatrix}
\end{aligned} \tag{20}
$$

This matrix is not $X(t)$ because it fails to satisfy the initial condition $X(0) = I$. We now assert that

$$X(t) = Y(t)Y^{-1}(0) \tag{21}$$

Proof. The matrix (21) equals I when $t = 0$. Further, since each column of $Y(t)$ is a solution of $x' = Ax$, the whole matrix Y satisfies $Y' = AY$. Therefore,

$$\frac{d}{dt} Y(t) \cdot Y^{-1}(0) = A Y(t) \cdot Y^{-1}(0)$$

Thus, the identity (21) is proved, and we may compute

$$X(t) = Y(t) \cdot \frac{1}{2} \begin{bmatrix} 1+i, & -i \\ 1-i, & i \end{bmatrix} \tag{22}$$

where $Y(t)$ is the matrix (20). From (22) we compute

$$X(t) = e^{-3t} \begin{bmatrix} \cos 4t - \sin 4t, & \sin 4t \\ -2 \sin 4t, & \cos 4t + \sin 4t \end{bmatrix} \tag{23}$$

In general, if $c^{(1)}, \ldots, c^{(n)}$ *are independent eigenvectors belonging to* $\lambda_1, \ldots, \lambda_n$, *the fundamental solution* $X(t)$ *solving* (19) *is given by*

$$X(t) = C \begin{bmatrix} e^{\lambda_1 t} & & O \\ & \cdot & \\ & & \cdot \\ O & & e^{\lambda_n t} \end{bmatrix} C^{-1} \tag{24}$$

where C *is the square matrix with columns of* $c^{(1)}, \ldots, c^{(n)}$.

Proof. The matrix of eigensolutions is given by

$$Y(t) = C \operatorname{diag} (e^{\lambda_1 t}, \ldots, e^{\lambda_n t})$$

and $Y^{-1}(0) = C^{-1}$.

EXAMPLE 3. We will solve the inhomogeneous initial-value problem

$$\frac{dx}{dt} = \begin{bmatrix} -7 & 4 \\ -8 & 1 \end{bmatrix} x + \begin{bmatrix} 0 \\ \sqrt{t} \end{bmatrix} \quad (t > 0)$$

$$x(0) = \begin{bmatrix} 1 \\ 0 \end{bmatrix}$$

(25)

According to Section 3.3, we have

$$x(t) = X(t) \begin{bmatrix} 1 \\ 0 \end{bmatrix} + \int_0^t X(t - \tau) \begin{bmatrix} 0 \\ \sqrt{\tau} \end{bmatrix} d\tau$$

From (23) we compute

$$x(t) = e^{-3t} \begin{bmatrix} \cos 4t - \sin 4t \\ -2 \sin 4t \end{bmatrix}$$

$$+ \int_0^t e^{-3(t-\tau)} \begin{bmatrix} \sin 4(t - \tau) \\ \cos 4(t - \tau) + \sin 4(t - \tau) \end{bmatrix} \sqrt{\tau} \, d\tau$$

PROBLEMS

1. Solve the initial-value problem

$$\begin{aligned} x_1' &= x_1 - 2x_2, & x_1(0) &= 4 \\ x_2' &= x_1 + 3x_2, & x_2(0) &= 5 \end{aligned}$$

First state the problem in vector-matrix form.

2. Find the fundamental matrix-solution $X(t)$ for the system in Problem 1.

3. Solve the initial-value problem

$$\begin{aligned} x_1' &= x_1 - 2x_2 + t^{1/3}, & x_1(0) &= 1 \\ x_2' &= x_1 + 3x_2 + t^{2/3}, & x_2(0) &= 1 \end{aligned}$$

Use the result of Problem 2.

4. Find *all* the eigensolutions $c \exp \lambda t$ of the system

$$\begin{aligned} x_1' &= 7x_1 \\ x_2' &= x_1 + 7x_2 \end{aligned}$$

Are the methods of this section directly applicable to this system?

5. For the system in Problem 4 find a fundamental matrix-solution satisfying $X' = AX$, $X(0) = I$. Is there a matrix Y of independent eigensolutions? Is the method of Section 3.3 for solving $x' = Ax + f$ still valid?

4 EIGENVALUES, EIGENVECTORS, AND CANONICAL FORMS

4.1 MATRICES WITH DISTINCT EIGENVALUES

The preceding chapter may be regarded as an introduction to the study of eigenvalues, eigenvectors, and canonical forms. If A is an $n \times n$ matrix, we define the *eigenvalues* of A *to be those numbers* λ for which the *characteristic equation* $Ac = \lambda c$ has a solution $c \neq 0$; the vector c is called an *eigenvector* belonging to the eigenvalue λ.

Theorem 1. *The number* λ *is an eigenvalue of the square matrix* A *if and only if* $\det(\lambda I - A) = 0$.

Proof. This result follows from Theorem 1 of Section 2.4 if A is replaced by $\lambda I - A$.

For application to differential equations it is important that the $n \times n$ matrix A have n linearly independent eigenvectors. Unfortunately, this is not always true.

EXAMPLE 1. Let

$$A = \begin{bmatrix} 7 & 3 \\ 0 & 7 \end{bmatrix}$$

Then

$$\det(\lambda I - A) = \begin{vmatrix} \lambda - 7, & -3 \\ 0, & \lambda - 7 \end{vmatrix} = (\lambda - 7)^2$$

Therefore, $\lambda = 7$ is the only eigenvalue. The characteristic equation becomes

$$(7I - A)c = \begin{bmatrix} 0 & -3 \\ 0 & 0 \end{bmatrix} \begin{bmatrix} c_1 \\ c_2 \end{bmatrix} = \begin{bmatrix} 0 \\ 0 \end{bmatrix}$$

Thus, the components of c must satisfy the equations

$$0c_1 - 3c_2 = 0, \qquad 0c_1 + 0c_2 = 0$$

Therefore, we must have $c_2 = 0$, and all eigenvectors of A have the form

$$c = \begin{bmatrix} \alpha \\ 0 \end{bmatrix} \qquad \text{(with } \alpha \neq 0\text{)}$$

Every two vectors of this form are dependent. The differential equation $x' = Ax$ is, of course, still solvable by means of the exponential matrix, c.f. Section 3.4, and we shall later find another solution by means of the Jordan canonical form.

EXAMPLE 2. Even if an $n \times n$ matrix does not have n distinct eigenvalues, it *may* have n linearly independent eigenvectors. Let

$$A = I = \begin{bmatrix} 1 & 0 \\ 0 & 1 \end{bmatrix}$$

then $\det (\lambda I - A) = (\lambda - 1)^2$. The only eigenvalue is $\lambda = 1$. The characteristic equation becomes

$$(1I - A)c = \begin{bmatrix} 0 & 0 \\ 0 & 0 \end{bmatrix} c = \begin{bmatrix} 0 \\ 0 \end{bmatrix}$$

Therefore, every nonzero c is an eigenvector. We may, for example, choose

$$c^1 = \begin{bmatrix} 9 \\ 17 \end{bmatrix}, \qquad c^2 = \begin{bmatrix} 8 \\ 3 \end{bmatrix}$$

as two linearly independent eigenvectors.

Theorem 2. *Let* A *be an* n × n *matrix. Then the characteristic determinant.* det $(\lambda I - A)$ *is a polynomial of degree* n *in* λ, *where the coefficient of* λ^n *equals* 1.

Proof. Let $B = \lambda I - A$. In the expansion

$$\det B = \sum s(j) b_{1j_1} \ldots b_{nj_n}$$

the only permutation j which yields the power λ^n is the identity permutation. The other permutations j give lower powers of λ. But

$$b_{11}b_{22} \ldots b_{nn} = (\lambda - a_{11})(\lambda - a_{22}) \ldots (\lambda - a_{nn}) = \lambda^n + \cdots \qquad (1)$$

Therefore, the coefficient of λ^n equals 1.

It is conventional to say that every $n \times n$ matrix A has n eigenvalues, namely the numbers $\lambda_1, \lambda_2, \ldots, \lambda_n$ which appear in the factorization

$$\det(\lambda I - A) = (\lambda - \lambda_1)(\lambda - \lambda_2) \ldots (\lambda - \lambda_n) \qquad (2)$$

Some of the numbers λ_j may be identical. Thus, the three eigenvalues of the 3×3 identity matrix are 1, 1, and 1. Alternatively, we may factor $\det(\lambda I - A)$ in the form

$$\det(\lambda I - A) = (\lambda - \lambda_1)^{m_1}(\lambda - \lambda_2)^{m_2} \ldots (\lambda - \lambda_r)^{m_r} \qquad (3)$$

where $\lambda_1, \ldots, \lambda_r$ are different, and where the positive integers $m_1, \ldots, m_r$ are the *multiplicities of the eigenvalues*. Of course, $m_1 + \cdots + m_r = n$. Thus, $\lambda_1 = 1$ is an eigenvalue of multiplicity $m_1 = 3$ of the 3×3 identity matrix. A matrix A is said to have *distinct eigenvalues* if all λ_j are different in the factorization (2) or, equivalently, if all $m_j = 1$ and $r = n$ in the factorization (3).

Theorem 3. *Let* A *be an* n $\times$ n *matrix with distinct eigenvalues* $\lambda_1, \ldots, \lambda_n$. *Then* A *has, correspondingly,* n *linearly independent eigenvectors* $c^1, \ldots, c^n$. *Moreover, the eigenvector* c^j *belonging to the eigenvalue* λ_j *is unique apart from a nonzero scalar multiplier.*

Thus, if A has distinct eigenvalues, the differential equation $x' = Ax$ with given initial state $x(0)$, has the solution given in Section 3.5 in terms of eigenvalues and eigenvectors.

Proof of the Theorem. Let $c^1, \ldots, c^n$ be eigenvectors:

$$Ac^1 = \lambda_1 c^1, \ldots, Ac^n = \lambda_n c^n \qquad \text{(all } c^j \neq 0\text{)} \qquad (4)$$

Suppose that $c^1, \ldots, c^n$ are dependent. Let $k \leqslant n$ be the *least* positive integer such that k of the c's are dependent. Without loss of generality, suppose that $c^1, \ldots, c^k$ are dependent:

$$\alpha_1 c^1 + \alpha_2 c^2 + \cdots + \alpha_k c^k = 0 \qquad \text{(not all } \alpha_j = 0\text{)} \qquad (5)$$

In the last equation $k \geqslant 2$, since all c^j are nonzero. Furthermore, *all* α_j are nonzero; otherwise, $k - 1$ of the c's would be dependent, and k would not be the least integer such that k of the c's were dependent.

To eliminate α_k, multiply (5) by the matrix $A - \lambda_k I$. Now

$$(A - \lambda_k I)c^1 = (\lambda_1 - \lambda_k)c^1, \ldots, (A - \lambda_k I)c^{k-1} = (\lambda_{k-1} - \lambda_k)c^{k-1} \qquad (6)$$

Therefore, multiplication of (5) by $A - \lambda_k I$ gives

$$\alpha_1(\lambda_1 - \lambda_k)c^1 + \cdots + \alpha_{k-1}(\lambda_{k-1} - \lambda_k)c^{k-1} = 0 \qquad (7)$$

Because the λ_j are distinct, $\lambda_1 - \lambda_k \neq 0, \ldots, \lambda_{k-1} - \lambda_k \neq 0$. But all α_j are nonzero. Therefore, all coefficients $\alpha_j(\lambda_j - \lambda_k)$ are nonzero in (7). Therefore, just $k - 1$ of the c's are dependent. This contradiction proves that $c^1, \ldots, c^n$ are independent.

Now we prove the uniqueness. We must show that

$$Ac = \lambda_j c, \qquad c \neq 0 \quad \text{implies} \quad c = \mu c^j \qquad (8)$$

Since the n vectors $c^1, \ldots, c^n$ are independent, they are a basis for E^n. Therefore, there is a representation

$$c = \beta_1 c^1 + \cdots + \beta_j c^j + \cdots + \beta_n c^n \qquad (9)$$

Multiplication of (9) by $A - \lambda_j I$ gives

$$0 = \beta_1(\lambda_1 - \lambda_j)c^1 + \cdots + \beta_n(\lambda_n - \lambda_j)c^n \qquad (10)$$

But $\lambda_i - \lambda_j \neq 0$ if $i \neq j$. Because $c^1, \ldots, c^n$ are independent, (10) implies $\beta_i = 0$ if $i \neq j$. Equation (9) now takes the form $c = \beta_j c^j$, so (8) is true with $\mu = \beta_j$.

PROBLEMS

1. Find independent eigenvectors for the matrix

$$A = \begin{bmatrix} 1 & 2 \\ -3 & 1 \end{bmatrix}$$

Express the vector $x = \text{col } (1, 2)$ as a linear combination of the eigenvectors of A.

2. Does the singular matrix

$$A = \begin{bmatrix} 1 & 1 \\ 1 & 1 \end{bmatrix}$$

have two independent eigenvectors?

3. Let

$$A = \begin{bmatrix} 0 & 1 & 0 & 0 \\ 0 & 0 & 1 & 0 \\ 0 & 0 & 0 & 1 \\ -\alpha_4 & -\alpha_3 & -\alpha_2 & -\alpha_1 \end{bmatrix}, \quad x = \begin{bmatrix} x_1 \\ x_2 \\ x_3 \\ x_4 \end{bmatrix}$$

Can x be an eigenvector of this matrix, A, if $x_1 = 0$? If λ is an eigenvalue of A, and if $x_1 = 1$, what is the form of the eigenvector x? What is the characteristic polynomial of A? Under what condition does A have four linearly independent eigenvectors?

4. Generalize the last problem, replacing 4 by n. (The matrix, A, is known as the *companion matrix* of the polynomial $\lambda^n + \alpha_1\lambda^{n-1} + \cdots + \alpha_n$.)

4.2 THE CANONICAL DIAGONAL FORM

Two $n \times n$ matrices A and B are called *similar* if there exists an $n \times n$ matrix T with det $T \neq 0$ for which

$$T^{-1}AT = B \tag{1}$$

We will show that *similar matrices represent the same linear transformation in different coordinate systems.*

We think of A as a linear transformation on the Euclidean space E^n. Each vector x is mapped into a vector x' by the transformation $x' = Ax$. Let the vectors $t^1, \ldots, t^n$ be a basis for E^n. Then x and x' have representations

$$\begin{aligned}
x &= y_1 t^1 + y_2 t^2 + \cdots + y_n t^n \\
x' &= y_1' t^1 + y_2' t^2 + \cdots + y_n' t^n
\end{aligned} \tag{2}$$

We may think of the numbers $y_1, \ldots, y_n$ as *coordinates* of the vector x with respect to the basis $t^1, \ldots, t^n$. The numbers $y_1', \ldots, y_n'$ are the coordinates of x'. The transformation $x \rightarrow x'$ is equivalent to a transformation $y \rightarrow y'$. The coordinates x_i, x_i' refer to the basis $e^1, \ldots, e^n$; the coordinates y_i, y_i' refer to the basis $t^1, \ldots, t^n$.

If $x' = Ax$, what is the relationship between y and y'? Let T be the matrix whose columns are $t^1, \ldots, t^n$. We have det $T \neq 0$ because the t's form a basis. Equation (2) states

$$x = Ty, \qquad x' = Ty' \tag{2'}$$

Now the transformation $x' = Ax$ has the representation

$$(Ty') = A(Ty) \tag{3}$$

Solving for y', we find $y' = (T^{-1}AT)y$.

EXAMPLE 1. Let

$$A = \begin{bmatrix} 0 & -1 \\ 1 & 0 \end{bmatrix} \tag{4}$$

The transformation $x' = Ax$ is a rotation of E^2 counterclockwise through $90°$. Choose the basis

$$t^1 = \begin{bmatrix} 1 \\ 3 \end{bmatrix}, \qquad t^2 = \begin{bmatrix} 2 \\ 7 \end{bmatrix} \tag{5}$$

Now x and x' have the coordinates y_1, y_2 and y_1', y_2' given by the equations

$$\begin{bmatrix} x_1 \\ x_2 \end{bmatrix} = y_1 \begin{bmatrix} 1 \\ 3 \end{bmatrix} + y_2 \begin{bmatrix} 2 \\ 7 \end{bmatrix}, \qquad \begin{bmatrix} x_1' \\ x_2' \end{bmatrix} = y_1' \begin{bmatrix} 1 \\ 3 \end{bmatrix} + y_2' \begin{bmatrix} 2 \\ 7 \end{bmatrix}$$

In other words, $x = Ty$ and $x' = Ty'$ where

$$T = \begin{bmatrix} 1 & 2 \\ 3 & 7 \end{bmatrix}$$

Now $x' = Ax$ becomes $y' = T^{-1}ATy$:

$$y' = \begin{bmatrix} 7 & -2 \\ -3 & 1 \end{bmatrix} \begin{bmatrix} 0 & -1 \\ 1 & 0 \end{bmatrix} \begin{bmatrix} 1 & 2 \\ 3 & 7 \end{bmatrix} y$$

Multiplying the three matrices, we find $y' = By$ with

$$B = \begin{bmatrix} 7 & -2 \\ -3 & 1 \end{bmatrix} \begin{bmatrix} -3 & -7 \\ 1 & 2 \end{bmatrix} = \begin{bmatrix} -23 & -53 \\ 10 & 23 \end{bmatrix} \tag{6}$$

This matrix B represents the counterclockwise rotation of E^2 through $90°$ *if* the vectors in E^2 are expressed in the coordinate system belonging to the basis (5).

Theorem 1. *Similar matrices have the same eigenvalues with the same multiplicities.*

Proof. Let $T^{-1}AT = B$. Now for all complex λ,

$$\begin{aligned} \det(\lambda I - B) &= \det(\lambda I - T^{-1}AT) \\ &= \det[T^{-1}(\lambda I - A)T] \\ &= (\det T^{-1})[\det(\lambda I - A)](\det T) \end{aligned}$$

But

$$(\det T^{-1})(\det T) = \det T^{-1}T = \det I = 1$$

Therefore, $\det(\lambda I - B) = \det(\lambda I - A)$; this completes the proof.

EXAMPLE 2. The matrices A and B in (4) and (6) both have the characteristic determinant $\lambda^2 + 1$.

We may ask whether, conversely, two matrices must be similar if they have the same eigenvalues with the same multiplicities. The answer is no.

EXAMPLE 3. The matrices

$$A = \begin{bmatrix} 1 & 0 \\ 0 & 1 \end{bmatrix} \quad \text{and} \quad B = \begin{bmatrix} 1 & 2 \\ 0 & 1 \end{bmatrix} \tag{7}$$

cannot be similar because $T^{-1}AT = T^{-1}T = I$ for all T.

Theorem 2. *An* n × n *matrix* A *is similar to a diagonal matrix if and only if* A *has* n *linearly independent eigenvectors. In particular,* A *is similar to a diagonal matrix if* A *has distinct eigenvalues.*

This remarkable theorem states that practically every linear transformation, looked at in the right coordinate system, can be represented by uncoupled stretchings of the coordinates. However, the "right" coordinates and the "stretching" factors may have to be complex numbers. A diagonal matrix, Λ, to which A is similar is known as a *canonical diagonal form* related to A.

Proof of the Theorem. First suppose that A is similar to a diagonal matrix:

$$T^{-1}AT = \begin{bmatrix} \alpha_1 & & & 0 \\ & \alpha_2 & & \\ & & \cdot & \\ & & & \cdot \\ 0 & & & \alpha_n \end{bmatrix} = \Lambda \tag{8}$$

Let $t^1, \ldots, t^n$ be the linearly independent columns of the nonsingular matrix T. Multiply both sides of (8) on the left by T. The jth column of AT is At^j; the jth column of $T\Lambda$ is $\alpha_j t^j$. Therefore, (8) implies

$$At^j = \alpha_j t^j \qquad (j = 1, \ldots, n) \tag{9}$$

Thus, the independent vectors t^j are eigenvectors of A. By Theorem 1, *the numbers α_j are the eigenvalues of* A *with the same multiplicities.*

Conversely, suppose that A has n independent eigenvectors $t^1, \ldots, t^n$. Let T be the nonsingular matrix with columns that are the vectors t^j. From the characteristic equations (9) we conclude that $AT = T\Lambda$, and hence $T^{-1}AT = \Lambda$.

EXAMPLE 4. Let

$$A = \begin{bmatrix} 0 & -1 \\ 1 & 0 \end{bmatrix} \tag{10}$$

The eigenvalues of A are $\alpha_1 = i$ and $\alpha_2 = -i$. Corresponding eigenvectors are

$$t^1 = \begin{bmatrix} 1 \\ -i \end{bmatrix} \quad \text{and} \quad t^2 = \begin{bmatrix} 1 \\ i \end{bmatrix} \tag{11}$$

Now

$$T^{-1}AT = \frac{1}{2i}\begin{bmatrix} i & -1 \\ i & 1 \end{bmatrix}\begin{bmatrix} 0 & -1 \\ 1 & 0 \end{bmatrix}\begin{bmatrix} 1 & 1 \\ -i & i \end{bmatrix} = \begin{bmatrix} i & 0 \\ 0 & -i \end{bmatrix} = \Lambda$$

If we represent any vector x by coordinates y_1, y_2 with respect to the basis t^1, t^2, we have

$$x = y_1 t^1 + y_2 t^2, \qquad Ax = (iy_1)t^1 + (-iy_2)t^2$$

The eigenvalues i and $-i$ give uncoupled "stretchings" of the coordinates y_1, y_2.

EXAMPLE 5. Let A be an $n \times n$ matrix with n linearly independent eigenvectors $c^1, \ldots, c^n$. Let C have the vectors c^j as columns. To solve the initial-value problem

$$\frac{dx}{dt} = Ax, \qquad x(0) = x^0 \tag{12}$$

make the change of coordinates $x = Cy$. Now (12) becomes

$$C\frac{dy}{dt} = ACy, \qquad Cy(0) = x^0 \tag{13}$$

Multiplication of (13) on the left by C^{-1} gives

$$\frac{dy}{dt} = \Lambda y, \qquad y(0) = C^{-1}x^0 \equiv y^0 \tag{14}$$

where $C^{-1}AC = \Lambda = \text{diag}\,(\lambda_1, \ldots, \lambda_n)$. But the system (14) is *uncoupled*; by components it reads

$$\frac{dy_k}{dt} = \lambda_k y_k, \qquad y_k(0) = y_k^0 \quad (k = 1, \ldots, n) \tag{15}$$

Therefore, we have the solution

$$y_k(t) = e^{\lambda_k t}y_k^0 \quad (k = 1, \ldots, n), \qquad x = Cy \tag{16}$$

The *uncoupling* property of the diagonal form is used to solve many sorts of linear equations.

EXAMPLE 6. Consider the coupled difference equations

$$u_{k+1} = -7u_k + 4v_k$$
$$v_{k+1} = -8u_k + v_k \qquad (k = 0, 1, \ldots) \qquad (17)$$

Let $x^{(k)} = \operatorname{col}(u_k, v_k)$. Then (17) takes the form

$$x^{(k+1)} = Ax^{(k)} \qquad \left(\text{where } A = \begin{bmatrix} -7 & 4 \\ -8 & 1 \end{bmatrix}\right) \qquad (18)$$

To uncouple this system, we introduce the canonical diagonal form of A. From Example 1, Section 3.5, we have

$$C^{-1}AC = \Lambda \qquad \left(\text{where } C = \begin{bmatrix} 1, & 1 \\ 1+i, & 1-i \end{bmatrix}\right) \qquad (19)$$

and $\Lambda = \operatorname{diag}(-3 + 4i, -3 - 4i)$. Make the change of coordinates

$$x^{(k)} = Cy^{(k)} \qquad (20)$$

Now (18) becomes $y^{k+1} = \Lambda y^k$, and this system is uncoupled. If $y^k = \operatorname{col}(r_k, s_k)$, then

$$r_{k+1} = (-3 + 4i)r_k$$
$$s_{k+1} = (-3 - 4i)s_k \qquad (k = 0, 1, \ldots) \qquad (21)$$

These equations are readily solvable:

$$r_k = (-3 + 4i)^k r_0, \qquad s_k = (-3 - 4i)^k s_0 \qquad (22)$$

To find u_k and v_k, we write out equation (20):

$$\begin{bmatrix} u_k \\ v_k \end{bmatrix} = \begin{bmatrix} 1, & 1 \\ 1+i, & 1-i \end{bmatrix} \begin{bmatrix} r_k \\ s_k \end{bmatrix}$$

Therefore, for $k = 0, 1, \ldots$,

$$u_k = (-3 + 4i)^k r_0 + (-3 - 4i)^k s_0$$
$$v_k = (1 + i)(-3 + 4i)^k r_0 + (1 - i)(-3 - 4i)^k s_0 \qquad (23)$$

The solutions u_k, v_k are completely determined by given initial values u_0, s_0. By (23), the initial values u_0, s_0 determine the numbers r_0, s_0 by the equations

$$u_0 = r_0 + s_0$$
$$v_0 = (1 + i)r_0 + (1 - i)s_0 \qquad (24)$$

PROBLEMS

1. Solve the system of difference equations in Example 6 under the initial conditions: $u_0 = 1$, $v_0 = 2$. Verify that the solution given by (23) is real valued even though it is expressed in terms of complex numbers.

2. Solve the difference equation $f_{n+1} = f_n + f_{n-1}$ for the *Fibonacci numbers* by obtaining a first-order system $x^{(n+1)} = Ax^{(n)}$ for the vectors

$$x^{(n)} = \begin{bmatrix} f_n \\ f_{n-1} \end{bmatrix}$$

Assume $f_0 = f_1 = 1$.

3. Let A have independent eigenvectors $u^1, \ldots, u^n$. Let $B = T^{-1}AT$. Does B have n independent eigenvectors $v^1, \ldots, v^n$? How are the eigenvectors of similar matrices related?

4. Using the technique of Example 5, solve the system of differential equations $dx/dt = Ax$, where A is the matrix in formula (18). Assume that $x(0) = \text{col}\,(1, 2)$.

5. If A is similar to B, show that the matrices A^k and B^k are similar for all powers $k = 0, 1, 2, \ldots$. If $\det A \neq 0$, also show that A^{-1} is similar to B^{-1}.

6. If A is similar to B, and if B is similar to C, show that A is similar to C.

7.* Let A be an $n \times n$ matrix with distinct eigenvalues λ_j. Let $x^{(0)}, x^{(1)}, \ldots$ solve the difference equation $x^{(k+1)} = Ax^{(k)}$. Under what condition on the eigenvalues λ_j can we be sure that all components of the vector $x^{(k)}$ tend to zero as $k \to \infty$?

8.* Let A be an $n \times n$ matrix with distinct eigenvalues λ_j. Let $x(t)$ solve the differential equation $dx/dt = Ax$. Under what condition on the eigenvalues λ_j can we be sure that all components of the vector $x(t)$ tend to zero as $t \to \infty$?

4.3 THE TRACE AND OTHER INVARIANTS

The sum of the eigenvalues of an $n \times n$ matrix A, is called its *trace:* $\text{tr}\,A = \sum \lambda_j$. This number is minus the coefficient of λ^{n-1} in the expansion

$$\begin{aligned} \det(\lambda I - A) &= (\lambda - \lambda_1)(\lambda - \lambda_2) \ldots (\lambda - \lambda_n) \\ &= \lambda^n + c_1\lambda^{n-1} + c_2\lambda^{n-2} + \cdots + c_n \end{aligned} \tag{1}$$

If matrices A and B are similar, they have the same trace because they have the same characteristic polynomial. In this sense, the trace is *invariant* in similarity transformations $B = T^{-1}AT$.

Another invariant is the determinant. Setting $\lambda = 0$ in (1) gives $\det(-A) = (-\lambda_1)\ldots(-\lambda_n)$. But $\det(-A) = (-)^n \det A$. Therefore,

$$\det A = \lambda_1 \lambda_2 \ldots \lambda_n \tag{2}$$

Evidently, all of the coefficients $c_1, c_2, \ldots, c_n$ are invariant in similarity transformations.

Theorem 1. *Let A be an* n $\times$ n *matrix. Then*

$$\operatorname{tr} A = a_{11} + a_{22} + \cdots + a_{nn} \tag{3}$$

Proof. In the expansion (1) we must show that

$$\lambda_1 + \lambda_2 + \cdots + \lambda_n = a_{11} + a_{22} + \cdots + a_{nn} \tag{4}$$

Let $B = \lambda I - A$. In the expansion

$$\det B = \sum_{(j)} s(j) b_{1j_1} b_{2j_2} \ldots b_{nj_n} \tag{5}$$

we shall find the coefficient c_1 of λ^{n-1}. The only permutation j which contributes $n - 1$ factors λ is the permutation $j_1 = 1, j_2 = 2, \ldots, j_n = n$. If $j_i \neq i$ for one i, then $j_i \neq i$ for at least two i, which implies that $\prod b_{ij_i}$ has degree $\leqslant n - 2$ in λ. Hence, c_1 is the coefficient of λ^{n-1} in the single term

$$b_{11} b_{22} \ldots b_{nn} = (\lambda - a_{11})(\lambda - a_{22}) \ldots (\lambda - a_{nn}) \tag{6}$$

Therefore, $c_1 = -a_{11} - \cdots - a_{nn}$. But the identity (1) yields $c_1 = -\lambda_1 - \cdots - \lambda_n$. This completes the proof.

EXAMPLE 1. Let

$$A = \begin{bmatrix} 5 & 7 \\ -2 & 3 \end{bmatrix}$$

Then the sum of the eigenvalues of A must equal $5 + 3 = 8$

All coefficients $c_1, c_2, \ldots, c_n$ of the characteristic polynomial are invariant under similarity transformations. This was proved in Theorem 1 of the last section. We have shown that $c_1 = -\sum a_{ii}$ and $c_n = (-)^n \det A$. These results can be generalized.

Theorem 2. *Let* $1 \leqslant$ m $\leqslant$ n. *Let* A *be an* n $\times$ n *matrix, with characteristic determinant* (1). *Then*

$$(-)^m c_m = \sum_{i_1 < \cdots < i_m} \Delta(i_1, i_2, \ldots, i_m) \tag{7}$$

where $\Delta(i_1, \ldots, i_m)$ *is the* m $\times$ m *determinant formed from rows* i $= i_1, i_2, \ldots, i_m$ *and columns* j $= i_1, i_2, \ldots, i_m$.

EXAMPLE 2. Let

$$A = \begin{bmatrix} 1 & 2 & 3 \\ 4 & 5 & 6 \\ 7 & 8 & 9 \end{bmatrix}, \qquad \det(\lambda I - A) = \lambda^3 + c_1\lambda^2 + c_2\lambda + c_3$$

For $m = 2$ formula (7) says

$$c_2 = \Delta(1,2) + \Delta(1,3) + \Delta(2,3)$$

$$= \begin{vmatrix} 1 & 2 \\ 4 & 5 \end{vmatrix} + \begin{vmatrix} 1 & 3 \\ 7 & 9 \end{vmatrix} + \begin{vmatrix} 5 & 6 \\ 8 & 9 \end{vmatrix} = -3 - 12 - 3 = -18$$

Proof of the Theorem. We have

$$\det(\lambda I - A) = \sum_{(j)} s(j)(\lambda\delta_{1j_1} - a_{1j_1})(\lambda\delta_{2j_2} - a_{2j_2}) \ldots (\lambda\delta_{nj_n} - a_{nj_n})$$

To find the coefficient c_m of λ^{n-m}, we must take $\delta_{ij_i}\lambda$ from $n - m$ of the factors $(\lambda\delta - a)$ and take $-a_{ij_i}$ from the remaining m factors in all possible ways. Thus,

$$c_m = \sum_{i_1 < \cdots < i_m} \sum_{(j)} s(j) \left(\prod_{i \neq i_1, \ldots, i_m} \delta_{ij_i} \right) (-a_{i_1j_{i_1}}) \ldots (a_{i_mj_{i_m}}) \tag{8}$$

The only nonzero terms come from permutations j for which the product of Kronecker deltas is nonzero, i.e., for which $i = j_i$ when $i \neq i_1, i_2, \ldots, i_m$. Now (8) becomes

$$c_m = \sum_{i_1 < \cdots < i_m} \sum_{(k)} s(k)(-a_{i_1k_1}) \ldots (-a_{i_mk_m}) \tag{9}$$

where k runs over all permutations of $i_1, \ldots, i_m$. Thus,

$$c_m = \sum_{i_1 < \cdots < i_m} (-)^m \Delta(i_1, i_2, \ldots, i_m) \tag{10}$$

This is the required identity (7). Note that $S(k)$ in formula (9) equals $S(j)$ in formula (8) when $j_i = i$ for all $i \neq i_1, \ldots, i_m$, since any sequence of t interchanges that reduces the permutation k to the natural order $i_1, \ldots, i_m$, simultaneously reduces j to the natural order $1, \ldots, n$.

PROBLEMS

1. Compute $\lambda_1\lambda_2 + \lambda_1\lambda_3 + \lambda_1\lambda_4 + \lambda_2\lambda_3 + \lambda_2\lambda_4 + \lambda_3\lambda_4$ for the matrix

$$A = \begin{bmatrix} 1 & 2 & 3 & 4 \\ 8 & 7 & 6 & 5 \\ 1 & 4 & 5 & 8 \\ 2 & 3 & 6 & 7 \end{bmatrix}$$

2. For the matrix in Problem 1, compute $\lambda_1 + \lambda_2 + \lambda_3 + \lambda_4$. Now, using the result of Problem 1, compute $\lambda_1^2 + \lambda_2^2 + \lambda_3^2 + \lambda_4^2$.

3. Show that tr $(AB) =$ tr (BA) even if $AB \neq BA$.

4. Suppose det $A = 0$. Show that, for all sufficiently small $|\epsilon| > 0$, det $(A + \epsilon I) \neq 0$.

5. Prove that det $(\lambda I - AB) \equiv$ det $(\lambda I - BA)$ for all λ. Hence, show that all the invariants $c_1, \ldots, c_n$ are the same for AB and for BA. (First prove the result by assuming det $A \neq 0$. If det $A = 0$, obtain the required identity by replacing A by $A + \epsilon I$ and by taking the limit as $\epsilon \to 0$.)

4.4 UNITARY MATRICES

The study of invariance under transformations leads to many interesting questions. For example, we may ask: *Which* n $\times$ n *matrices* U *transform vectors* x *into vectors* y *with the same length?* If x has real components, we mean by *length* the Euclidean norm

$$\| x \| = \sqrt{x_1^2 + x_2^2 + \cdots + x_n^2} \tag{1}$$

If x has complex components, we must replace this definition by

$$\| x \| = \sqrt{|x_1|^2 + |x_2|^2 + \cdots + |x_n|^2} \tag{2}$$

Otherwise certain nonzero vectors, e.g., $x = $ col $(1, i)$, could have zero length. We ask: For which $n \times n$ matrices U is

$$\| Ux \| = \| x \| \qquad \text{(for all } x) \tag{3}$$

EXAMPLE 1. For $n = 2$ and real x the rotation matrices

$$U = \begin{bmatrix} \cos\theta & -\sin\theta \\ \sin\theta & \cos\theta \end{bmatrix} \tag{4}$$

have the property (3). They also satisfy (3) for complex x; since

$$|x_1 \cos\theta - x_2 \sin\theta|^2 + |x_1 \sin\theta + x_2 \cos\theta|^2 = |x_1|^2 + |x_2|^2$$

EXAMPLE 2. For all x the matrix

$$U = \frac{1}{2} \begin{bmatrix} 1 - i, & 1 + i \\ 1 + i, & -1 + i \end{bmatrix} \tag{5}$$

preserves length:

$$\tfrac{1}{4}|(1 - i)x_1 + (1 + i)x_2|^2 + \tfrac{1}{4}|(1 + i)x_1 - (1 - i)x_2|^2 = |x_1|^2 + |x_2|^2$$

Before answering the question let us discuss the n-dimensional length (2). Can we define an "angle" ϕ between two n-dimensional vectors x and y? For $n = 2$ and 3 we have, for real x and y,

$$\cos \phi = \frac{x_1 y_1 + \cdots + x_n y_n}{\|x\| \|y\|}$$

The numerator of this fraction is the *inner product* (x, y) defined as

$$(x, y) = x_1 y_1 + \cdots + x_n y_n \tag{6}$$

If the components x_j, y_j are allowed to be complex numbers, the inner product is defined as

$$(x, y) = x_1 \bar{y}_1 + \cdots + x_n \bar{y}_n \tag{7}$$

The inner product has several important elementary properties:

$$
\begin{aligned}
(x, x) &= \|x\|^2, &\quad (x, y) &= \overline{(y, x)} \\
(\lambda x, y) &= \lambda(x, y), &\quad (x, \lambda y) &= \bar{\lambda}(x, y) \\
\|x + y\|^2 &= \|x\|^2 + \|y\|^2 + 2\,\mathrm{Re}\,(x, y) \\
(x + y, z) &= (x, z) + (y, z)
\end{aligned}
\tag{8}
$$

For $n > 3$, even for real x and y, it is not obvious that the "cosine" (6) has absolute value $\leqslant 1$.

Theorem 1. (*The Cauchy-Schwarz Inequality*)

$$|(x, y)| \leqslant \|x\| \|y\| \tag{9}$$

with equality if and only if x *and* y *are dependent.*

Proof. If $x = 0$ or $y = 0$ then both sides of (9) are equal to zero. Therefore, suppose $x \neq 0$ and $y \neq 0$. Now (9) takes the form

$$\left| \sum_{\nu} x_\nu \bar{y}_\nu \right| \leqslant \left(\sum_{\alpha} |x_\alpha|^2 \right)^{1/2} \left(\sum_{\beta} |y_\beta|^2 \right)^{1/2} \tag{10}$$

or

$$\left| \sum_{\nu} a_\nu \bar{b}_\nu \right| \leqslant 1 \tag{11}$$

where $a = x/\|x\|$ and $b = y/\|y\|$:

$$a_\nu = \frac{x_\nu}{\left(\sum_{\alpha} |x_\alpha|^2 \right)^{1/2}}, \qquad b_\nu = \frac{y_\nu}{\left(\sum_{\beta} |y_\beta|^2 \right)^{1/2}} \quad (\nu = 1, \ldots, n) \tag{12}$$

Evidently,

$$|\sum a_\nu \bar{b}_\nu| \leqslant \sum |a_\nu||b_\nu| \tag{13}$$

with equality if and only if the argument is constant:

$$\arg (a_\nu \bar{b}_\nu) = \psi \text{ independent of } \nu \tag{14}$$

where the argument of zero may be chosen at will. Next,

$$|a_\nu||b_\nu| \leqslant \tfrac{1}{2}(|a_\nu|^2 + |b_\nu|^2) \qquad (\nu = 1, \ldots, n) \tag{15}$$

with equality if and only if $|a_\nu| = |b_\nu|$. But $a = x/\|x\|$ and $b = y/\|y\|$ are unit vectors! Therefore, summation of (15) for $\nu = 1, \ldots, n$ gives

$$\sum |a_\nu||b_\nu| \leqslant \tfrac{1}{2}(\sum |a_\nu|^2 + \sum |b_\nu|^2) = 1 \tag{16}$$

This establishes the required inequality (11), equivalent to (9), with equality if and only if, for $\nu = 1, \ldots, n$,

$$\frac{|x_\nu|}{\|x\|} = \frac{|y_\nu|}{\|y\|} \quad \text{and} \quad \arg x_\nu \bar{y}_\nu = \psi \text{ independent of } \nu \tag{17}$$

If $|x_\nu| = r_\nu$, $\arg x_\nu = \theta_\nu$, and $\lambda = \|y\|/\|x\|$, formula (17) states

$$x_\nu = r_\nu e^{i\theta_\nu}, \qquad y_\nu = (\lambda e^{-i\psi})r_\nu e^{i\theta_\nu} \quad (\nu = 1, \ldots, n) \tag{18}$$

Thus, (9) holds, with equality if and only if y equals $\lambda \exp(-i\psi)$ times x. This completes the proof.

Lemma 1. *An* n $\times$ n *matrix* U *preserves lengths if and only if it preserves inner products, i.e.,*

$$\|Ux\| = \|x\| \qquad (\textit{for all } x) \tag{19}$$

if and only if

$$(Ux, Uy) = (x, y) \qquad (\textit{for all } x \textit{ and all } y) \tag{20}$$

Proof. The identity (20) implies (19) as follows: For all x, define $y = x$. Then (20) states

$$\|Ux\|^2 = \|x\|^2 \qquad (\text{for all } x)$$

which is equivalent to (19).

To show that (19) implies (20) is harder. The inner product can be related to the length by the identity

$$\|x + y\|^2 = \sum |x_\nu + y_\nu|^2 = \sum |x_\nu|^2 + \sum x_\nu \bar{y}_\nu + \sum \bar{x}_\nu y_\nu + \sum |y_\nu|^2$$

or

$$\|x + y\|^2 = \|x\|^2 + 2 \operatorname{Re}(x, y) + \|y\|^2 \tag{21}$$

To obtain $\operatorname{Im}(x, y)$ from the last identity, replace the vector y by the vector iy:

$$\|x + iy\|^2 = \|x\|^2 + 2 \operatorname{Re}(x, iy) + \|iy\|^2$$

But $(x, iy) = -i(x, y)$, so $\operatorname{Re}(x, iy) = \operatorname{Im}(x, y)$. Therefore,

$$\|x + iy\|^2 = \|x\|^2 + 2 \operatorname{Im}(x, y) + \|y\|^2 \tag{22}$$

If we replace x by Ux, and y by Uy, in the preceding identities, we find

$$\|U(x + y)\|^2 = \|Ux\|^2 + 2 \operatorname{Re}(Ux, Uy) + \|Uy\|^2 \tag{21'}$$

$$\|U(x + iy)\|^2 = \|Ux\|^2 + 2 \operatorname{Im}(Ux, Uy) + \|Uy\|^2 \tag{22'}$$

But the preservation of *all* lengths (19) implies

$$\|U(x + y)\| = \|x + y\|, \qquad \|U(x + iy)\| = \|x + iy\|,$$
$$\|Ux\| = \|x\|, \qquad \|Uy\| = \|y\|$$

Now the identities (21'), (22') become

$$\|x + y\|^2 = \|x\|^2 + 2 \operatorname{Re}(Ux, Uy) + \|y\|^2 \tag{21''}$$

$$\|x + iy\|^2 = \|x\|^2 + 2 \operatorname{Im}(Ux, Uy) + \|y\|^2 \tag{22''}$$

From (21) and (22) we now conclude

$$\operatorname{Re}(x, y) = \operatorname{Re}(Ux, Uy), \qquad \operatorname{Im}(x, y) = \operatorname{Im}(Ux, Uy)$$

which is the required result (20).

Since a length-preserving matrix U preserves inner products,

$$(Ue^j, Ue^k) = (e^j, e^k) = \delta_{jk} \qquad (j, k = 1, \ldots, n) \tag{23}$$

where $e^1, e^2, \ldots, e^n$ are the columns of the identity matrix. But Ue^j and Ue^k are simply the jth and kth columns of U. Formula (23) shows that *the columns of a length-preserving matrix are mutually orthogonal unit vectors.* Is the converse true? Given (23), we have for all x

$$\| Ux \|^2 = (Ux, Ux)$$
$$= (U \sum_j x_j e^j, \; U \sum_k x_k e^k)$$
$$= \sum_j \sum_k x_j \bar{x}_k (Ue^j, Ue^k)$$
$$= \sum_j \sum_k x_j \bar{x}_k \, \delta_{jk} = \sum_j |x_j|^2 = \| x \|^2$$

This establishes the converse. We have proved

Theorem 2. *The* $n \times n$ *matrix* U *preserves Euclidean length* $\| x \| = (\sum |x_\nu|^2)^{1/2}$ *if and only if the columns* u^j *of* U *are mutually orthogonal unit vectors:* $(u^j, u^k) = \delta_{jk}$.

For any matrix A we define the *adjoint matrix* A^* to be the complex conjugate of the transpose of A. For example,

$$\begin{bmatrix} 3 + i, & -8 \\ 2 + i, & 4i \\ -3i, & 2 + 5i \end{bmatrix}^* = \begin{bmatrix} 3 - i, & 2 - i, & 3i \\ -8, & -4i, & 2 - 5i \end{bmatrix}$$

In particular, for column-matrices (vectors) x and y, we have

$$(x, y) = y^* x = \sum \bar{y}_j x_j \tag{24}$$

The orthogonality and unit length of the columns of U can now be summarized in the formula

$$U^* U = I \tag{25}$$

In fact, by the rule of matrix multiplication, the j, k component of U^*U is simply the sum $u^{j*} u^k = (u^k, u^j)$, which is required by (25) to equal $\delta_{jk} = \delta_{kj}$. Square matrices U for which $U^*U = I$ are called *unitary*.

Theorem 3. *If* U *and* V *are* $n \times n$ *unitary matrices, so are* U^* *and* UV.

Proof. UV is unitary because it preserves length:

$$\| (UV)x \| = \| U(Vx) \| = \| Vx \| = \| x \|$$

U^* is unitary because the given equation $U^*U = I$ characterizes U^* as the inverse of U. Since a left-inverse is a right-inverse, we have $UU^* = I$. But $U = (U^*)^*$, as we see by taking complex conjugates and taking the transpose twice. Therefore, $(U^*)^*(U^*) = I$.

This theorem has the amusing corollary that the columns of a square matrix are mutually orthogonal unit vectors if and only if the *rows* are mutually orthogonal unit vectors.

PROBLEMS

1. Let A be an $m \times n$ matrix. Show that $(Ax, y) \equiv (x, By)$ for all n-component vectors x and all m-component vectors y if and only if $B = A^* \equiv \overline{A^T}$.

2. If A^{-1} exists, show that $(A^*)^{-1} = (A^{-1})^*$.

3. Show that $(AB)^* = B^*A^*$.

4. Show that all the eigenvalues of a unitary matrix are numbers $\lambda = e^{i\theta}$ on the unit circle.

5. Assume that $\rho_1 > 0, \ldots, \rho_n > 0$. Redefine the "length" of a vector as

$$|x| \equiv (\rho_1|x_1|^2 + \cdots + \rho_n|x_n|^2)^{1/2}$$

Which matrices V preserve this "length"?

6. Let U be unitary, and let $B = UA$ and $C = AU$. Show that

$$\text{tr } A^*A = \text{tr } B^*B = \text{tr } C^*C = \sum \sum |a_{\mu\nu}|^2$$

where the trace is the sum of the diagonal elements.

7.* Define the Lorentz-metric $x^2 - c^2t^2$ from the special theory of relativity. We ask for linear transformations $x' = \alpha x + \beta t$, $t' = \gamma x + \delta t$ such that $x'^2 - c^2t'^2 \equiv x^2 - c^2t^2$ for all x and t, where $\alpha > 0$ and $\delta > 0$. Show that all such linear transformations have the form

$$\begin{bmatrix} x' \\ t' \end{bmatrix} = \begin{bmatrix} \cosh \phi & c \sinh \phi \\ c^{-1} \sinh \phi, & \cosh \phi \end{bmatrix} \begin{bmatrix} x \\ t \end{bmatrix}$$

8.* Show that rigid motions are necessarily *linear* transformations: For $i = 1, \ldots, n$ let $y_i = f_i(x_1, \ldots, x_n)$ be real-valued, twice continuously differentiable functions of the real vector $x = (x_1, \ldots, x_n)$. For all vectors x and all increments Δx suppose that

$$\sum (\Delta y_i)^2 \equiv \sum (\Delta x_i)^2$$

Then prove that the functions $f_i(x)$ have the form

$$f_i(x) \equiv c_i + \sum_{j=1}^{n} u_{ij}x_j$$

where the c_i and the u_{ij} are *constants*, with $\sum_{(i)} u_{ij}u_{ik} = \delta_{jk}$. (Method: Expand each $f_i(x + \Delta x)$ in a Taylor series with a remainder involving the second derivatives. Letting $\Delta x \to 0$, show that the second derivatives are all zero.)

4.5 THE GRAM-SCHMIDT ORTHOGONALIZATION PROCESS

In this section we will show that every finite-dimensional linear vector space with real or complex scalars has a basis consisting of mutually orthogonal unit vectors. In the following theorem we will do somewhat more. Suppose that we are given linearly independent vectors $a^1, a^2, \ldots, a^m$. We will show how to orthogonalize these vectors successively. First we will find a unit vector u^1 which is a multiple of a^1. Then we will find a unit vector u^2, orthogonal to u^1, such that u^1 and u^2 span the same plane as a^1 and a^2. Then we construct a unit vector u^3, orthogonal to u^1 and u^2, such that u^1, u^2, u^3 span the same linear space as a^1, a^2, a^3. Finally we shall have mutually orthogonal unit vectors $u^1, \ldots, u^m$ spanning the same linear space as $a^1, \ldots, a^m$.

The Gram-Schmidt process has many applications. For example, it is used to construct the orthogonal polynomials and other orthogonal sets of functions used in mathematical physics. Because of these applications, we will be rather general in our definitions of "inner product" and "orthogonality."

Consider a linear vector space, L, defined over a field of scalars, F. For us, F will be either the field of real numbers or the field of complex numbers. We suppose that for every two vectors x and y a complex or real number (x, y) is defined, and that the following laws hold:

$$
\begin{aligned}
&(x, y) = \overline{(y, x)} \\
&(\lambda x, y) = (x, \bar{\lambda} y) = \lambda \, (x, y) \qquad \text{(for all } \lambda \text{ in } F) \\
&(x + y, z) = (x, z) + (y, z) \\
&(x, x) \geqslant 0 \qquad [\text{with } (x, x) = 0 \quad \text{if and only if} \quad x = 0]
\end{aligned}
\tag{1}
$$

In this case, the functional (x, y) is called an *inner product*. Two vectors, x and y, are called *orthogonal* if $(x, y) = 0$. The vector u is called a *unit vector* if $(u, u) = 1$.

EXAMPLE 1. Let L be the space of vectors with n real components, defined over the field, F, of real numbers. Then we may define

$$(x, y) = x_1 y_1 + x_2 y_2 + \cdots + x_n y_n$$

EXAMPLE 2. Let L be the space of vectors with two complex components, defined over the field, F, of complex numbers. Then we may define

$$(x, y) = 2x_1 \bar{y}_1 + x_1 \bar{y}_2 + x_2 \bar{y}_1 + 3x_2 \bar{y}_2$$

Note that

$$(x, x) = 2|x_1|^2 + 2 \operatorname{Re} x_1 \bar{x}_2 + 3|x_2|^2$$
$$= |x_1|^2 + 2|x_2|^2 + |x_1 + x_2|^2 \geq 0$$

with $(x, x) = 0$ only when $x = 0$.

EXAMPLE 3. Let L be the linear space of continuous, complex-valued functions $x = \phi(t)$ defined for $0 \leqslant t \leqslant 1$. Let F be the field of complex numbers. Then we may define the inner product

$$(x, y) = [\phi(t), \psi(t)] \equiv \int_0^1 \phi(t)\overline{\psi(t)}\, dt$$

In this space the "vectors"

$$x^{(k)} = \phi_k(t) = e^{2\pi i k t} \qquad (k = 0, \pm 1, \pm 2, \ldots)$$

are "orthogonal."

Theorem 1. *Let L be a linear vector space defined over the field, F, of real numbers or of complex numbers. Let an inner product* (x, y) *be defined which obeys the laws* (1). *Let* $a^1, a^2, \ldots, a^m$ *be linearly independent vectors in L. Then there are mutually orthogonal unit vectors* $u^1, u^2, \ldots, u^m$ *such that, for each* j = 1, 2, \ldots, m,

$$u^j = \text{a linear combination of } a^1, \ldots, a^j$$

and (2)

$$a^j = \text{a linear combination of } u^1, \ldots, u^j$$

Proof. Since $a^1 \neq 0$, we have $(a^1, a^1) > 0$. For any vector x, define

$$\|x\| = \sqrt{(x, x)}$$

Then we set

$$u^1 = \alpha a^1 \qquad (\text{with } \alpha = 1/\|a^1\|) \tag{3}$$

For any $k \geqslant 1$ suppose that we have constructed unit vectors $u^1, \ldots, u^k$ such that (2) holds for all $j \leqslant k$. If $k < m$, we will show how to construct u^{k+1} so that (2) holds for all $j \leqslant k + 1$. Let v be a vector of the form

$$v = a^{k+1} - \alpha_1 u^1 - \alpha_2 u^2 - \cdots - \alpha_k u^k \tag{4}$$

Since $u^1, \ldots, u^k$ are linear combinations of $a^1, \ldots, a^k$, we have

$$v = a^{k+1} + \text{lin comb } (a^1, a^2, \ldots, a^k) \tag{5}$$

Therefore, $v \neq 0$ because $a^{k+1}, a^1, \ldots, a^k$ are linearly independent. We now choose the coefficients $\alpha_1, \ldots, \alpha_k$ so that v is orthogonal to $u^1, u^2, \ldots, u^k$. For $j \leq k$, we have, from (4),

$$(v, u^j) = (a^{k+1}, u^j) - \alpha_j$$

since $(u^s, u^j) = \delta_{sj} \equiv 0$ or 1, depending on whether $s \neq j$ or $s = j$. Thus, the nonzero vector v is orthogonal to all the unit vectors $u^j (j \leq k)$ if we define

$$\alpha_j = (a^{k+1}, u^j) \qquad (j = 1, \ldots, k)$$

To make v into a unit vector, we divide it by its length

$$u^{k+1} = \frac{v}{\|v\|} \tag{6}$$

The relations (2) hold now for all $j \leq k + 1$, where $(u^s, u^j) = \delta_{sj}$. The theorem now follows by induction.

Corollary. *Every finite-dimensional linear vector space with an inner product has a basis consisting of orthogonal unit vectors* $u^1, \ldots, u^m$.

Proof. The desired result follows at once from the theorem if we let $a^1, \ldots, a^m$ be any basis for the space.

EXAMPLE 4. The vectors

$$a^1 = \begin{bmatrix} 1 \\ 0 \\ -1 \end{bmatrix}, \qquad a^2 = \begin{bmatrix} 0 \\ 1 \\ -1 \end{bmatrix}$$

are a basis for the plane $x_1 + x_2 + x_3 = 0$ in three-dimensional, real Euclidean space, where we define the inner product to be

$$(x, y) = x_1 y_1 + x_2 y_2 + x_3 y_3$$

Using the Gram-Schmidt process, we first compute

$$\|a^1\| = \sqrt{2}, \qquad u^1 = \frac{a_1}{\sqrt{2}} = \text{col}\,(2^{-1/2}, 0, -2^{-1/2})$$

To find u^2, set

$$v = a^2 - \alpha_1 u^1 \tag{7}$$

We compute

$$\alpha_1 = (a^2, u^1) = \frac{1}{\sqrt{2}}$$

Thus, from (7),

$$v = \text{col}\left(-\tfrac{1}{2}, 1, -\tfrac{1}{2}\right)$$

Setting $u^2 = v/\|v\|$, where $\|v\| = \sqrt{\tfrac{3}{2}}$, we find

$$u^1 = \frac{1}{\sqrt{2}} \begin{bmatrix} 1 \\ 0 \\ -1 \end{bmatrix}, \qquad u^2 = \frac{1}{\sqrt{6}} \begin{bmatrix} -1 \\ 2 \\ -1 \end{bmatrix}$$

EXAMPLE 5. Consider the linear vector space of polynomials $x = \phi(t)$ of degree $\leq N$ defined over the field of real numbers. Introduce the inner product

$$[\phi(t), \psi(t)] = \int_0^\infty \phi(t)\psi(t)e^{-t}\, dt$$

We wish to obtain an orthogonal basis

$$u^{(0)} = \phi_0(t), \qquad u^{(1)} = \phi_1(t), \ldots, u^{(N)} = \phi_N(t)$$

We begin with the basis

$$a^{(0)} = 1, \qquad a^{(1)} = t, \ldots, a^{(N)} = t^N$$

We then compute

$$\|a^{(0)}\|^2 = \int_0^\infty 1^2 e^{-t}\, dt = 1$$

And then

$$u^{(0)} = a^{(0)} = 1$$

Now write

$$v = a^{(1)} - \alpha_0 u^{(0)} = t - \alpha_0$$

We compute

$$\alpha_0 = (t, 1) = \int_0^\infty t e^{-t}\, dt = 1$$

Now

$$\|v\|^2 = \int_0^\infty (t - 1)^2 e^{-t}\, dt = 1$$

Hence,

$$u^{(1)} = t - 1$$

To compute $u^{(2)}$, we define the "vector"

$$v = a^{(2)} - \alpha_0 u^{(0)} - \alpha_1 u^{(1)}$$
$$v = t^2 - \alpha_0 - \alpha_1(t - 1)$$

Here

$$\alpha_0 = (t^2, 1) = \int_0^\infty t^2 e^{-t}\, dt = 2$$

$$\alpha_1 = (t^2, t - 1) = \int_0^\infty t^2(t - 1)e^{-t}\, dt = 4$$

Thus

$$v = t^2 - 2 - 4(t - 1) = t^2 - 4t + 2$$
$$\|v\|^2 = 24 - 24 + 4 = 4$$

Hence,

$$u^{(2)} = \tfrac{1}{2}(t^2 - 4t + 2)$$

and the process could be continued indefinitely. The polynomials $u^{(0)}, u^{(1)}, u^{(2)}, \ldots$ are normalized *Laguerre* polynomials.

PROBLEMS

1. The vectors

$$a^1 = \begin{bmatrix} 1 \\ 0 \\ 0 \\ -1 \end{bmatrix}, \quad a^2 = \begin{bmatrix} 0 \\ 1 \\ 0 \\ -1 \end{bmatrix}, \quad a^3 = \begin{bmatrix} 0 \\ 0 \\ 1 \\ -1 \end{bmatrix}$$

are a basis for the plane $x_1 + x_2 + x_3 + x_4 = 0$ in four-space. Using the Gram-Schmidt process, find a basis consisting of orthogonal unit vectors u^1, u^2, u^3.

2. Consider the three-dimensional space spanned by the "vectors" $a^{(0)} = 1$, $a^{(1)} = t$, $a^{(2)} = t^2$ in the space of polynomials in t of degree ≤ 100. Use real scalars. Define the inner product

$$[\phi(t), \psi(t)] = \int_{-1}^1 \phi(t)\psi(t)\, dt$$

Using the Gram-Schmidt process, find an orthogonal set of unit vectors $u^{(0)}, u^{(1)}, u^{(2)}$ spanning the same space as $a^{(0)}, a^{(1)}, a^{(2)}$.

3. Let L be any n-dimensional vector space defined over the field of complex numbers. Let $b^{(1)}, \ldots, b^{(n)}$ be any basis. If arbitrary vectors x and y have representations

$$x = \sum_{k=1}^{n} \xi_k b^{(k)}, \qquad y = \sum_{k=1}^{n} \eta_k b^{(k)}$$

show that the definition

$$(x, y) \equiv \sum_{k=1}^{n} \xi_k \bar{\eta}_k$$

has all the properties (1) required of an inner product. Find orthogonal unit vectors with respect to this inner product.

4. Let $a^1, \ldots, a^m$ be linearly independent vectors over the field of complex numbers. Define $\alpha_{ij} = (a^i)^* a^j = (a^j, a^i)$. Show that $\det (\alpha_{ij}) \neq 0$ by showing that an eigenvector x of the matrix (α_{ij}) belonging to the eigenvalue 0, would satisfy the relation $\| \sum x_i a^i \|^2 = 0$.

5.* Define $a^1, \ldots, a^m$ and α_{ij} as in Problem 4. Let $v^1 = a^1$. Define the vectors $v^2, \ldots, v^n$ by the "determinants"

$$v^k = \begin{vmatrix} \alpha_{11} & \alpha_{12} & \cdots & \alpha_{1k} \\ \alpha_{21} & \alpha_{22} & \cdots & \alpha_{2k} \\ \cdot & \cdot & \cdots & \cdot \\ \alpha_{k-1,1} & \alpha_{k-1,2} & \cdots & \alpha_{k-1,k} \\ a^1, & a^2, & \ldots, & a^k \end{vmatrix}$$

where we expand by the last row. For instance, $v^2 = \alpha_{11}a^2 - \alpha_{12}a^1$. Show that the vectors $u^1, \ldots, u^m$ created by the Gram-Schmidt process are scalar multiples

$$u^k = \rho_k v^k \qquad (k = 1, \ldots, m)$$

Find the scalars $\rho_1, \ldots, \rho_m$ in terms of $\Delta_k = \det (\alpha_{ij})(i, j = 1, \ldots, k)$. Note that $(v^k, v^k) = (v^k, \Delta_{k-1}a^k)$ because v^k is orthogonal to $a^1, \ldots, a^{k-1}$ and because the coefficient of a^k is Δ_{k-1} in the expansion of v^k as a linear combination of $a^1, \ldots, a^k$.

4.6 PRINCIPAL AXES OF ELLIPSOIDS

For dimension $n = 2$ or $n = 3$, an ellipse or an ellipsoid centered at the origin is represented by an equation

$$a_{11}x_1^2 + a_{22}x_2^2 + \cdots + a_{nn}x_n^2 + 2 \sum_{i<j} a_{ij}x_i x_j = 1$$

or, if we define $a_{ij} = a_{ji}$ for $i > j$,

$$\sum_{i,j=1}^{n} a_{ij}x_i x_j = 1 \tag{1}$$

Let $A = (a_{ij})(i, j = 1, \ldots, n)$. The real matrix A is called *symmetric* because $a_{ij} = a_{ji}$ for all $i \neq j$. In terms of the inner product, the equation (1) takes the form

$$(Ax, x) = 1 \tag{2}$$

since x has real components.

A *principal axis* of the ellipsoid is a vector extending from the origin to a point x on the ellipsoid such that the vector is normal to the ellipsoid at the point x. For $n = 2$, there is an illustration in Figure 4.1.

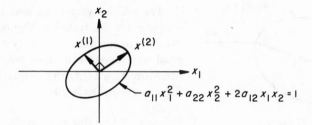

Figure 4.1

An ellipse has two independent principal axes. An ellipsoid, in three dimensions, has three independent principal axes. From analytic geometry we know that *the principal axes are, or may be chosen to be, mutually orthogonal,* and we shall prove and generalize this result in the next section. The cautious phrase "or may be chosen to be" refers to spheres or other ellipsoids of revolution, for which the choice of three mutually orthogonal principal axes is not unique.

We will now show that *the principal axes of an ellipsoid are the eigenvectors of the real, symmetric matrix* $A = (a_{ij})$. From calculus we know that a differential $dx = (dx_1, \ldots, dx_n)$ on a surface $\phi(x_1, \ldots, x_n) = \text{const}$, satisfies the relation

$$d\phi = \frac{\partial \phi}{\partial x_1} dx_1 + \cdots + \frac{\partial \phi}{\partial x_n} dx_n = 0 \tag{3}$$

The vector grad $\phi = (\partial \phi / \partial x_k)(k = 1, \ldots, n)$, being normal to all differentials $dx = (dx_k)$ near the point x, is therefore a vector normal to the surface $\phi = \text{const}$ at the point x. Letting $\phi(x)$ be the *quadratic form* $\sum \sum a_{ij} x_i x_j$, we may compute the normal vector to the ellipsoid $\phi = 1$:

$$\left(\frac{\partial \phi}{\partial x_k} \right) = \left(\sum_i \sum_j a_{ij} \frac{\partial (x_i x_j)}{\partial x_k} \right) \qquad (k = 1, \ldots, n) \tag{4}$$

By the rule for differentiating a product,

$$\frac{\partial (x_i x_j)}{\partial x_k} = \frac{\partial x_i}{\partial x_k} x_j + x_i \frac{\partial x_j}{\partial x_k} = \delta_{ik} x_j + x_i \delta_{jk} \tag{5}$$

Inserting (5) in (4) and summing, we find

$$\left(\frac{\partial \phi}{\partial x_k}\right) = (\sum_j a_{kj}x_j + \sum_i a_{ik}x_i) \tag{6}$$

Since $a_{ik} = a_{ki}$, we thus have

$$\left(\frac{\partial \phi}{\partial x_k}\right) = (2 \sum_j a_{kj}x_j) = 2Ax \tag{7}$$

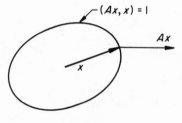

The normal vector Ax and the radial vector x are illustrated in Figure 4.2. The vector x in the figure is clearly not a principal axis because it does not have the same direction as Ax. The equation defining a *principal axis* x is

Figure 4.2

$$Ax = \lambda x \quad \text{(for some scalar } \lambda) \tag{8}$$

where $(Ax, x) = 1$. Since $x \neq 0$, *a principal axis is an eigenvector of* A.

The length of the principal axis associated with the eigenvalue λ_i *is* $1/\sqrt{\lambda_i}$. To see this, take the inner product of both sides of (8) with x:

$$(Ax, x) = (\lambda x, x) \tag{9}$$

But $(Ax, x) = 1$ for a point x on the ellipsoid, and $(\lambda x, x) = \lambda \|x\|^2$. Now (9) states $1 = \lambda \|x\|^2$, which yields the length $\|x\| = 1/\sqrt{\lambda}$. Evidently, *a quadratic form* $(Ax, x) = 1$ *representing an ellipsoid must come from a matrix with positive eigenvalues.*

EXAMPLE 1. Consider the ellipse

$$x_1^2 + 2x_1x_2 + 3x_2^2 = 1 \tag{10}$$

This equation states that $(Ax, x) = 1$, where

$$A = \begin{bmatrix} 1 & 1 \\ 1 & 3 \end{bmatrix} \tag{11}$$

The eigenvalues of A are the roots of $\lambda^2 - 4\lambda + 2 = 0$. Thus,

$$\lambda_1 = 2 + \sqrt{2}, \qquad \lambda_2 = 2 - \sqrt{2}$$

The principal axis $x^{(1)}$ belonging to λ_1 satisfies

$$(\lambda_1 I - A)x = \begin{bmatrix} 1 + \sqrt{2}, & -1 \\ -1, & -1 + \sqrt{2} \end{bmatrix}\begin{bmatrix} x_1^{(1)} \\ x_2^{(1)} \end{bmatrix} = \begin{bmatrix} 0 \\ 0 \end{bmatrix}$$

Therefore, the first principal axis equals

$$x^{(1)} = \alpha \begin{bmatrix} 1 \\ 1 + \sqrt{2} \end{bmatrix} \qquad (\alpha = \text{const}) \tag{12}$$

Similarly, it is possible to compute the second principal axis

$$x^{(2)} = \beta \begin{bmatrix} 1 \\ 1 - \sqrt{2} \end{bmatrix} \qquad (\beta = \text{const}) \tag{13}$$

Observe that the axes $x^{(1)}$ *and* $x^{(2)}$ *are orthogonal.* The constants α and β could be determined so that $x^{(1)}$ and $x^{(2)}$ both lie on the ellipse (10). Further,

$$\| x^{(1)} \| = \frac{1}{\sqrt{\lambda_1}} = (2 + 2^{1/2})^{-1/2}, \qquad \| x^{(2)} \| = \frac{1}{\sqrt{\lambda_2}} = (2 - \sqrt{2})^{-1/2} \tag{14}$$

The principal axes yield natural coordinates for an ellipsoid $(Ax, x) = 1$. Define mutually orthogonal unit vectors $u^1, u^2, \ldots, u^n$ by dividing the principal axes by their lengths. Let an arbitrary vector x be represented as a linear combination

$$x = y_1 u^1 + y_2 u^2 + \cdots + y_n u^n \tag{15}$$

The numbers $y_1, y_2, \ldots$ are coordinates with respect to the orthogonal basis $u^1, u^2, \ldots$. We now have

$$Ax = y_1 \lambda_1 u^1 + y_2 \lambda_2 u^2 + \cdots + y_n \lambda_n u^n \tag{16}$$

because the principal axes are eigenvectors of A. Since $(u^j, u^k) = \delta_{jk}$, the equation $(Ax, x) = 1$ becomes

$$(\textstyle\sum y_j \lambda_j u^j, \sum y_k u^k) = 1 \tag{17}$$

or

$$\textstyle\sum \sum y_j \lambda_j y_k \delta_{jk} = 1 \tag{18}$$

or

$$\boxed{\lambda_1 y_1^2 + \lambda_2 y_2^2 + \cdots + \lambda_n y_n^2 = 1} \tag{19}$$

In matrix notation, let U be the unitary matrix with columns that are the normalized axes $u^1, \ldots, u^n$. Then (15) states $x = Uy$. Now

$$(Ax, x) = (AUy, Uy) \tag{20}$$

But we readily verify that $(z, Uy) = (U^*z, y)$ for any z, by the definition of the inner product. Setting $z = AUy$, we have

$$(Ax, x) = (U^*AUy, y) \tag{21}$$

But $AU = U\Lambda$, where $\Lambda = \text{diag} \, (\lambda_1, \ldots, \lambda_n)$. Since U is unitary,

$$U^*AU = U^*U\Lambda = \Lambda \tag{22}$$

Thus $(Ax, x) = 1$ becomes $(\Lambda y, y) = 1$, a restatement of (19).

PROBLEMS

1. Consider the ellipse
$$4x_1^2 + 3x_1x_2 + 2x_2^2 = 1$$
If this equation is written in the form $(Ax, x) = 1$, what is the matrix A? What are the eigenvalues and eigenvectors of A? Find principal axes for the ellipse, and compute their lengths by the method of Example 1. If $U^*AU = \Lambda$, where U is unitary and Λ is diagonal, what are U and Λ? What is the equation (19)?

2. Show that every *symmetric*, real 2×2 matrix A has real eigenvalues. Prove that the eigenvalues are both positive if and only if $a_{11} > 0$ and $\det A > 0$.

3. Answer all the questions in Problem 1 for the ellipse $2x_1^2 - 2x_1x_2 + x_2^2 = 1$.

4.7 HERMITIAN MATRICES

If A is an $n \times n$ matrix with real or complex components, we define the *adjoint matrix*, A^*, to be the complex conjugate of the transpose of A. Thus

$$\begin{bmatrix} 1+i, & 2-i \\ 3+4i, & 5-6i \end{bmatrix}^* = \begin{bmatrix} 1-i, & 3-4i \\ 2+i, & 5+6i \end{bmatrix}$$

and

$$\begin{bmatrix} -8 & 9 \\ 6 & 7 \end{bmatrix}^* = \begin{bmatrix} -8 & 6 \\ 9 & 7 \end{bmatrix}$$

If A^T is the transpose of A, we have

$$A^* = \overline{A^T} \tag{1}$$

If we define the *inner product* of two vectors, x and y, to be

$$(x, y) = \sum_{k=1}^{n} x_k \bar{y}_k \tag{2}$$

then the adjoint matrix satisfies the identity

$$(Ax, y) = (x, A^*y) \tag{3}$$

because

$$(Ax, y) = \sum_{k=1}^{n} (\sum_{j=1}^{n} a_{kj}x_j)\bar{y}_k$$

$$= \sum_{j=1}^{n} x_j (\overline{\sum_{k=1}^{n} \bar{a}_{kj}y_k}) = (x, A^*y)$$

Conversely, the identity

$$(Ax, y) \equiv (x, By) \quad \text{implies} \quad B = \overline{A^T} = A^*$$

This follows from setting $x = e^j$ and $y = e^k$, which yields $a_{kj} = b_{jk}$.

A real, symmetric matrix A is its own adjoint: $A = A^T = A^*$. *In general, Hermitian matrices are defined as self-adjoint matrices:*

$$H = H^* \qquad (Hx, y) = (x, Hy) \quad \text{(for all } x \text{ and } y\text{)}$$
$$h_{kj} = \bar{h}_{jk} \quad (j, k = 1, \ldots, n) \tag{4}$$

EXAMPLE 1. The matrices

$$\begin{bmatrix} 1 & 2 \\ 2 & -3 \end{bmatrix}, \qquad \begin{bmatrix} 1 & 2+i \\ 2-i, & -3 \end{bmatrix}$$

are Hermitian, but the complex, symmetric matrix

$$\begin{bmatrix} 1 & 2+i \\ 2+i, & -3 \end{bmatrix}$$

is not Hermitian.

Theorem 1. *The eigenvalues of a Hermitian matrix are real, and eigenvectors belonging to different eigenvalues are orthogonal.*

Proof. Suppose that $H = H^*$ and

$$Hx = \lambda x, \qquad (x \neq 0) \tag{5}$$

Then $(Hx, x) = (\lambda x, x) = \lambda(x, x)$, and λ is the *Rayleigh quotient*

$$\frac{(Hx, x)}{(x, x)} = \lambda \tag{6}$$

The denominator (x, x) is positive. The numerator is real because it equals its own conjugate:

$$(Hx, x) = (x, Hx) = (\overline{Hx, x}) \tag{7}$$

Therefore, λ is the quotient of two real numbers.

Next, suppose

$$Hx = \lambda x, \qquad Hy = \mu y \quad (\text{with } \lambda \neq \mu, \, x \neq 0, \, y \neq 0)$$

Then

$$(Hx, y) = (\lambda x, y), \qquad (x, Hy) = (x, \mu y) \tag{8}$$

But $(Hx, y) = (x, Hy)$, and therefore

$$(\lambda x, y) = \lambda(x, y) = (x, \mu y) = \bar{\mu}(x, y) \tag{9}$$

But $\bar{\mu} = \mu$ because μ is an eigenvalue of a Hermitian matrix! Since $\lambda \neq \mu$ by assumption, we have the orthogonality: $(x, y) = 0$.

The last result shows that, if $H = H^*$ has distinct eigenvalues, then it can be diagonalized by a unitary similarity transformation

$$U^{-1}HU = U^*HU = \Lambda = \text{diag}(\lambda_1, \ldots, \lambda_n) \tag{10}$$

In fact, we may take for the columns of U a set of n mutually orthogonal unit eigenvectors belonging to the n different eigenvalues of H.

The remarkable fact is that *the canonical diagonalization* (10) *of Hermitian matrices is* always *possible, even if the eigenvalues* $\lambda_1, \ldots, \lambda_n$ *are not distinct.* We shall prove this result in the next theorem, but the following heuristic argument shows why it is true: If the eigenvalues of H are not distinct, think of H as the limit of nearby Hermitian matrices H_ϵ with distinct eigenvalues. For every small $\epsilon > 0$ there are n mutually perpendicular eigenvectors. As $\epsilon \to 0$, by the perpendicularity, there is no way in which any two of the eigenvectors can coalesce in the limit; the eigenvectors are held rigidly apart at 90° angles.

Theorem 2. *Let* H *be an* n × n *Hermitian matrix, with eigenvalues* $\lambda_1, \lambda_2, \ldots, \lambda_n$. *Then* H *has* n *mutually orthogonal unit eigenvectors* $u^1, \ldots, u^n$, *with*

$$Hu^j = \lambda_j u^j \quad (j = 1, \ldots, n) \quad \text{and} \quad U^*HU = \Lambda \tag{11}$$

where U *is the unitary matrix with columns* $u^1, \ldots, u^n$ *and* $\Lambda = \text{diag}(\lambda_1, \ldots, \lambda_n)$.

To prove this theorem, we need a preliminary result:

Lemma 1. *If any* n × n *matrix* A *maps a subspace* L_d *of* $E^n(C)$ *into itself, then* A *has an eigenvector in* L_d *if* L_d *has dimension* d ≥ 1.

Proof. If L_d has dimension d, let $b^1, \ldots, b^d$ be any basis for L_d. Then Ab^j is a linear combination of $b^1, \ldots, b^d$:

$$Ab^j = m_{j_1}b^1 + m_{j_2}b^2 + \cdots + m_{j_k}b^k$$

If B is the $n \times d$ matrix with columns of $b^1, \ldots, b^d$, we have $AB = BM$, where M is the $d \times d$ matrix

$$M = \begin{bmatrix} m_{11} & m_{21} & \cdot & m_{d1} \\ m_{12} & m_{22} & \cdot & m_{d2} \\ \cdot & \cdot & \cdot & \cdot \\ m_{1d} & m_{2d} & \cdot & m_{dd} \end{bmatrix}$$

Since the characteristic equation det $(\lambda I - M) = 0$ has at least one root, M has some eigenvector y:

$$My = \lambda y, \qquad (y \neq 0)$$

Now, because $AB = BM$, we have

$$A(By) = BMy = \lambda(By)$$

The vector $x = By$ is nonzero because $y \neq 0$ and because the columns of B are independent. Therefore,

$$x = y_1 b^1 + \cdots + y_d b^d$$

is an eigenvector of A lying in the space L_d.

Proof of Theorem 2. The $n \times n$ matrix H has a unit eigenvector, u^1, belonging to some eigenvalue, λ_1. Suppose that we have found k mutually orthogonal unit eigenvectors $u^1, \ldots, u^k$, with $1 \leq k < n$. Define L_{n-k} to be the linear space of vectors orthogonal to all the eigenvectors $u^1, \ldots, u^k$. Since H is Hermitian, we can show that H maps L_{n-k} into itself: If $(x, u^j) = 0$, where $Hu^j = \lambda_j u^j$, then

$$(Hx, u^j) = (x, Hu^j) = (x, \lambda_j u^j) = \lambda_j(x, u^j) = 0$$

By the lemma, we can show that H has an eigenvector in L_{n-k} if L_{n-k} contains any nonzero vector x. Since $k < n$, the vectors $u^1, \ldots, u^k$ cannot be a basis for the n-dimensional space E^n, and there is some vector y in E^n which is *not* a linear combination of $u^1, \ldots, u^k$. Therefore, the vector

$$x = y - (y, u^1)u^1 - \cdots - (y, u^k)u^k$$

is nonzero. But this vector is orthogonal to all the vectors $u^1, \ldots, u^k$, since $(u^r, u^s) = \delta_{rs}$ by assumption. Since L_{n-k} is, therefore, of dimension ≥ 1, the matrix H contains a unit eigenvector, u^{k+1}, in L_{n-k}.

We continue the process until we have found a full set of n mutually orthogonal unit eigenvectors $u^1, \ldots, u^n$. If U is the matrix with columns of these eigenvectors, then $U^*U = I$. Moreover, $HU = U\Lambda$ if Λ is the diagonal matrix formed from the eigenvalues $\lambda_1, \ldots, \lambda_n$ belonging to $u^1, \ldots, u^n$. Therefore, $U^*HU = \Lambda$, and the proof is complete.

Suppose that H is a real, symmetric matrix. Does H have n mutually orthogonal *real* unit eigenvectors? The answer is yes. A study of the preceding proof shows that, if H is real, complex numbers need never appear, since the eigenvalues λ are real. The inner product becomes $(x, y) = \sum x_i y_i$, without any conjugates. The unitary matrix U which diagonalizes H will have all components real. Thus we have:

Theorem 3. *If* H *is a real, symmetric matrix there is a real, unitary matrix* U *for which* U^{T}HU *is a diagonal matrix* Λ *formed from the eigenvalues of* H.

PROBLEMS

1. Let H be the Hermitian matrix

$$H = \begin{bmatrix} 0 & 2 & -1 \\ 2 & 5 & -6 \\ -1 & -6 & 8 \end{bmatrix}$$

Let L_2 be the space of vectors orthogonal to the eigenvector $u^1 = 3^{-1/2}$ col $(1, 1, 1)$. Define some basis for L_2, and verify that H maps L_2 into itself. Let B be defined as in the proof of Lemma 1. Find a 2×2 matrix M such that $HB = BM$. Compute an eigenvector y of M. Hence, compute a second unit eigenvector u^2 of H, where $(u^1, u^2) = 0$. Find a basis for the space, L_1, of vectors orthogonal to u^1 and u^2. Finally, compute a third unit eigenvector, u^3, orthogonal to u^1 and u^2. Define the unitary matrix U of equation (11), and verify the identity $U^*HU = \Lambda$.

2. Prove that the space L_{n-k} appearing in the proof of Theorem 2, has dimension $n - k$ by showing that $u^{k+1}, \ldots, u^n$ provides a basis for L_{n-k}.

3. If A is a square *non*-Hermitian matrix, does A map the space L orthogonal to an eigenvector, into itself? Illustrate.

4. Let A be an $n \times n$ non-Hermitian matrix. Suppose that A has distinct eigenvalues $\lambda_1, \ldots, \lambda_n$. Show that A^* has the eigenvalues $\bar{\lambda}_1, \ldots, \bar{\lambda}_n$. If u^j is an eigenvector of A belonging to λ_j, and if v^k is an eigenvector of A^* belonging to $\bar{\lambda}_k$, show that $(u^j, v^k) = 0$ if $j \neq k$, and show that $(u^j, v^j) \neq 0$. This is known as the *principle of biorthogonality*.

4.8 MASS-SPRING SYSTEMS; POSITIVE DEFINITENESS; SIMULTANEOUS DIAGONALIZATION

In this section we will apply the results in the last section to mechanical systems of masses and springs, and we will generalize this application to *the simultaneous diagonalization of two quadratic forms.*

Consider the mass-spring system in Figure 4.3. We have three masses and four springs vibrating horizontally between two rigid walls. At equilibrium, the masses would have certain position coordinates, say r_1, r_2, and r_3.

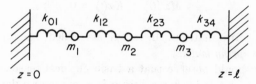

Figure 4.3

Let x_1, x_2, and x_3 be the *deviations* of the vibrating masses from their positions at rest. Thus, $x_1 = 0$, $x_2 = 0$, and $x_3 = 0$ when the system is at rest. Let $z_i = r_i + x_i$ $(i = 1, 2, 3)$. Let $l_{01}, \ldots, l_{34}$ be the lengths of the four springs when they are under no tension. Then, by Hooke's law, the forces exerted by the springs are

$$\pm k_{01}(z_1 - l_{01}), \quad \pm k_{12}(z_2 - z_1 - l_{12}), \quad \pm k_{23}(z_3 - z_2 - l_{23}),$$
$$\text{and} \pm k_{34}(l - z_3 - l_{34}) \tag{1}$$

where $k_{01}, \ldots, k_{34}$ are constants, and where the two ends of the system have coordinates 0 and l.

Setting force equal to mass times acceleration, we find the three differential equations

$$m_i \frac{d^2 z_i}{dt^2} = k_{i,i+1}(z_{i+1} - z_i - l_{i,i+1})$$
$$-k_{i-1,i}(z_i - z_{i-1} - l_{i-1,i}) \quad (i = 1, 2, 3) \tag{2}$$

where $z_0 = 0$ and $z_4 = l$. At equilibrium, the left-hand sides are zero, and $z_i = r_i$. Therefore,

$$0 = k_{i,i+1}(r_{i+1} - r_i - l_{i,i+1}) - k_{i-1,i}(r_i - r_{i-1} - l_{i-1,i}) \tag{3}$$

for $i = 1, 2, 3$, with $r_0 = 0$ and $r_4 = l$. This is a set of three equations in the three unknown constants r_1, r_2, r_3. We will show later that the determinant of this system is nonzero.

We wish to focus our attention on the *deviations* from equilibrium, $x_i(t)$ $(i = 1, 2, 3)$. Subtraction of the equations (3) from the equations (2) gives

$$m_i \frac{d^2 x_i}{dt^2} = k_{i-1,i} x_{i-1} - (k_{i-1,i} + k_{i,i+1}) x_i + k_{i,i+1} x_{i+1} \qquad (i = 1, 2, 3) \qquad (4)$$

with $x_0 = x_4 = 0$. These equations may be written with matrices:

$$\begin{bmatrix} m_1 & 0 & 0 \\ 0 & m_2 & 0 \\ 0 & 0 & m_3 \end{bmatrix} \begin{bmatrix} x_1'' \\ x_2'' \\ x_3'' \end{bmatrix} + \begin{bmatrix} k_{01} + k_{12}, & -k_{12}, & 0 \\ -k_{12}, & k_{12} + k_{23}, & -k_{23} \\ 0, & -k_{23}, & k_{23} + k_{34} \end{bmatrix} \begin{bmatrix} x_1 \\ x_2 \\ x_3 \end{bmatrix} = \begin{bmatrix} 0 \\ 0 \\ 0 \end{bmatrix} \qquad (5)$$

or

$$M x''(t) + K x(t) = 0 \qquad (6)$$

The real, symmetric matrices M and K are called, respectively, the *mass matrix* and the *spring matrix*.

The reader should observe that a basic physical reason why the spring matrix K is symmetric is that a spring is a symmetric device; it acts the same way with respect to both ends. A resistor is also a symmetric device. Therefore, a matrix $R = (r_{ij})$ of resistances between pairs of nodes i, j is a symmetric matrix. These two examples, K and R, illustrate why many matrices occurring in practice are symmetric.

The differential equation (6) can tell us a great deal directly, without our solving it. We shall derive a law of *conservation of energy*. The kinetic energy of our system is

$$\tau = \frac{1}{2} \sum_{i=1}^{3} m_i \left(\frac{dx_i}{dt} \right)^2 \qquad (7)$$

To see how the kinetic energy varies, differentiate (7):

$$\frac{d\tau}{dt} = \sum_{i=1}^{3} m_i x_i'' x_i' = (M x'', x') \qquad (8)$$

This *bilinear form* appears if we take the inner product of the differential equation (6) with the vector $x' = dx/dt$:

$$(M x'', x') + (K x, x') = 0. \qquad (9)$$

But, since K is real and symmetric,

$$\frac{d}{dt}(K x, x) = (K x', x) + (K x, x') = 2(K x, x'). \qquad (10)$$

Similarly, since M is real and symmetric, $(M x', x')' = 2(M x'', x')$. Therefore, (9) says

$$\frac{d}{dt}\left[\frac{1}{2}(Mx', x') + \frac{1}{2}(Kx, x)\right] = 0 \tag{11}$$

or

$$\tfrac{1}{2}[Mx'(t), x'(t)] + \tfrac{1}{2}[Kx(t), x(t)] = \text{constant} \tag{12}$$

The term $\frac{1}{2}(Kx, x)$ is called *potential energy*. We shall show that this quadratic form is always positive if $x \neq 0$. We have

$$\begin{aligned}
(Kx, x) &= [(k_{01} + k_{12})x_1 - k_{12}x_2]x_1 \\
&\quad + [-k_{12}x_1 + (k_{12} + k_{23})x_2 - k_{23}x_3]x_2 \\
&\quad + [-k_{23}x_2 + (k_{23} + k_{34})x_3]x_3 \\
&= k_{01}x_1^2 + k_{12}(x_1 - x_2)^2 + k_{23}(x_2 - x_3)^2 + k_{34}x_3^2
\end{aligned} \tag{13}$$

Since all k_{ij} are >0, we have $(Kx, x) > 0$ unless $0 = x_1 = x_1 - x_2 = x_2 - x_3 = x_3$, i.e., unless all $x_i = 0$. The form $\frac{1}{2}(Kx, x)$ is the work which must be done to stretch our system to deviations x_1, x_2, x_3 from equilibrium.

We shall say that a Hermitian matrix H is *positive definite* if $(Hx, x) > 0$ unless $x = 0$. The examples M and K illustrate that positive definite matrices may arise in practice because their quadratic forms represent energy.

We will show in Theorem 2 that a change of variable $x = Cy$ can simultaneously convert both energies into sums of squares:

$$(Mx', x') = y_1'^2 + y_2'^2 + y_3'^2, \qquad (Kx, x) = \lambda_1 y_1^2 + \lambda_2 y_2^2 + \lambda_3 y_3^2 \tag{14}$$

Theorem 1. *A Hermitian matrix is positive definite if and only if all its eigenvalues are positive.*

Proof. If all the eigenvalues λ_i are positive, and if $U^*HU = \Lambda$ is the canonical diagonalization, then

$$\begin{aligned}
(Hx, x) &= (HUy, Uy) \qquad \text{(if } x = Uy) \\
&= (U^*HUy, y) = (\Lambda y, y) \\
&= \sum_1^n \lambda_i |y_i|^2 > 0 \qquad \text{(unless } y = 0)
\end{aligned} \tag{15}$$

But $y = 0$ implies $x = Uy = 0$.

Conversely, if $(Hx, x) > 0$, unless $x = 0$, then

$$(Hu^i, u^i) = \lambda_i > 0 \quad (i = 1, \ldots, n) \tag{16}$$

if u^i is a unit eigenvector belonging to λ_i. This completes the proof.

Theorem 2. *Let* M *and* K *be* n × n *Hermitian matrices. If* M *is positive definite, then there is an* n × n *matrix* C *for which*

$$C^*MC = I \quad \text{and} \quad C^*KC = \Lambda = \text{diag}\,(\lambda_1, \ldots, \lambda_n) \qquad (17)$$

The numbers λ_j *are real. If* K *is positive definite, the* λ_j *are positive. The* λ_j *are generalized eigenvalues satisfying*

$$Kc^j = \lambda_j Mc^j, \quad c^j \neq 0 \quad (j = 1, \ldots, n) \qquad (18)$$

If K *and* M *are real, then a* real *matrix* C, *with* real *columns* c^j, *may be found satisfying* (17) *and* (18).

Note that the identities (14) for the mass-spring system now follow at once if $x(t) = Cy(t)$. In (14) all λ_i are positive because K, as well as M, is positive definite. Also C and, hence, y are real, since M and K and $x(t)$ are real

Proof of the Theorem. Since M is Hermitian, there is a unitary matrix U such that

$$U^*MU = \text{diag}\,(\mu_1, \mu_2, \ldots, \mu_n) \qquad (19)$$

The effect of the transformation

$$L = U^*KU \qquad (20)$$

is to transform the Hermitian matrix K into a matrix L which is also Hermitian because

$$L^* = (U^*KU)^* = U^*K^*(U^*)^* = U^*KU = L \qquad (21)$$

Here we have used two elementary identities satisfied by the adjoint:

$$(AB)^* = B^*A^* \quad \text{and} \quad (A^*)^* = A \qquad (22)$$

The proofs of these identities are as follows: For all vectors x and y,

$$(ABx, y) = (Bx, A^*y) = (x, B^*A^*y) \qquad (23)$$

and

$$(A^*x, y) = \overline{(y, A^*x)} = \overline{(Ay, x)} = (x, Ay) \qquad (24)$$

We now reduce the diagonal matrix (19) to the identity by a transformation which preserves the Hermitian character of L. Since M is assumed positive definite, its eigenvalues μ_i are positive. Taking the positive roots, $\mu_i^{-1/2}$, we define the diagonal matrix

$$D = \text{diag}\,(\mu_1^{-1/2},\, \mu_2^{-1/2},\, \ldots,\, \mu_n^{-1/2}) = D^* \tag{25}$$

From (19) and (20), we now find

$$D^*(U^*MU)D = I, \qquad D^*(U^*KU)D = H \tag{26}$$

The matrix H is Hermitian by the reasoning used in (21).

Without affecting I, we now may reduce H to a real diagonal matrix Λ by a unitary similarity transformation. If $V^*V = I$ and $V^*HV = \Lambda$, formula (26) yields

$$(V^*D^*U^*)M(UDV) = I, \qquad (V^*D^*U^*)K(UDV) = \Lambda \tag{27}$$

Setting $C = UDV$, we have the required equations (17).

The matrix C has $\det C \neq 0$, since $C^*MC = I$ implies

$$\overline{(\det C)}(\det M)(\det C) = 1 \tag{28}$$

Therefore, all the columns c^j of C are nonzero vectors. To obtain the eigenvalue equation (18), multiply the equation $C^*KC = \Lambda$ by $(C^*)^{-1}$. Since $(C^*)(MC) = I$, we have $(C^*)^{-1} = MC$. Therefore,

$$KC = MC\Lambda \quad \text{or} \quad Kc^j = \lambda_j Mc^j \quad (j = 1, \ldots, n) \tag{29}$$

Note the *generalized orthogonality*

$$(c^i)^*Mc^j = \delta_{ij} \qquad (i, j = 1, \ldots, n) \tag{30}$$

which is implied by $C^*MC = I$.

If K, as well as M, is positive definite, the numbers λ_j are positive because, by (29), they equal the quotients

$$\lambda_j = \frac{(Kc^j, c^j)}{(Mc^j, c^j)} \tag{31}$$

If K and M are real, all the matrices $U, D, V,$ and Λ may be found as real matrices, according to Theorem 3 of the last section. This completes the proof of the theorem.

The simultaneous diagonalization of M and K provides an explicit, meaningful solution of the differential equation $Mx'' + Kx = 0$ of mass-spring and analogous systems. Make the change of variable $x(t) = Cy(t)$. The differential equation now becomes

$$MCy''(t) + KCy(t) = 0 \tag{32}$$

Multiplication on the left by C^* yields the uncoupled equations

$$y''(t) + \Lambda y(t) = 0 \tag{33}$$

Since K, as well as M, is positive definite, the numbers λ_i are positive: $\lambda_i = \omega_i^2 > 0$. By components, (33) reads

$$y_i''(t) + \omega_i^2 y_i(t) = 0 \qquad (i = 1, \ldots, n) \tag{34}$$

Therefore, we have the general solution

$$y_i(t) = \alpha_i \cos \omega_i t + \beta_i \sin \omega_i t \qquad (i = 1, \ldots, n) \tag{35}$$

Since $x(t) = Cy(t)$, where C has columns c^j,

$$x(t) = y_1(t)c^1 + \cdots + y_n(t)c^n \tag{36}$$

$$x(t) = \sum_{j=1}^{n} (\alpha_j \cos \sqrt{\lambda_j}\, t + \beta_j \sin \sqrt{\lambda_j}\, t)\, c^j \tag{37}$$

Equation (37) gives the solution $x(t)$ in terms of the generalized eigenvalues λ_j and eigenvectors c^j. The motion $x(t)$ is thus composed of harmonic oscillations with angular frequencies $\sqrt{\lambda_j}$, where $\lambda_1, \ldots, \lambda_n$ are the roots of the polynomial equation

$$\det (\lambda M - K) = 0 \tag{38}$$

In fact, if $\Lambda = \operatorname{diag}(\lambda_1, \ldots, \lambda_n)$,

$$\begin{aligned} \det (\lambda I - \Lambda) &= \det [C^*(\lambda M - K)C] \\ &= |\det C|^2 \det (\lambda M - K) \end{aligned} \tag{39}$$

The constants α_j, β_j may be used to fit given initial conditions

$$x(0) = \sum_{j=1}^{n} \alpha_j c^j, \qquad x'(0) = \sum_{j=1}^{n} \sqrt{\lambda_j}\, \beta_j c^j \tag{40}$$

Finally, we remark that the determinant of the equilibrium equations (3) is nonzero. These equations may be written in the form $Kr = $ a given vector. But the spring matrix K is positive definite, and *the determinant of a positive-definite matrix*, being the product of its eigenvalues, *is positive.*

PROBLEMS

1. Let

$$M = \begin{bmatrix} 2, & -3 \\ -3, & 5 \end{bmatrix}, \qquad K = \begin{bmatrix} 3, & 1 \\ 1, & 21 \end{bmatrix}$$

Find the roots, λ_1 and λ_2, of the characteristic equation $\det (\lambda M - K) = 0$.

Find nonzero vectors, v^1 and v^2, such that $Kv^i = \lambda_i Mv^i$ $(i = 1, 2)$. Find normalized vectors $c^i = \rho_i v^i$ $(i = 1, 2)$ such that $(Mc^i, c^i) = 1$. Form the matrix C with columns c^1 and c^2. Verify that $C^*MC = I$ and $C^*KC = \Lambda = \mathrm{diag}\,(\lambda_1, \lambda_2)$.

2. Let M and K be defined as in Problem 1. Solve initial-value problem

$$Mx''(t) + Kx(t) = 0$$
$$x(0) = \begin{bmatrix} 1 \\ 0 \end{bmatrix}, \qquad x'(0) = \begin{bmatrix} 0 \\ 1 \end{bmatrix}$$

3. Let M and K be positive-definite Hermitian matrices. Let $x(t)$ satisfy the differential equation

$$Mx''(t) + Lx'(t) + Kx(t) = 0$$

where L is any matrix for which the Hermitian matrix $L + L^*$ is positive definite. Show that the total energy

$$\tfrac{1}{2}[Mx'(t), x'(t)] + \tfrac{1}{2}[Kx(t), x(t)]$$

decreases steadily as t increases.

4. If a Hermitian matrix H is positive definite, show that $H = P^2$, where P is also positive definite.

5. If a Hermitian matrix H is positive definite, show that it satisfies the generalized Schwarz inequality,

$$|(Hx, y)| \le (Hx, x)^{1/2}(Hy, y)^{1/2}$$

and the generalized triangle-inequality,

$$[H(x + y), x + y]^{1/2} \le (Hx, x)^{1/2} + (Hy, y)^{1/2}$$

6.* Let $M = I$, and let

$$K = \begin{bmatrix} 3 & 2 \\ 2 & 3 \end{bmatrix}, \qquad L = \begin{bmatrix} 3 & 2 \\ 2 & 2 \end{bmatrix}$$

For these *three* matrices $M, K,$ and L, show that *no* two nonsingular matrices, P and Q, exist for which all three matrices $PMQ, PKQ\ PLQ$ are diagonal matrices. (Hence, the differential equation $Mx'' + Lx' + Kx = 0$ cannot be uncoupled by setting $x = Qy$ and multiplying the differential equation on the left by P.)

4.9 UNITARY TRIANGULARIZATION

We have shown that not every square matrix is similar to a diagonal matrix. However, as we will now show, every square matrix *is* similar to a triangular matrix. For many purposes triangularization is sufficient.

Theorem 1. *Let* A *be an* n $\times$ n *matrix. Then there is a unitary matrix* U *for which*

$$U^*AU = T = (t_{ij}) \qquad \text{(with } t_{ij} = 0 \text{ for } i > j) \tag{1}$$

In other words T *has all zeros below the main diagonal. The diagonal elements* t$_{11}$ *are the eigenvalues of* A.

It is noteworthy that the similarity transformation $A \rightarrow T$ can always be accomplished by a *unitary* matrix, with $U^* = U^{-1}$. If A happens to be Hermitian, T is necessarily diagonal because T is triangular and $T = U^*AU$ is Hermitian. Therefore, our proof will provide an independent proof that a Hermitian matrix H can be diagonalized by a unitary similarity transformation $U^*HU = \Lambda$.

Proof of the Theorem. The theorem is true for $n = 1$, with $1 \cdot a_{11} \cdot 1 = \lambda_1$ $= T$. Supposing the theorem true for $n \leq m$, we will prove it for $n = m + 1$. Let u^1 be a unit eigenvector of A:

$$Au^1 = \lambda_1 u^1, \qquad \|u^1\| = 1 \tag{2}$$

The vector u^1 exists because the polynomial det $(\lambda I - A)$ is zero for at least one complex number $\lambda = \lambda_1$.

Since $u^1 \neq 0$, u^1 has at least one nonzero component, say the rth component. Consider the vectors

$$u^1, e^1, e^2, \ldots, e^{r-1}, e^{r+1}, \ldots, e^n \qquad (e^r \text{ missing}) \tag{3}$$

These n vectors clearly form a basis for E^n. If these vectors are orthogonalized by the Gram-Schmidt process, the result is n vectors

$$v^1, v^2, \ldots, v^n \qquad [\text{with } v^1 = u^1 \text{ and } (v^i, v^j) = \delta_{ij}] \tag{4}$$

Let V be the unitary matrix with columns v^j. Then AV has the columns

$$Av^1 = \lambda_1 v^1, Av^2, \ldots, Av^n \tag{5}$$

The matrix $V^*(AV)$ has the first column

$$V^*(Av^1) = V^*(\lambda_1 v^1) = [\lambda_1(v^i)^*v^1] \qquad (i = 1, \ldots, n)$$

which equals λ_1 col $(1, 0, 0, \ldots, 0)$. Thus, V^*AV has the form

$$V^*AV = \begin{bmatrix} \lambda_1 & * & \cdots\cdots & * \\ 0 & & & \\ 0 & & & \\ \cdot & & B & \\ \cdot & & & \\ \cdot & & & \\ 0 & & & \end{bmatrix} \tag{6}$$

where the numbers * are irrelevant and where B is an $(n - 1) \times (n - 1)$ matrix.

By induction, we have an $(n - 1) \times (n - 1)$ unitary matrix W for which $W^*BW = T_1$, a triangular matrix with all zeros below the main diagonal. Now form the $n \times n$ matrix

$$
Y = \begin{bmatrix} 1 & 0 & \cdots\cdots & 0 \\ 0 & & & \\ \cdot & & & \\ \cdot & & W & \\ \cdot & & & \\ 0 & & & \end{bmatrix} \tag{7}
$$

The matrix Y is unitary because its columns are mutually orthogonal unit vectors. Multiplying (6) on the right by Y and on the left by Y^*, we find

$$
Y^*(V^*AV)Y = \begin{bmatrix} \lambda_1 & * & \cdots\cdots & * \\ 0 & & & \\ \cdot & & & \\ \cdot & & W^*BW & \\ \cdot & & & \\ 0 & & & \end{bmatrix} = T \tag{8}
$$

But $W^*BW = T_1$, which has all zeros below the main diagonal. Therefore, T has all zeros below the main diagonal. The product of unitary matrices $U = VY$ is unitary. Therefore, (8) gives the required triangularization (1).

The diagonal elements $t_{11}, \ldots, t_{nn}$ are the eigenvalues of A because we have the expansion

$$
\det(\lambda I - T) = (\lambda - t_{11})(\lambda - t_{22}) \ldots (\lambda - t_{nn}) \tag{9}
$$

for the determinant of the triangular matrix $\lambda I - T$. Since the characteristic polynomial is invariant under a similarity transformation, we must also have

$$
\det(\lambda I - T) = \det(\lambda I - A) = (\lambda - \lambda_1)(\lambda - \lambda_2) \ldots (\lambda - \lambda_n)
$$

This theorem has many applications, of which we shall give only a few.

Theorem 2. *Let* A *be an* n $\times$ n *matrix with multiple eigenvalues. Then there is a matrix* B *as near as we wish to* A *such that* B *has distinct eigenvalues.*

Proof. Let A be given. For any $\epsilon > 0$, we must show that there is a matrix $B = (b_{ij})$ with $|b_{ij} - a_{ij}| < \epsilon\,(i, j = 1, \ldots, n)$ and such that B has distinct eigenvalues.

From the unitary triangularization $U^*AU = T$, we may represent A in the form

$$A = U \begin{bmatrix} \lambda_1 & * & \cdots & * \\ 0 & \lambda_2 & \cdots & * \\ . & . & \cdots & . \\ 0 & 0 & \cdots & \lambda_n \end{bmatrix} U^* = UTU^* \qquad (10)$$

Keep U fixed and the numbers * fixed, but change the eigenvalues $\lambda_1, \ldots, \lambda_n$ into *distinct* numbers $\lambda_1', \ldots, \lambda_n'$. The result is a new matrix

$$B = U \begin{bmatrix} \lambda_1' & * & \cdots & * \\ 0 & \lambda_2' & \cdots & * \\ . & . & \cdots & . \\ 0 & 0 & \cdots & \lambda_n' \end{bmatrix} U^* = UT'U^* \qquad (11)$$

The eigenvalues of B are the *distinct* numbers λ_j' because B is similar to T'. By the representations (10) and (11), if the λ_k' are chosen sufficiently near the λ_k, we shall have $|b_{ij} - a_{ij}| < \epsilon$ for all i, j. This completes the proof.

Theorem 3. *Let* A *be an* n × n *matrix. Then the powers* A[r] *tend to the zero matrix as* r → ∞ *if and only if all the eigenvalues* λ_k *of* A *lie in the unit circle* $|\lambda| < 1$.

This is the basic theorem of numerical matrix-iteration methods.

Proof. If $|\lambda_1| \geq 1$ for any eigenvalue λ_1, the powers A^r cannot tend to zero because, if $Au^1 = \lambda_1 u^1$ with $u^1 \neq 0$, then

$$A^r u^1 = \lambda_1^r u^1 \qquad (r = 1, 2, \ldots) \qquad (12)$$

which does not tend to the zero vector as $r \to \infty$.

Suppose, conversely, that all $|\lambda_j| < 1$; show $A^r \to O$ as $r \to \infty$. This is trivial if A has *distinct* eigenvalues. For then, if $\Lambda = \text{diag}(\lambda_1, \ldots, \lambda_n)$,

$$C^{-1}AC = \Lambda, \qquad A = C\Lambda C^{-1} \qquad (13)$$

and

$$A^r = (C\Lambda C^{-1})(C\Lambda C^{-1}) \ldots (C\Lambda C^{-1}) = C\Lambda^r C^{-1} \qquad (14)$$

which tends to zero as $r \to \infty$ because $\Lambda^r = \text{diag}(\lambda_1^r, \ldots, \lambda_n^r)$.

If A has multiple eigenvalues, we still have the unitary triangularization (1). The identities

$$A^r = UT^rU^* \quad \text{and} \quad T^r = U^*A^rU \tag{15}$$

imply that $A^r \to O$ if and only if $T^r \to O$. We now *majorize* T by the triangular matrix

$$M = \begin{bmatrix} \mu_1 & \alpha & \alpha & \cdots & \alpha \\ 0 & \mu_2 & \alpha & \cdots & \alpha \\ 0 & 0 & \mu_3 & \cdots & \alpha \\ \cdot & \cdot & \cdot & \cdots & \cdot \\ 0 & 0 & 0 & \cdots & \mu_n \end{bmatrix} \tag{16}$$

where $\alpha \ge$ all $|t_{ij}|$ for $j > i$ and where $\mu_1, \mu_2, \ldots, \mu_n$ are any n *distinct* positive numbers such that

$$|\lambda_k| \le \mu_k < 1 \qquad (k = 1, \ldots, n) \tag{17}$$

The powers M^r tend to O as $r \to \infty$ because M has the n *distinct* eigenvalues μ_k inside the unit circle. But the inequalities

$$|t_{ij}| \le m_{ij} \qquad \text{(for all } i, j) \tag{18}$$

between T and M imply the inequalities

$$|t_{ij}^{(r)}| \le m_{ij}^{(r)} \quad \text{(for all } i, j) \tag{19}$$

between corresponding components of the powers T^r and M^r. Since the i, j component $m_{ij}^{(r)}$ tends to 0 as $r \to \infty$, (19) shows that the i, j component of T^r also tends to zero as $r \to \infty$. This completes the proof.

As a final application we will prove the famous Cayley-Hamilton theorem, which states that a square matrix satisfies its own characteristic equation.

Theorem 4. *Let* A *be an* n × n *matrix. Let*

$$\det (\lambda I - A) = \lambda^n + \alpha_1\lambda^{n-1} + \alpha_2\lambda^{n-2} + \cdots + \alpha_{n-1}\lambda + \alpha_n \tag{20}$$

Then

$$A^n + \alpha_1A^{n-1} + \alpha_2A^{n-2} + \cdots + \alpha_{n-1}A + \alpha_nI = O \tag{21}$$

EXAMPLE 1. For

$$A = \begin{bmatrix} 1 & 2 \\ 3 & 4 \end{bmatrix}$$

we have $\det (\lambda I - A) = \lambda^2 - 5\lambda - 2$. Now (21) becomes

$$A^2 - 5A - 2I = O$$

or

$$\begin{bmatrix} 7 & 10 \\ 15 & 22 \end{bmatrix} - 5\begin{bmatrix} 1 & 2 \\ 3 & 4 \end{bmatrix} - 2\begin{bmatrix} 1 & 0 \\ 0 & 1 \end{bmatrix} = \begin{bmatrix} 0 & 0 \\ 0 & 0 \end{bmatrix}.$$

Proof of the Theorem. We will later give a purely algebraic proof of this theorem. Let $\phi(\lambda) = \det(\lambda I - A)$. We wish to prove that $\phi(A) = O$. This is obvious if A has distinct eigenvalues. For then $A = C\Lambda C^{-1}$, where $\Lambda = \text{diag}(\lambda_1, \ldots, \lambda_n)$; and

$$\phi(A) = C\phi(\Lambda)C^{-1} \tag{22}$$

But $\phi(\Lambda) = \text{diag}[\phi(\lambda_1), \ldots, \phi(\lambda_n)] = O$, because the numbers $\phi(\lambda_j)$ are all 0.

If A has multiple eigenvalues, Theorem 2 states that A is the limit of matrices B with distinct eigenvalues. If

$$\psi(\lambda) = \det(\lambda I - B) = \lambda^n + \beta_1\lambda^{n-1} + \beta_2\lambda^{n-2} + \cdots + \beta_n \tag{23}$$

then $\beta_j \to \alpha_j$ as $B \to A$ because the coefficients of the characteristic polynomial are continuous, multinomial functions of the components of a matrix. Therefore,

$$\begin{aligned} \phi(A) &= A^n + \alpha_1 A^{n-1} + \alpha_2 A^{n-2} + \cdots + \alpha_n I \\ &= \lim_{B \to A}(B^n + \beta_1 B^{n-1} + \beta_2 B^{n-2} + \cdots + \beta_n I) \end{aligned} \tag{24}$$

But $B^n + \beta_1 B^{n-1} + \cdots + \beta_n I = \psi(B) = O$ because B has distinct eigenvalues. Therefore, $\phi(A) = O$.

PROBLEMS

1. If A is an $n \times n$ matrix, prove that there is a unitary matrix V such that $VAV^* = L$, where L is *lower* triangular ($l_{ij} = 0$ for $j > i$). Use Theorem 1.

2. Find a unitary triangularization $U^*AU = T$ for the matrix

$$A = \begin{bmatrix} 1 & 0 \\ 2 & 3 \end{bmatrix}$$

3. Find a unitary triangularization $U^*AU = T$ for the matrix

$$A = \begin{bmatrix} 1 & 4 \\ 3 & 2 \end{bmatrix}$$

4. If $U^*AU = T$ is a unitary triangularization, show that

$$\sum_{i=1}^{n} \sum_{j=1}^{n} |a_{ij}|^2 = \sum_{i \leq j} |t_{ij}|^2$$

5. Consider a system of differential equations $dx/dt = Ax$, where A is *not* similar to a diagonal matrix. Let $U^*AU = T$ be a unitary triangularization of A. Show how the change of variable $x = Uy$ allows the system to be solved recursively for y_n, then $y_{n-1}, \ldots$, and finally y_1.

4.10 NORMAL MATRICES

What is the most general class of n $\times$ n *matrices* N *which have* n *orthogonal eigenvectors?* We shall call these matrices *normal matrices*. Let $\lambda_1, \ldots, \lambda_n$ be the eigenvalues of N, and let $u^1, \ldots, u^n$ be corresponding eigenvectors satisfying $(u^j, u^k) = \delta_{jk}$. Let $\Lambda = \text{diag}(\lambda_1, \ldots, \lambda_n)$, and let U be the unitary matrix with columns $u^1, \ldots, u^n$. Then

$$U^*NU = \Lambda \quad \text{or} \quad N = U\Lambda U^* \tag{1}$$

Since $N^* = U\Lambda^*U^*$, the normal matrix N is Hermitian if and only if $\Lambda = \Lambda^*$, which means that Λ is real. Let $\Lambda = \Lambda' + i\Lambda'' = \text{Re}\,\Lambda + i\,\text{Im}\,\Lambda$. Suppose that Λ is pure-imaginary: $\Lambda = i\Lambda''$. Then $\Lambda^* = -\Lambda$, and (1) shows that $N = -N^*$. Suppose that all λ_k lie on the unit circle. Then $\Lambda^*\Lambda = I$, so that $N^*N = I$ and N is unitary. Conversely, we shall show later that every skew-Hermitian or unitary matrix is a normal matrix.

Since $\Lambda = \Lambda' + i\Lambda''$, we can write any normal matrix in the form

$$N = U(\Lambda' + i\Lambda'')U^* = H' + iH'' \tag{2}$$

where H' and H'' are commuting Hermitian matrices:

$$H' = U\Lambda'U^*, \quad H'' = U\Lambda''U^*; \qquad H'H'' = H''H' \tag{3}$$

A simple property held in common by all Hermitian, skew-Hermitian, and unitary matrices is that they commute with their adjoints: $NN^* = N^*N$. We now show the converse:

Theorem 1. *An* n $\times$ n *matrix* N *is* normal, *i.e., has a complete set of orthogonal eigenvectors, if and only if* NN* = N*N.

Proof. If N is normal, equation (1) gives

$$NN^* = N^*N = U\,\text{diag}(|\lambda_1|^2, \ldots, |\lambda_n|^2)U^* \tag{4}$$

Supposing, instead, that $NN^* = N^*N$, let us prove that N is normal.

For any square matrix N we have $N = H' + iH''$, where H' and H'' are the Hermitian matrices

$$H' = \tfrac{1}{2}(N + N^*), \qquad H'' = \frac{1}{2i}(N - N^*) \tag{5}$$

Since $NN^* = N^*N$, the matrices H' and H'' commute:

$$(4i)H'H'' = N^2 - NN^* + N^*N - (N^*)^2 = N^2 - (N^*)^2$$
$$(4i)H''H' = N^2 - N^*N + NN^* - (N^*)^2 = N^2 - (N^*)^2$$

We will now show that $H'H'' = H''H'$ implies that the Hermitian matrices H' and H'' can be diagonalized by the *same* unitary matrix U. Let $\lambda'_1 \geq \cdots \geq \lambda'_n$ be the eigenvalues of H', and let $\Lambda' = \text{diag}(\lambda'_1, \ldots, \lambda'_n)$. Since H' is Hermitian there is a unitary matrix V for which $V^*H'V = \Lambda'$. Let $V^*H''V = K''$. The matrix K'' is, of course, Hermitian; but we cannot be sure that K'' is diagonal. For example, the matrices

$$H' = \begin{bmatrix} 1 & 0 \\ 0 & 1 \end{bmatrix}, \qquad H'' = \begin{bmatrix} 0 & 7 \\ 7 & 0 \end{bmatrix}$$

commute; but if we take $V = I$, then $K'' = H'' \neq$ a diagonal matrix.

Since H' and H'' commute, Λ' and K'' commute:

$$\Lambda'K'' = (V^*H'V)(V^*H''V) = V^*(H'H'')V$$
$$K''\Lambda' = (V^*H''V)(V^*H'V) = V^*(H''H')V$$

If K'' has components k_{ij}, the commuting of Λ' and K'' implies

$$\lambda'_i k_{ij} = k_{ij}\lambda'_j \qquad (i,j = 1, \ldots, n) \tag{6}$$

Therefore, $k_{ij} = 0$ unless $\lambda'_i = \lambda'_j$.

What does this mean? If the λ'_i are distinct, then $k_{ij} = 0$ unless $i = j$; then K'' is diagonal. If the λ'_i are not distinct, we may write

$$\Lambda' = \begin{bmatrix} \Lambda_1 & 0 & \cdots & 0 \\ 0 & \Lambda_2 & \cdots & 0 \\ \cdot & \cdot & \cdots & \cdot \\ 0 & 0 & \cdots & \Lambda_s \end{bmatrix} \tag{7}$$

where Λ_i consists of a string of m_i *equal* eigenvalues, say γ_i, where $\gamma_1 > \gamma_2 > \cdots > \gamma_s$. Since $k_{ij} = 0$ unless $\lambda'_i = \lambda'_j$, there is a corresponding partitioning

$$K'' = \begin{bmatrix} K_1 & 0 & \cdots & 0 \\ 0 & K_2 & \cdots & 0 \\ \cdot & \cdot & \cdots & \cdot \\ 0 & 0 & \cdots & K_s \end{bmatrix} \tag{8}$$

where K_i is an $m_i \times m_i$ Hermitian matrix.

For each K_i there is a unitary matrix W_i such that $W_i^* K_i W_i$ is diagonal. Define

$$W = \begin{bmatrix} W_1 & 0 & \cdots & 0 \\ 0 & W_2 & \cdots & 0 \\ \cdot & \cdot & \cdots & \cdot \\ 0 & 0 & \cdots & W_s \end{bmatrix} \tag{9}$$

The matrix W is an $n \times n$ unitary matrix. The matrix $W^*K''W$ is diagonal; it consists of zeros except for the blocks $W_i^* K_i W_i$ along the diagonal, and each block $W_i^* K_i W_i$ is a diagonal matrix.

Form the matrix $W^*\Lambda'W$. This matrix consists of zeros except for the blocks $W_i^* \Lambda_i W_i$. But $\Lambda_i = \gamma_i I_i$ where I_i is the identity matrix of order m_i. Therefore,

$$W_i^* \Lambda_i W_i = W_i^*(\gamma_i I_i) W_i = \gamma_i I_i = \Lambda_i \tag{10}$$

Therefore, $W^*\Lambda'W = \Lambda'$. In summary, if $U = VW$, we have shown

$$U^*H'U = W^*\Lambda'W = \Lambda'$$
$$U^*H''U = W^*K''W = \Lambda''$$

where Λ' and Λ'' are real diagonal matrices. From the representation $N = H' + iH''$ we find the required diagonalization

$$U^*NU = \Lambda' + i\Lambda'' = \Lambda$$

The columns of the unitary matrix U form a complete set of orthogonal eigenvectors for N.

Corollary. Let A be an n $\times$ n *matrix for which* A* $= -$A *or for which* A*A $=$ I. *Then* A *has* n *mutually orthogonal unit eigenvectors.*

Proof. In either case, $A^*A = AA^*$.

RIGID MOTIONS IN EUCLIDEAN SPACE

As an application of the theory of normal matrices, we shall discuss the rigid motions of real, three-dimensional space. The rigid motions $x \rightarrow Rx$

preserve length. We shall assume that there is no translation, so that $0 \longrightarrow 0$. Therefore, according to Section 4.4, the rigid motions are prescribed by real, unitary matrices R:

$$R^*R = R^TR = RR^T = RR^* = I$$

A physically realizable rigid motion can be achieved by a continuous sequence of rigid motions, $M(t)(0 \le t \le 1)$, where

$$M(0) = I \quad \text{and} \quad M(1) = R$$

The eigenvalues of each matrix unitary M must lie on the unit circle because $Mx = \lambda x$ implies

$$\|x\| = \|Mx\| = \|\lambda x\| = |\lambda| \|x\|$$

Since M is real, if M has complex eigenvalues, they occur in complex conjugate pairs $e^{i\theta}$, $e^{-i\theta}$. Therefore, the three eigenvalues of M are all ± 1, or they are ± 1, $e^{i\theta}$, $e^{-i\theta}$, where $0 < \theta < \pi$. In either case, $\det M(t) = \pm 1$ for all t. But $\det M(0) = \det I = 1$. Since $M(t)$ varies continuously, $\det M(t)$ varies continuously. Therefore, $\det M(t) = 1$ for all t, since a continuous function cannot jump from $+1$ to -1.

In particular,

$$\det R = \det M(1) = 1$$

Therefore, the eigenvalues of R have one of these forms:

$$(\alpha) \qquad 1, 1, 1$$
$$(\beta) \qquad 1, -1, -1$$
$$(\gamma) \qquad 1, e^{i\theta}, e^{-i\theta} \quad (0 < \theta < \pi)$$

Let U be a unitary matrix which diagonalizes the normal matrix R:

$$U^*RU = \Lambda, \qquad R = U\Lambda U^*, \qquad U^*U = I$$

Case (α). In this case $\Lambda = I$, and

$$R = UIU^* = I$$

Case (β). Since the normal matrix R has real eigenvalues, R is Hermitian. For example,

$$R = \begin{bmatrix} \cos\theta & \sin\theta & 0 \\ \sin\theta & -\cos\theta & 0 \\ 0 & 0 & -1 \end{bmatrix} \qquad (11)$$

has the eigenvalues $1, -1, -1$. Then the real, Hermitian matrix R can be diagonalized by a *real* unitary matrix U. This was proved in Theorem 3 of Section 4.7. Let the columns of U be the real unit vectors u, v, and w. Since

$$Ru = u, \qquad Rv = -v, \quad \text{and} \quad Rw = -w$$

we see that R is a rotation about the u axis, through $180°$, in the v, w plane.

Case (γ). Since there is a single eigenvalue $\lambda = 1$, there is a real eigenvector u for which $Ru = u$. Every other eigenvector belonging to $\lambda = 1$ is a scalar multiple of u. Let the complex unitary matrix U have columns u, v, and w. Since

$$Rv = e^{i\theta}v, \qquad Rw = e^{-i\theta}w \quad (0 < \theta < \pi)$$

while taking conjugates gives

$$R\bar{v} = e^{-i\theta}\bar{v}$$

the vector w is a scalar multiple of $\bar{v}$; we shall take $w = \bar{v}$. Let the vector v have real part a and imaginary part b: $v = a + ib$. Then

$$R(a + ib) = (\cos\theta + i\sin\theta)(a + ib)$$

implies

$$Ra = (\cos\theta)a - (\sin\theta)b, \qquad Rb = (\sin\theta)a + (\cos\theta)b \qquad (12)$$

Since v and w are orthogonal, we have

$$0 = (v, w) = (a + ib, a - ib)$$
$$= (a, a) + i(b, a) + i(a, b) - (b, b)$$

But $(a, b) = (b, a)$ since the vectors a and b are real. Therefore,

$$(a, b) = 0 \quad \text{and} \quad (a, a) = (b, b)$$

But $1 = (v, v)$ implies

$$(a, a) + (b, b) = 1$$

Therefore a and b are real, orthogonal unit vectors with $\|a\| = \|b\| = 1/\sqrt{2}$. Since u is orthogonal to $v = a + ib$, the real vectors u, a, and b are mutually orthogonal. Let V be the *real* unitary matrix with columns u, $\sqrt{2}\,a$, and $\sqrt{2}\,b$. Then, by (12),

$$RV = V \begin{bmatrix} 1 & 0 & 0 \\ & \cos\theta & \sin\theta \\ 0 & -\sin\theta & \cos\theta \end{bmatrix}$$

Thus, R is a rotation about the u axis, through the angle θ, in the a, b plane.

In summary, a real 3×3 unitary matrix, R, with det $R = 1$, represents a *rotation*. The eigenvalues and eigenvectors give the angle of rotation, the axis of rotation, and two orthogonal vectors in the plane of rotation.

PROBLEMS

1. Find the axis of rotation in the rigid motion given by the matrix

$$R = \begin{bmatrix} \cos \theta & \sin \theta & 0 \\ \sin \theta & -\cos \theta & 0 \\ 0 & 0 & -1 \end{bmatrix}$$

2. Find the angle of rotation, the axis of rotation, and two orthogonal vectors in the plane of rotation for the rigid motion

$$R = \begin{bmatrix} 1/\sqrt{3}, & 1/\sqrt{2}, & -1/\sqrt{6} \\ 1/\sqrt{3}, & 0, & 2/\sqrt{6} \\ 1/\sqrt{3}, & -1/\sqrt{2}, & -1/\sqrt{6} \end{bmatrix}$$

3.* Consider the differential equation $dx(t)/dt = Nx(t)$. This equation has the solution $x(t) = X(t)x(0)$, where $X(t)$ is the exponential matrix e^{Nt} (See Section 3.4). If N is a normal matrix, show that $X(t)$ is normal for each time, t. If N is Hermitian, show that $X(t)$ is Hermitian. If N is skew-Hermitian, show that $X(t)$ is unitary.

4. Let $N^*N = NN^*$. Show that there are a positive-semidefinite Hermitian matrix, P, and a unitary matrix, V, such that $N = PV = VP$. (Use the factorization $N = U\Lambda U^*$. If $NN^* = U\Lambda\Lambda^*U^* = P^2$, how can P be defined?)

5. Let T be a triangular matrix, with $t_{ij} = 0$ for $i > j$. Show that $TT^* = T^*T$ only if T is a diagonal matrix. Hence, give an independent proof of Theorem 1 based on the unitary triangularization $N = UTU^*$.

THE JORDAN CANONICAL FORM

5.1 INTRODUCTION

Not every matrix can be diagonalized by a similarity transformation. This fact has an important consequence in the theory of differential equations: Not every system of differential equations

$$\frac{d}{dt}\, x(t) = Ax(t) \qquad \text{with } x(0) = b \tag{1}$$

has a solution which is a linear combination of exponential functions

$$x(t) = \sum_{\nu=1}^{n} \xi_\nu c^{(\nu)} e^{\lambda_\nu t} \tag{2}$$

For example, the problem

$$\frac{d}{dt}\, x(t) = \begin{bmatrix} 7 & 1 \\ 0 & 7 \end{bmatrix} x(t) \qquad \text{with } x(0) = \begin{bmatrix} 0 \\ 1 \end{bmatrix} \tag{3}$$

has the nonexponential solution

$$x(t) = \begin{bmatrix} t \\ 1 \end{bmatrix} e^{7t} \tag{4}$$

The matrix A in the example (3) cannot be diagonalized by a similarity transformation

$$C^{-1} \begin{bmatrix} 7 & 1 \\ 0 & 7 \end{bmatrix} C = \begin{bmatrix} \lambda_1 & 0 \\ 0 & \lambda_2 \end{bmatrix} = \Lambda \tag{5}$$

If (5) were possible, then we must have $\lambda_1 = \lambda_2 = 7$ because A and Λ must have the same characteristic polynomial. Then (5) implies the false equation

$$\begin{bmatrix} 7 & 1 \\ 0 & 7 \end{bmatrix} = C \begin{bmatrix} 7 & 0 \\ 0 & 7 \end{bmatrix} C^{-1} = \begin{bmatrix} 7 & 0 \\ 0 & 7 \end{bmatrix}$$

To obtain the solutions of differential equations (1) in all cases, we may use the following theorem of C. Jordan:

Theorem 1. *Let* A *be an* n × n *matrix whose different eigenvalues are* $\lambda_1, \ldots, \lambda_s$ *with multiplicities* $m_1, \ldots, m_s$:

$$\det(\lambda I - A) = \prod_{j=1}^{s} (\lambda - \lambda_j)^{m_j} \tag{6}$$

Then A *is similar to a matrix of the form*

$$J = \begin{bmatrix} \Lambda_1 & 0 & \cdots & 0 \\ 0 & \Lambda_2 & \cdots & 0 \\ . & . & \cdots & . \\ 0 & 0 & \cdots & \Lambda_s \end{bmatrix} \tag{7}$$

where Λ_i *is an* $m_i \times m_i$ *matrix of the form*

$$\Lambda_i = \begin{bmatrix} \lambda_i & 0 & 0 & \cdots & 0 & 0 & 0 \\ * & \lambda_i & 0 & \cdots & 0 & 0 & 0 \\ 0 & * & \lambda_i & \cdots & 0 & 0 & 0 \\ . & . & . & \cdots & . & . & . \\ 0 & 0 & 0 & \cdots & * & \lambda_i & 0 \\ 0 & 0 & 0 & \cdots & 0 & * & \lambda_i \end{bmatrix} \tag{8}$$

with each * *equal to* 0 *or* 1. (Some *'s may equal 0 while other *'s equal 1.)

This chapter will be devoted to the proof of Jordan's Theorem, which is a generalization of the preceding results. If A has *distinct* eigenvalues, we have $s = n$ and all $m_j = 1$ in (6). Then the matrix Λ_i is the 1×1 matrix λ_i, and $J = \text{diag}(\lambda_1, \ldots, \lambda_n)$. If A has multiple eigenvalues *but* has n linearly independent eigenvectors (e.g., if A is Hermitian), then A is similar to J with every number * equal to 0.

Let us show how Jordan's Theorem applies to differential equations (1). If $C^{-1}AC = J$, we make the change of variable $x(t) = Cy(t)$. Then (1) becomes

$$\frac{dy(t)}{dt} = Jy(t), \qquad y(0) = C^{-1}b \tag{9}$$

We now partition the n-component column vector $y(t)$ into parts

$$y(t) = \begin{bmatrix} y^{(1)}(t) \\ y^{(2)}(t) \\ \cdot \\ \cdot \\ \cdot \\ y^{(s)}(t) \end{bmatrix} \qquad \begin{array}{l} m_1 \text{ components} \\ m_2 \text{ components} \\ \\ \\ \\ m_s \text{ components} \end{array} \tag{10}$$

Similarly, we partition the initial vector $y(0) = C^{-1}b \equiv g$ into s parts: $g^{(1)}, g^{(2)}, \ldots, g^{(s)}$. The block form (7) for J now yields s *disjoint* systems

$$\frac{dy^{(i)}(t)}{dt} = \Lambda_i y^{(i)}(t) \qquad \text{with } y^{(i)}(0) = g^{(i)} \tag{11}$$

For $i = 1$, equation (11) involves only the first m_1 components of y; for $i = 2$, (11) involves only the next m_2 components of y, etc. Therefore, the s systems (11) may be solved separately.

Every one of the systems (11) has the form

$$\frac{dz_k(t)}{dt} = *z_{k-1}(t) + \lambda z_k(t) \qquad (k = 1, \ldots, m) \tag{12}$$

where

$$z_k = y_k^{(i)}, \qquad \lambda = \lambda_i, \qquad m = m_i, \quad \text{each } * = 0 \text{ or } 1 \tag{13}$$

with $* = 0$ for $k = 1$. Make the change of variable

$$z_k(t) = e^{\lambda t} w_k(t) \tag{14}$$

Then (12) becomes

$$\frac{d}{dt} w_k(t) = *w_{k-1}(t) \qquad (k = 1, \ldots, m) \tag{15}$$

Since $* = 0$ for $k = 1$, (15) yields $w_1(t) = \text{constant}$. Integrating (15) successively gives

$$\begin{aligned} w_k(t) &= \text{polynomial in } t \text{ of degree} < k \\ z_k(t) &= (\text{polynomial in } t \text{ of degree} < k) \cdot e^{\lambda t} \end{aligned} \tag{16}$$

The Jordan canonical form thus shows that, if A has the different eigenvalues

$\lambda_1, \ldots, \lambda_s$ *with multiplicities* $m_1, \ldots, m_s$, *then the vector* x(t) *solving* x′(t) = Ax(t), x(0) = b, *has components of the form*

$$x_v(t) = \sum_{i=1}^{s} \left(\sum_{j=0}^{m_i-1} \xi_{vij} t^j \right) e^{\lambda_i t} \qquad (v = 1, \ldots, n) \qquad (17)$$

EXAMPLE 1. Let A be similar to the matrix

$$J = \begin{bmatrix} 2 & 0 & 0 & 0 \\ 0 & 2 & 0 & 0 \\ 0 & 0 & 3 & 0 \\ 0 & 0 & 1 & 3 \end{bmatrix}$$

Here $n = 4$, $\lambda_1 = 2$, $\lambda_2 = 3$, $m_1 = 2$, $m_2 = 2$,

$$\Lambda_1 = \begin{bmatrix} 2 & 0 \\ 0 & 2 \end{bmatrix}, \qquad \Lambda_2 = \begin{bmatrix} 3 & 0 \\ 1 & 3 \end{bmatrix}$$

The differential equation $dy/dt = Jy$ can be solved by setting

$$y^{(1)} = \begin{bmatrix} y_1 \\ y_2 \end{bmatrix}, \qquad y^{(2)} = \begin{bmatrix} y_3 \\ y_4 \end{bmatrix}, \quad \text{where } y = \begin{bmatrix} y_1 \\ y_2 \\ y_3 \\ y_4 \end{bmatrix}$$

The equations (11) are the independent systems

$$\begin{array}{c|c} y_1' = 2y_1 & y_3' = 3y_3 \\ y_2' = 2y_2 & y_4' = y_3 + 4y_4 \end{array}$$

If $y_1(0) = 1, \ldots, y_4(0) = 4$, we find

$$\begin{array}{c|c} y_1 = e^{2t} & y_3 = 3e^{3t} \\ y_2 = 2e^{2t} & y_4 = (4 + 3t)e^{3t} \end{array}$$

Suppose that $x(t)$ is related to $y(t)$ by the equation

$$x(t) = Cy(t) = \begin{bmatrix} 4 & 1 & 1 & 1 \\ -1 & 3 & 0 & 1 \\ 1 & 0 & 3 & 1 \\ 1 & 0 & 0 & 2 \end{bmatrix} y(t)$$

Then, for example, for $x_3(t)$ we find

$$x_3(t) = e^{2t} + 9e^{3t} + (4 + 3t)e^{3t} = \sum_{i=1}^{2} \sum_{j=0}^{1} \xi_{3ij} t^j e^{\lambda_i t}$$

where

$$\xi_{310} = 1, \qquad \xi_{311} = 0, \qquad \xi_{320} = 13, \qquad \xi_{321} = 3$$

PROBLEMS

1. Suppose that $y(t)$ satisfies the differential equation

$$\frac{dy(t)}{dt} = \begin{bmatrix} 2 & 0 & 0 & 0 & 0 \\ 1 & 2 & 0 & 0 & 0 \\ 0 & 0 & 3 & 0 & 0 \\ 0 & 0 & 1 & 3 & 0 \\ 0 & 0 & 0 & 1 & 3 \end{bmatrix} y(t) \qquad \text{with } y(0) = \begin{bmatrix} 1 \\ 2 \\ 3 \\ 4 \\ 5 \end{bmatrix}$$

Solve for $y(t)$. In this example identify the matrices Λ_i and the vectors $y^{(i)}(t)$.

2. Let $y(t)$ be the solution of Problem 1. Suppose that $x(t) = Cy(t)$, where

$$C = \begin{bmatrix} 0 & 1 & 0 & 0 & 0 \\ 0 & 0 & 1 & 0 & 0 \\ 0 & 0 & 0 & 1 & 0 \\ 0 & 0 & 0 & 0 & 1 \\ 1 & 0 & 0 & 0 & 0 \end{bmatrix}$$

In this example, identify all the different numbers s, m_i, ξ_{vij}, λ_i, n in the general formula (17).

3. Assume that Jordan's Theorem is true. Let ρ be some very large positive number, and let $D = \text{diag}(1, \rho, \rho^2, \ldots, \rho^{n-1})$. If we form the matrix $D^{-1}JD$, describe the resulting modified Jordan form for the matrix A. What happens when $\rho \to \infty$?

5.2 PRINCIPAL VECTORS

As in the preceding section, assume that A is an $n \times n$ matrix with the different eigenvalues $\lambda_1, \ldots, \lambda_s$ with multiplicities $m_1, \ldots, m_s$. In this section we will define *principal vectors* as generalizations of eigenvectors. We say that a zero or nonzero vector p is a *principal vector of grade* g $\geqslant 0$ *belonging to the eigenvalue* λ_i if

$$(\lambda_i I - A)^g p = 0 \tag{1}$$

and if there is no smaller non-negative integer $\gamma < g$ for which $(\lambda_i I - A)^\gamma p = 0$.

The vector $p = 0$ is the principal vector of grade 0. The eigenvectors are the principal vectors of grade 1.

We shall define the linear space $P_g(\lambda_i)$ as the linear space of all principal vectors of grade $\leqslant g$ belonging to λ_i. Thus,

$$P_g(\lambda_i) = [p \,|\, (\lambda_i I - A)^g p = 0] \qquad (2)$$

and $P_g(\lambda_i)$ is the null space of the matrix $(\lambda_i I - A)^g$. We have

$$P_0(\lambda_i) \subset P_1(\lambda_i) \subset P_2(\lambda_i) \subset \cdots \qquad (3)$$

because

$$(\lambda_i I - A)^g p = 0 \quad \text{implies} \quad (\lambda_i I - A)^{g+1} p = 0$$

If A has distinct eigenvalues, i.e., if $s = n$ and all $m_1 = 1$, we know from Section 4.1 that A has n linearly independent eigenvectors $c^1, \ldots, c^n$. Then any x has an expansion

$$x = \xi_1 c^1 + \cdots + \xi_n c^n = p^{(1)} + \cdots + p^{(n)} \qquad (4)$$

where $p^i = \xi_i c^i$ is a principal vector belonging to λ_i; the grade of p^i is 1 if $\xi_i \neq 0$, or 0 if $\xi_i = 0$. In either case, p^i lies in the space $P_1(\lambda_i)$; recall that $1 = m_i$.

In the general case, in which m_i may be > 1, we have a *representation by principal vectors*:

Theorem 1. *Let* A *be an* n $\times$ n *matrix with the different eigenvalues* $\lambda_1, \ldots, \lambda_s$ *with multiplicities* $m_1, \ldots, m_s$. *Then every* n-*component column vector* x *has a representation*

$$x = p^{(1)} + p^{(2)} + \cdots + p^{(s)} \qquad (5)$$

where p^i *is a uniquely defined principal vector belonging to* λ_i *of grade* $\leqslant m_i$.

We shall prove this theorem after some algebraic preliminaries.

EXAMPLE 1. Let

$$A = \begin{bmatrix} 1 & 0 & 0 \\ 7 & 1 & 0 \\ 0 & 0 & 2 \end{bmatrix} \qquad (6)$$

There are two eigenvalues, $\lambda_1 = 1$ and $\lambda_2 = 2$. We have $m_1 = 2$, $m_2 = 1$.

The eigenvectors belonging to $\lambda_1 = 1$ satisfy

$$0 = (1 \cdot I - A)c = \begin{bmatrix} 0 & 0 & 0 \\ -7 & 0 & 0 \\ 0 & 0 & -1 \end{bmatrix} \begin{bmatrix} c_1 \\ c_2 \\ c_3 \end{bmatrix} = \begin{bmatrix} 0 \\ -7c_1 \\ -c_3 \end{bmatrix}$$

Thus, the eigenvectors of λ_1 are the nonzero multiples of col $(0, 1, 0)$. The eigenvectors belonging to $\lambda_2 = 2$ are the nonzero multiples of col $(0, 0, 1)$. Thus, a representation (4) of x by eigenvectors is impossible if $x_1 \neq 0$. Since $m_1 = 2$, we look for principal vectors of grade $\leqslant 2$ belonging to λ_1. They satisfy the equation

$$0 = (1 \cdot I - A)^2 p^1 = \begin{bmatrix} 0 & 0 & 0 \\ 0 & 0 & 0 \\ 0 & 0 & 1 \end{bmatrix} p^1 = \begin{bmatrix} 0 \\ 0 \\ p^1_3 \end{bmatrix}$$

Thus we have

$$P_2(\lambda_1) = [p^1 \,|\, p^1 = \text{col}\,(\alpha, \beta, 0)] \tag{7}$$

while for the second eigenvalue $\lambda_2 = 2$ of multiplicity $m_2 = 1$,

$$P_1(\lambda_2) = [p^2 \,|\, p^2 = \text{col}\,(0, 0, \gamma)] \tag{8}$$

Theorem 1 merely states that every $x = \text{col}\,(\alpha, \beta, \gamma)$ has a unique representation $x = p^{(1)} + p^{(2)}$.

Lemma 1. *If* $\phi(\lambda) = \det\,(\lambda I - A)$, *then* $\phi(A) = 0$.

Proof. This is the Cayley-Hamilton Theorem, which was stated, illustrated, and proved in Section 4.9. Here, for the sake of completeness, we shall give an independent, purely algebraic proof. Define the $n \times n$ matrix of signed cofactors

$$C(\lambda) = \text{cof}\,(\lambda I - A) \tag{9}$$

For any square matrix, M, we have $M\,(\text{cof}\,M)^T = (\det M)I$. Therefore,

$$(\lambda I - A)C^T(\lambda) = \phi(\lambda)I \tag{10}$$

If A is an $n \times n$ matrix, every component of $C(\lambda)$ is a polynomial of degree $\leqslant n - 1$ in λ. Then we may write

$$C^T(\lambda) = \lambda^{n-1}C_0 + \lambda^{n-2}C_1 + \cdots + \lambda C_{n-2} + C_{n-1} \tag{11}$$

where each C_i is an $n \times n$ matrix of constants. If

$$\phi(\lambda)I = \lambda^n I + \alpha_1 \lambda^{n-1} I + \cdots + \alpha_{n-1} \lambda I + \alpha_n I \tag{12}$$

then identification of the coefficients of equal powers of λ in (10) gives

$$
\begin{aligned}
&\text{for } \lambda^n\text{:} && C_0 = I \\
&\text{for } \lambda^{n-1}\text{:} && C_1 - AC_0 = \alpha_1 I \\
&\quad \cdots \\
&\text{for } \lambda\text{:} && C_{n-1} - AC_{n-2} = \alpha_{n-1} I \\
&\text{for } 1\text{:} && -AC_{n-1} = \alpha_n I
\end{aligned}
\tag{13}
$$

Multiply the first equation by A^n on the left, the second by A^{n-1}, etc., and add. The result is

$$A^n C_0 + A^{n-1}(C_1 - AC_0) + \cdots + A(C_{n-1} - AC_{n-2}) - AC_{n-1} = \phi(A)I \tag{14}$$

All terms on the left-hand side of (14) cancel, giving $0 = \phi(A)I$.

Lemma 2. *Let* s $\geqslant 2$. *Let* $\phi_1(\lambda), \ldots, \phi_s(\lambda)$ *be polynomials. Suppose that there is no number* λ_0 *which is a root of all these polynomials. Then there are polynomials* $\psi_1(\lambda), \ldots, \psi_s(\lambda)$ *for which*

$$\psi_1(\lambda)\phi_1(\lambda) + \psi_2(\lambda)\phi_2(\lambda) + \cdots + \psi_s(\lambda)\phi_s(\lambda) \equiv 1 \tag{15}$$

Note that the identity (15) is clearly impossible if for some λ_0,

$$\phi_i(\lambda) = 0 \qquad (i = 1, \ldots, s)$$

EXAMPLE 2. The polynomials

$$\phi_1(\lambda) = \lambda^2 + 1 \quad \text{and} \quad \phi_2(\lambda) = \lambda^3 + 2\lambda + 5$$

have no common root. One may verify the identity

$$[\tfrac{1}{26}(\lambda^2 - 5\lambda + 1)]\phi_1(\lambda) + [-\tfrac{1}{26}(\lambda - 5)]\phi_2(\lambda) \equiv 1 \tag{15'}$$

Proof of Lemma 2. Let

$$N = (\text{degree of } \phi_1) + \cdots + (\text{degree of } \phi_s) \tag{16}$$

If $N = 0$, all $\phi_i(\lambda)$ are constants, and at least one of these constants, say ϕ_k, is nonzero. Then the identity (15) holds if we let $\psi_k(\lambda)$ be the constant $1/\phi_k$ and let all other $\psi_i(\lambda) \equiv 0$.

If $N \geqslant 1$, assume without loss of generality that

$$\text{degree of } \phi_1(\lambda) \leqslant \cdots \leqslant \text{degree of } \phi_s(\lambda) \tag{17}$$

Let $\phi_k(\lambda)$ be the first one of the polynomials $\phi_1, \phi_2, \ldots, \phi_s$ which is not identically zero. Then $k < s$; otherwise, if $k = s$, every root of ϕ_s would be a root of all ϕ_i. If $\phi_k(\lambda) = $ constant, we set $\psi_k(\lambda) \equiv 1/\phi_k$ and set all other $\psi_i(\lambda) \equiv 0$. If $\phi_k(\lambda)$ is not a constant, we divide all other $\phi_i(\lambda)$ by $\phi_k(\lambda)$ to obtain identities

$$\phi_i(\lambda) = q_i(\lambda)\phi_k(\lambda) + r_i(\lambda) \qquad (i \neq k) \tag{18}$$

If $i < k$, then $\phi_i(\lambda) \equiv r_i(\lambda) \equiv 0$. If $i > k$, the degree of the remainder $r_i(\lambda)$ is less than the degree of $\phi_k(\lambda)$, and therefore less than the degree of $\phi_i(\lambda)$.

Now consider the polynomials

$$\phi_k(\lambda), r_i(\lambda) \qquad (i \neq k) \tag{19}$$

These polynomials cannot have a common root λ_0; otherwise λ_0 would, by (18), be a root of all the polynomials $\phi_1, \ldots, \phi_s$. Further, the sum of the degrees of the polynomials (19) is less than the sum of the degrees of $\phi_i, \ldots, \phi_s$. By induction on the sum of the degrees, we may assume that there are polynomials $\psi_j^*(\lambda)$ such that

$$\psi_k^*(\lambda)\phi_k(\lambda) + \sum_{i \neq k} \psi_i^*(\lambda)r_i(\lambda) \equiv 1 \tag{20}$$

By (18), this identity becomes

$$\psi_k^*(\lambda)\phi_k(\lambda) + \sum_{i \neq k} \psi_i^*(\lambda)[\phi_i(\lambda) - q_i(\lambda)\phi_k(\lambda)] \equiv 1 \tag{21}$$

which gives the required identity (15) if we define

$$\psi_k(\lambda) = \psi_k^*(\lambda) - \sum_{i \neq k} \psi_i^*(\lambda)q_i(\lambda) \tag{22}$$

and

$$\psi_i(\lambda) = \psi_i^*(\lambda) \qquad \text{for } i \neq k$$

Proof of Theorem 1. If $s = 1$ and $m_1 = n$, then $\det(\lambda I - A) = (\lambda - \lambda_1)^n$, and the Cayley-Hamilton Theorem states that

$$(A - \lambda_1 I)^n = 0 \tag{23}$$

Then every x is, itself, a principal vector of grade $\leqslant m_1 = n$ belonging to λ_1, and (5) holds with $s = 1$ and $p^{(1)} = x$.

If $s \geqslant 2$, define the polynomials

$$\phi_i(\lambda) = \prod_{j=1, j \neq i}^{s} (\lambda - \lambda_j)^{m_j} \qquad (i = 1, \ldots, s) \tag{24}$$

These polynomials have no common root. By Lemma 2, there are polynomials $\psi_i(\lambda)$ for which

$$\psi_1(\lambda)\phi_1(\lambda) + \cdots + \psi_s(\lambda)\phi_s(\lambda) \equiv 1 \tag{25}$$

If $\omega(\lambda) =$ a polynomial $\equiv 1$, we must have $\omega(A) = I$ for any square matrix A, since the permissible manipulations of addition, subtraction, and multiplication are the same for a scalar variable λ as for a single square matrix A. For example,

$$\lambda(\lambda - 1) - 2\lambda^2 + \lambda(\lambda + 1) \equiv 1$$

implies

$$A(A - I) - 2A^2 + A(A + I) = I$$

Thus, (25) implies

$$\phi_1(A)\psi_1(A) + \cdots + \phi_s(A)\psi_s(A) = I \tag{26}$$

Multiplying the matrix (26) into the vector x gives

$$[\phi_1(A)\psi_1(A)x] + \cdots + [\phi_s(A)\psi_s(A)x] = x \tag{27}$$

But each [   ] is a principal vector! In fact,

$$(A - \lambda_i I)^{m_i}[\phi_i(A)\psi_i(A)x] = [(A - \lambda_i I)^{m_i}\phi_i(A)]\psi_i(A)x \tag{28}$$

But [   ] $= \phi(A) = O$ by the Cayley-Hamilton Theorem, where

$$\phi(\lambda) = \det(\lambda I - A) = (\lambda - \lambda_i)^{m_i}\phi_i(\lambda) \tag{29}$$

Thus, the vector (28) is zero, and

$$p^{(i)} = [\phi_i(A)\psi_i(A)x] \tag{30}$$

is a principal vector of grade $\leqslant m_i$ belonging to λ_i. Thus, (27) is the required representation (5).

To show that the representation (5) is unique, suppose

$$x = q^{(1)} + \cdots + q^{(s)} \tag{5'}$$

where $q^1 \neq p^1$, and where each q^i is a principal vector of grade $\leqslant m_i$ belonging to λ_i. Taking (5) $-$ (5'), we find

$$0 = r^1 + \cdots + r^s \tag{31}$$

where $r^i = p^i - q^i$. Now r^1 is a nonzero principal vector belonging to λ_1. Let r^1 have grade $g_1 \geqslant 1$. Let

$$c^1 = (A - \lambda_1 I)^{g_1 - 1} \qquad r^1 \neq 0 \qquad (32)$$

Then c^1 is an *eigenvector* belonging to λ_1, since $(A - \lambda_1 I)c^1 = 0$. Multiply (31) by the matrix

$$(A - \lambda_1 I)^{g_1 - 1} \prod_{j=2}^{s} (A - \lambda_j I)^{m_j}$$

The result is

$$0 = \prod_{j=2}^{s} (\lambda_1 - \lambda_j)^{m_j} c^1 + 0 + \cdots + 0 \qquad (33)$$

This is a contradiction because the right-hand side is nonzero. Note the use of the identity $\phi_1(A)c^1 = \phi_1(\lambda_1)c^1$ for the eigenvector c^1 in the derivation of (33).

PROBLEMS

1. Verify the Cayley-Hamilton Theorem for the matrix

$$A = \begin{bmatrix} -1 & 3 \\ 2 & -4 \end{bmatrix}$$

2. Suppose that $\det(\lambda I - A) = \phi(\lambda) = (\lambda - 1)^4(\lambda - 2)(\lambda^2 + 1)^3$. Identify the polynomials $\phi_i(\lambda)$ discussed in the proof of Theorem 1.

3. Identify the spaces $P_g(\lambda_i)$ for the matrix

$$A = \begin{bmatrix} 1 & 0 & 1 \\ 0 & 2 & 0 \\ 0 & 0 & 1 \end{bmatrix}$$

Also identify the principal vectors of grade 2.

4. For the matrix A in Problem 3, find the unique representations of the vectors

$$x = \begin{bmatrix} \sqrt{2} \\ -9 \\ 84 \end{bmatrix}, \qquad x = \begin{bmatrix} 0 \\ 0 \\ 0 \end{bmatrix}, \qquad x = \begin{bmatrix} 8+i \\ 3-i \\ 2+7i \end{bmatrix}, \qquad x = \begin{bmatrix} 0 \\ 9.3 \\ 0 \end{bmatrix}$$

as sums of principal vectors: $x = p^{(1)} + \cdots + p^{(s)}$.

5. Let A be defined as in Problem 3, and let $A_1 = TAT^{-1}$, where

$$T = \begin{bmatrix} 1 & 1 & 1 \\ 1 & 2 & 4 \\ 1 & 3 & 9 \end{bmatrix}$$

Identify the spaces $P_g(\lambda_i)$ for the matrix A_1. Also identify the principal vectors of grade 2.

6. In general, what relationship exists between the principal vectors of a matrix A and the principal vectors of a similar matrix $A_1 = TAT^{-1}$?

7.* Explain how the method of proof of Lemma 2 can be made into a constructive procedure. Illustrate by finding polynomials ψ_1, ψ_2, ψ_3 such that $\sum \psi_1(\lambda)\phi_1(\lambda) \equiv 1$, where

$$\phi_1(\lambda) = (\lambda - 2)(\lambda - 3)^2, \quad \phi_2(\lambda) = (\lambda - 1)(\lambda - 3)^2,$$
$$\phi_3(\lambda) = (\lambda - 1)(\lambda - 2)$$

8. Prove that a matrix cannot have principal vectors of grade greater than the greatest of the multiplicites of its eigenvalues.

5.3 PROOF OF JORDAN'S THEOREM

The notation in this section will be that of the preceding two sections; A is an $n \times n$ matrix with the different eigenvalues $\lambda_1, \ldots, \lambda_s$ with multiplicities $m_1, \ldots, m_s$.

Lemma 1. *For* $i = 1, \ldots, s$ *let* B_i *be any basis for the linear space of principal vectors of grade* $\leqslant m_i$ *belonging to* λ_i. *Then the collection of vectors* $B_1, B_2, \ldots, B_s$ *is a basis for the* n-*dimensional space* E^n.

Proof. According to Theorem 1 of the last section each x in E^n has a *unique* representation

$$x = p^{(1)} + p^{(2)} + \cdots + p^{(s)} \tag{1}$$

where p^i is a principal vector of grade $\leqslant m_i$ belonging to λ_i. Since B_i is a basis, p^i has a unique representation as a linear combination of the vectors comprising B_i. Now (1) implies that each x in E^n has a unique representation of the vectors comprising $B_1, B_2, \ldots,$ and B_s. Note that the vectors in $B_1, \ldots, B_s$ are linearly independent because $x = 0$ has the unique representation (1) with all $p^i = 0$.

This result allows us to consider *separately* the spaces of principal vectors belonging to $\lambda_1, \ldots, \lambda_s$. For any λ_i define the matrix

$$M = A - \lambda_i I \tag{2}$$

and define the linear spaces

$$P_g = [x \mid M^g x = 0] \qquad (g = 0, 1, \ldots, m) \tag{3}$$

where $m = m_i = $ the multiplicity of λ_i. In the notation of the lemma,

B_i is a basis for the linear space P_m of principal vectors of grade $\leqslant m = m_i$ belonging to the eigenvalue λ_i of A.

We shall call the basis

$$J: (v^1, v^2, \ldots, v^z) \tag{4}$$

a *Jordan basis* for P_g if the vectors v^j can be arranged in chains as follows:

$$
\begin{array}{llll}
v^1 & v^{a+1} & \cdot & v^{y+1} \\
v^2 = Mv^1 & v^{a+2} = Mv^{a+1} & \cdot & v^{y+2} = Mv^{y+1} \\
v^3 = Mv^2 & v^{a+3} = Mv^{a+2} & \cdot & v^{y+3} = Mv^{y+2} \\
\cdot & \cdot & \cdot & \cdot \\
\cdot & \cdot & \cdot & \cdot \\
\cdot & \cdot & \cdot & \cdot \\
v^a = Mv^{a-1} & v^b = Mv^{b-1} & \cdot & v^z = Mv^{z-1}
\end{array} \tag{5}
$$

where

$$Mv^a = 0, \qquad Mv^b = 0, \ldots, \qquad Mv^z = 0$$

and where each chain has length $\leqslant g$. The vector at the bottom of each chain is an eigenvector of M belonging to the eigenvalue 0. A vector next to the bottom is a principal vector of grade 2, etc.

EXAMPLE 1. Let

$$
M = \begin{bmatrix}
0 & 0 & 0 & 0 & 0 & 0 \\
1 & 0 & 0 & 0 & 0 & 0 \\
0 & 1 & 0 & 0 & 0 & 0 \\
0 & 0 & 0 & 0 & 0 & 0 \\
0 & 0 & 0 & 1 & 0 & 0 \\
0 & 0 & 0 & 0 & 0 & 7
\end{bmatrix} \tag{6}
$$

M has the eigenvalue 0 with multiplicity $m = 5$ and has another eigenvalue of 7. We assert that

$$
v^1 = \begin{bmatrix} 1 \\ 0 \\ 0 \\ 0 \\ 0 \\ 0 \end{bmatrix}, \qquad
v^2 = \begin{bmatrix} 0 \\ 1 \\ 0 \\ 0 \\ 0 \\ 0 \end{bmatrix}, \ldots, \qquad
v^5 = \begin{bmatrix} 0 \\ 0 \\ 0 \\ 0 \\ 1 \\ 0 \end{bmatrix}
$$

is a Jordan basis J for the space P_5 of vectors x satisfying $M^5x = 0$. In fact, (5) takes the form

$$v^1$$
$$v^2 = Mv^1 \quad \vdots \quad v^4$$
$$v^3 = Mv^2 \quad \vdots \quad v^5 = Mv^4$$

where

$$Mv^3 = 0 \quad \text{and} \quad Mv^5 = 0$$

In this example, P_5 is the space of vectors in E^6 whose last component equals 0. In fact, the matrix M^5 consists of zeros except for the number 7^5 in the lower-right corner.

Lemma 2. *The space* P_m *defined in* (3) *has a Jordan basis.*

Proof. If $m = 1$, P_1 is the set of vectors x satisfying $Mx = 0$. If x^1, ..., x^z is a basis for P_1, each x^j is an eigenvector of M; therefore, any basis for P_1 is a Jordan basis.

If $m > 1$, we make the following assertion: *Let* $\mathrm{y}^1, \ldots, \mathrm{y}^\beta$ *be any basis for* P_{g-1}, *where* $\mathrm{g} \geqslant 2$. *Let a basis*

$$x^1, \ldots, x^\alpha, y^1, \ldots, y^\beta \tag{7}$$

for P_g *be formed by appending any necessary additional vectors* $\mathrm{x}^1, \ldots, \mathrm{x}^\alpha$, *where* $\alpha \geqslant 0$. *(If* $\alpha = 0$, $P_g = P_{g-1}$ *and there are no* x's.) *Then the vectors* $\mathrm{y}^1, \ldots, \mathrm{y}^\beta$ *may be replaced in* (7) *by vectors* $\mathrm{z}^1, \ldots, \mathrm{z}^\beta$ *such that*

$$x^1, \ldots, x^\alpha, z^1, \ldots, z^\beta \tag{8}$$

is a Jordan basis for P_g. The assertion, which we will prove by induction, yields the lemma when $g = m$.

Let us prove the assertion when $g = 2$. If $\alpha = 0$, we have $P_2 = P_1$, and the required Jordan basis (8) is found simply by setting $z^i = y^i (i = 1, \ldots, \beta)$. Suppose $\alpha > 1$. Form the vectors $Mx^1, \ldots, Mx^\alpha$. We assert that the 2α vectors $x^1, \ldots, x^\alpha, Mx^1, \ldots, Mx^\alpha$ are independent. Suppose

$$a_1x^1 + \cdots + a_\alpha x^\alpha + b_1Mx^1 + \cdots + b_\alpha Mx^\alpha = 0 \tag{9}$$

Multiplication by M gives

$$M(a_1x^1 + \cdots + a_\alpha x^\alpha) + 0 + \cdots + 0 = 0 \tag{10}$$

since $M^2x^i = 0$, x^i being in P_2. Now (10) states that $a_1x^1 + \ldots + a_\alpha x^\alpha$ lies in P_1. Therefore, $\sum a_i x^i$ equals some linear combination of $y^1, \ldots, y^\beta$

(a basis for P_1). Therefore, all $a_i = 0$, since $x^1, \ldots, x^\alpha, y^1, \ldots, y^\beta$ are given as independent.

Now (9) states $M(\sum b_i x^i) = 0$. Then $\sum b_i x^i$ is some combination of $y^1, \ldots, y^\beta$. Since $x^1, \ldots, x^\alpha, y^1, \ldots, y^\beta$ are independent, all $b_i = 0$ in (9). This proves the independence of the 2α vectors x^i, Mx^i.

The vectors $Mx^1, \ldots, Mx^\alpha$ are independent vectors in P_1. If they do not span P_1, adjoin vectors $z^{\alpha+1}, \ldots, z^\beta$ so that $Mx^1, \ldots, Mx^\alpha, z^{\alpha+1}, \ldots, z^\beta$ are a basis for P^1. Now the required Jordan basis for P_2 is

$$
\begin{array}{cccc}
x^1 & x^2 & & x^\alpha \\
Mx^1 & Mx^2 & \cdots & Mx^\alpha & z^{\alpha+1}, \ldots, z^\beta
\end{array}
\tag{11}
$$

In the notation of (8), $z^1 = Mx^1, \ldots, z^\alpha = Mx^\alpha$.

Finally, we prove the assertion for $g > 2$. If $\alpha = 0$, $P_g = P_{g-1}$ and the assertion follows by induction, since there is a Jordan basis for P_{g-1}. Suppose $\alpha \geqslant 1$. Form the vectors $Mx^1, \ldots, Mx^\alpha$. Again we assert that the 2α vectors $x^1, \ldots, x^\alpha, Mx^1, \ldots, Mx^\alpha$ are independent. For suppose $\sum a_i x^i + \sum b_i Mx^i = 0$. Multiplication by M^{g-1} gives

$$
M^{g-1}(\sum a_i x^i) + \sum 0 = 0
\tag{12}
$$

since all $M^g x^i = 0$. Now (12) implies that $\sum a_i x^i$ is a combination of the y's. Since the $\alpha + \beta$ vectors (x^i, y^j) are independent, all $a_i = 0$.

We now have just $\sum b_i Mx^i = 0$. Therefore, $\sum b_i x^i$ lies in $P_1 \subset P_{g-1}$. Therefore, $\sum b_i x^i$ is a combination of the y's. Therefore, all $b_i = 0$. This proves the independence of the 2α vectors $x^1, \ldots, x^\alpha, Mx^1, \ldots, Mx^\alpha$.

Let $w^1, \ldots, w^\gamma$ be any basis for P_{g-2}. The vectors

$$
Mx^1, \ldots, Mx^\alpha; \; w^1, \ldots, w^\gamma
\tag{13}
$$

lie in P_{g-1}. Further, these vectors are independent because

$$
\sum a_i Mx^i + \sum b_j w^j = 0
\tag{14}
$$

implies $M^{g-1}(\sum a_i x^i) = 0$, which implies all $a_i = 0$, as before; now (14) states $\sum b_i w^j = 0$, which implies all $b_j = 0$.

If the independent vectors (13) are not a basis for P_{g-1}, adjoin certain vectors $q^1, \ldots, q^\delta$ so that the combined list

$$
Mx^1, \ldots, Mx^\alpha, q^1, \ldots, q^\delta; \; w^1, \ldots, w^\gamma
\tag{15}
$$

is a basis for P_{g-1}. By induction, we can replace $w^1, \ldots, w^\gamma$ in (15) by a new basis $z^1, \ldots, z^\gamma$ for P_{g-2} so that the new list

$$
Mx^1, \ldots, Mx^\alpha, q^1, \ldots, q^\delta; \; z^1, \ldots, z^\gamma
\tag{16}
$$

is a *Jordan* basis for P_{g-1}.

We now replace the original basis $y^1, \ldots, y^\beta$ of P_{g-1} by the Jordan basis (16) for P_{g-1}. Then

$$
\begin{array}{cccc}
x^1 & x^2 & \cdots & x^\alpha \\
Mx^1 & Mx^2 & & Mx^\alpha, \quad q^1, \ldots, q^\delta \\
& z^1, \ldots, z^\gamma &
\end{array} \tag{17}
$$

is a Jordan basis for P_g. This completes the proof of the lemma.

EXAMPLE 2. Let

$$
M = \begin{bmatrix} 0 & 7 & 0 \\ 0 & 0 & 0 \\ 0 & 0 & 0 \end{bmatrix}
$$

The vectors

$$
y^1 = \begin{bmatrix} 3 \\ 0 \\ 5 \end{bmatrix}, \qquad y^2 = \begin{bmatrix} 2 \\ 0 \\ 9 \end{bmatrix}
$$

are a basis for the space P_1. Consider the basis for P_2:

$$
x^1 = \begin{bmatrix} 0 \\ 1 \\ 0 \end{bmatrix}, \qquad y^1 = \begin{bmatrix} 3 \\ 0 \\ 5 \end{bmatrix}, \qquad y^2 = \begin{bmatrix} 2 \\ 0 \\ 9 \end{bmatrix}
$$

To construct a Jordan basis, form

$$
Mx^1 = \begin{bmatrix} 7 \\ 0 \\ 0 \end{bmatrix} = z^1
$$

Define z^2 in any way so that z^1, z^2 are a new basis for P_1; say $z^2 = \operatorname{col}(0, 0, 1)$. Then

$$
x^1 = \begin{bmatrix} 0 \\ 1 \\ 0 \end{bmatrix}, \qquad z^1 = \begin{bmatrix} 7 \\ 0 \\ 0 \end{bmatrix}, \qquad z^2 = \begin{bmatrix} 0 \\ 0 \\ 1 \end{bmatrix}
$$

is a Jordan basis for P_2.

Lemma 3. *Let λ_i be an eigenvalue of multiplicity m_i belonging to the $n \times n$ matrix A. Let B_i be a Jordan basis for the set of vectors x such that*

$$(A - \lambda_i I)^{m_i} x = 0 \qquad (18)$$

Then, if we regard B_i as the matrix whose columns are the basis vectors,

$$AB_i = B_i \Lambda_i \qquad (19)$$

where Λ_i has the form

$$\Lambda_i = \begin{bmatrix} \lambda_i & 0 & 0 & \cdots & 0 & 0 \\ * & \lambda_i & 0 & \cdots & 0 & 0 \\ 0 & * & \lambda_i & \cdots & 0 & 0 \\ \cdot & \cdot & \cdot & \cdots & \cdot & \cdot \\ 0 & 0 & 0 & \cdots & \lambda_i & 0 \\ 0 & 0 & 0 & \cdots & * & \lambda_i \end{bmatrix} \qquad \text{(with each } * = 0 \text{ or } 1) \quad (20)$$

Proof. Let $M = A - \lambda_i I$, and let the Jordan basis B_i be given by the chains (5). Thus

$$B_i = [v^1, \ldots, v^{a-1}, v^a; \ldots; v^{y+1}, \ldots, v^{z-1}, v^z] \qquad (21)$$

By (5) we have

$$\begin{aligned} MB_i &= [Mv^1, \ldots, Mv^{a-1}, Mv^a; \ldots; Mv^{y+1}, \ldots, Mv^{z-1}, Mv^z] \\ &= [\quad v^2, \ldots, \quad v^2 \quad , \quad 0 \ ; \ldots; \quad v^{y+2}, \ldots, \quad v^z \quad , \quad 0\ ] \end{aligned} \qquad (22)$$

But $A = \lambda_i I + M$. Therefore,

$$\begin{aligned} AB_i &= \lambda_i B_i + M B_i \\ &= [\lambda_i v^1 + v^2, \ldots, \lambda_i v^{a-1} + v^a, \lambda_i v^a; \ldots; \\ &\qquad \lambda_i v^{y+1} + v^{y+2}, \ldots, \lambda_i v^{z-1} + v^z, \lambda_i v^z] \end{aligned}$$

But this matrix equals

$$[v^1, \ldots, v^{a-1}, v^a; \ldots; v^{y+1}, \ldots, v^{z-1}, v^z] \Lambda_i \qquad (23)$$

provided that the sequence of $*$'s in (20) is chosen as follows:

$$** \cdots * = \underbrace{1 \cdots 1}_{a-1} 0; \underbrace{1 \cdots 1}_{b-a-1} 0; \cdots; \underbrace{1 \cdots 1}_{y-x-1}, 0; \underbrace{1 \cdots 1}_{z-y-1} \qquad (24)$$

Observe that there are $z - 1$ numbers $*$. The proof is complete, since (23) has the required form $B_i \Lambda_i$. Please observe that we have not yet proved that the number of columns in B_i equals m_i.

EXAMPLE 3. Suppose that

$$
\begin{array}{llll}
v^1 & & & \text{(grade 3)} \\
v^2 & & v^5 & \text{(grade 2)} \\
v^3 & v^4 & v^6 & v^7 \quad \text{(grade 1: eigenvectors)}
\end{array}
$$

is a Jordan basis of the space of all vectors x satisfying

$$
M^{m_i}x = (A - \lambda_i I)^{m_i}x = 0
$$

Then B_i has n rows and seven columns:

$$
B_i = [v^1, v^2, v^3; v^4; v^5, v^6; v^7]
$$

We have

$$
AB_i = \lambda_i B_i + MB_i = [\lambda_i v^1 + v^2, \lambda_i v^2 + v^3, \lambda_i v^3; \lambda_i v^4; \lambda_i v^5 + v^6,
$$
$$
\lambda_i v^6; \lambda_i v^7]
$$

But this equals $B_i \Lambda_i$ if we define the 7×7 matrix

$$
\Lambda_i =
\begin{bmatrix}
\lambda_i & & & & & & \\
1 & \lambda_i & & & & \mathbf{0} & \\
 & 1 & \lambda_i & & & & \\
 & & 0 & \lambda_i & & & \\
 & & & 0 & \lambda_i & & \\
\mathbf{0} & & & & 1 & \lambda_i & \\
 & & & & & 0 & \lambda_i
\end{bmatrix}
$$

Proof of Jordan's Theorem. Now we can prove Theorem 1 of Section 5.1. For $i = 1, \ldots, s$ let B_i be the matrix whose columns are a *Jordan* basis for the principal vectors of grade $\leqslant m_i$ belonging to the eigenvalue λ_i of A. We have just derived the identity $AB_i = B_i \Lambda_i$ where Λ_i is a square matrix of the form (20).

Form the matrix

$$
B = [B_1, B_2, \ldots, B_s] \tag{25}
$$

By Lemma 1, the columns of this matrix are a basis for E^n. The matrix B is, therefore, an $n \times n$ matrix with an inverse B^{-1}. Multiplication by A gives

$$
\begin{aligned}
AB &= [AB_1, AB_2, \ldots, AB_s] \\
&= [B_1 \Lambda_1, B_2 \Lambda_2, \ldots, B_s \Lambda_s]
\end{aligned} \tag{26}
$$

But this equals

$$[B_1, B_2, \ldots, B_s] \begin{bmatrix} \Lambda_1 & 0 & \cdots & 0 \\ 0 & \Lambda_2 & \cdots & 0 \\ \cdot & \cdot & \cdots & \cdot \\ 0 & 0 & \cdots & \Lambda_s \end{bmatrix} = BJ \qquad (27)$$

Multiplication of the identity $AB = BJ$ by B^{-1} gives the required result, $B^{-1}AB = J$.

It remains only to show that Λ_i is an $m_i \times m_i$ matrix. That follows immediately from the just-proved similarity of A and J. We have

$$\det (\lambda I - A) = \det (\lambda I - J)$$

or

$$\prod_{i=1}^{s} (\lambda - \lambda_i)^{m_i} = \prod_{i=1}^{s} \det (\lambda I - \Lambda_i) \qquad (28)$$

by the block-diagonal form of J. Let Λ_i be an $o_i \times o_i$ matrix. Then the triangular matrix Λ_i has characteristic determinant

$$\det (\lambda I - \Lambda_i) = (\lambda - \lambda_i)^{o_i} \qquad (29)$$

Since $\lambda_1, \ldots, \lambda_s$ are the different eigenvalues of the $n \times n$ matrix A, the identity (28) implies $m_i = o_i$.

We conclude further that *the multiplicity*, m_i, *of* λ_i *equals the dimension of the space of principal vectors of grade* $\leqslant m_i$ *belonging to* λ_i. This follows because the number of columns in B_i equals the order of Λ_i in the identity (19).

PROBLEMS

1. Consider the matrix

$$A = \begin{bmatrix} 17 & -25 \\ 9 & -13 \end{bmatrix}$$

What are the eigenvalues? What are the eigenvectors? What are the principal vectors? Is $v^1 = \text{col}\,[1, 0]$ a principal vector of grade 2? Form $v^2 = Mv^1 = (A - \lambda_1 I)v^1$. Let B be the matrix whose columns are v^1 and v^2. Compute $J = B^{-1}AB$.

2. Let

$$A = \begin{bmatrix} 17 & 0 & -25 \\ 0 & 3 & 0 \\ 9 & 0 & -13 \end{bmatrix}$$

Find Jordan bases B_1 and B_2 corresponding to the two different eigenvalues of A. Let $B = [B_1, B_2]$, as in (25). Compute $J = B^{-1}AB$.

3. Let

$$J_1 = \begin{bmatrix} 7 & 0 & 0 \\ 0 & 7 & 0 \\ 0 & 0 & 7 \end{bmatrix} \quad \text{and} \quad J_2 = \begin{bmatrix} 7 & 0 & 0 \\ 1 & 7 & 0 \\ 0 & 1 & 7 \end{bmatrix}$$

Show that J_1 and J_2 cannot be Jordan canonical forms for the same matrix A. (Discuss the dimension of the space P_1.)

4. Let

$$J_3 = \begin{bmatrix} 7 & 0 & 0 \\ 0 & 7 & 0 \\ 0 & 1 & 7 \end{bmatrix}$$

and let J_1 be defined as in the last problem. Show that J_1 and J_3 are Jordan forms of a single matrix, A.

5.* To what extent is the Jordan form of a given matrix, A, uniquely defined?

6   VARIATIONAL PRINCIPLES AND PERTURBATION THEORY

6.1 INTRODUCTION

In this chapter we shall be concerned with maximum principles, with minimax principles, and with other variational properties of eigenvalues and eigenvectors. These principles have mathematical interest, and they often have physical significance.

Perturbation theory is concerned with what happens to the eigenvalues and eigenvectors of a matrix when the elements of the matrix are varied slightly. This topic is important in numerical computation. Seldom in science or engineering are we given a matrix with perfect accuracy. From a given matrix of data we compute eigenvalues and eigenvectors. We must be able to estimate the error in the computed eigenvalues and eigenvectors which results from error in the data.

6.2 THE RAYLEIGH PRINCIPLE

Let H be a Hermitian matrix. We have shown that H has real eigenvalues $\lambda_1 \geqslant \lambda_2 \geqslant \cdots \geqslant \lambda_n$ and has mutually orthogonal unit eigenvectors $u^1, u^2, \ldots, u^n$:

$$Hu^i = \lambda_i u^i, \qquad (u^i, u^j) = \delta_{ij} \quad (i, j = 1, \ldots, n) \tag{1}$$

The eigenvalues of H are thus values of the quadratic form (Hu, u) defined on the unit sphere $\|u\| = (u, u)^{1/2} = 1$:

$$\lambda_1 = (Hu^1, u^1) \geqslant \lambda_2 = (Hu^2, u^2) \geqslant \cdots \geqslant \lambda_n = (Hu^n, u^n) \tag{2}$$

141

Thus, λ_1 is the greatest of these n values of the quadratic form on the unit sphere. It is natural to ask whether λ_1 is the greatest of *all* values of the quadratic form (Hu, u) on the unit sphere $\|u\| = 1$.

Theorem 1. *Let* H *be Hermitian. Let* λ_1 *be the largest eigenvalue of* H. *Then*

$$\lambda_1 = \max_{\|u\| = 1} (Hu, u) \tag{3}$$

and the maximum is achieved when u *is an eigenvector belonging to* λ_1.

Proof. Let $u^1, \ldots, u^n$ be a complete set of eigenvectors satisfying (1). These vectors form a basis for E^n. Then every unit vector u has a representation

$$u = c_1 u^1 + c_2 u^2 + \cdots + c_n u^n \tag{4}$$

where

$$
\begin{aligned}
1 = (u, u) &= \left(\sum_i c_i u^i, \sum_j c_j u^j\right) \\
&= \sum_i \sum_j c_i \bar{c}_j (u^i, u^j) = \sum_i \sum_j c_i \bar{c}_j \delta_{ij} \\
&= |c_1|^2 + |c_2|^2 + \cdots + |c_n|^2
\end{aligned} \tag{5}
$$

But $Hu = \sum c_i \lambda_i u^i$. Therefore,

$$
\begin{aligned}
(Hu, u) &= \left(\sum c_i \lambda_i u^i, \sum c_j u^j\right) \\
&= \lambda_1 |c_1|^2 + \lambda_2 |c_2|^2 + \cdots + \lambda_n |c_n|^2 \\
&\leqslant \lambda_1 (|c_1|^2 + |c_2|^2 + \cdots + |c_n|^2) = \lambda_1
\end{aligned} \tag{6}
$$

with equality in (6) when $c_2 = c_3 = \cdots = c_n = 0$ and $c_1 = 1$. Thus $(Hu, u) \leqslant \lambda_1$ with equality when $u = 1 \cdot u^1 + 0 + \cdots + 0$ in (4).

The proof is complete. We observe that if H is *real* and symmetric, the maximum (3) may be taken over *real* unit vectors u because H has a complete set of real eigenvectors u^i.

Corollary: *If* H *is Hermitian and* λ_1 *is its greatest eigenvalue, then*

$$\lambda_1 = \max_{x \neq 0} \frac{(Hx, x)}{(x, x)} \tag{7}$$

Proof. This follows from the homogeneity of the form. If $x \neq 0$ then, if $\rho = \|x\| > 0$,

$$\frac{(Hx, x)}{(x, x)} = \frac{1}{\rho^2}(Hx, x)$$

$$= (H\rho^{-1}x, \rho^{-1}x) = (Hu, u) \tag{8}$$

where u is the unit vector $\rho^{-1} x$. Thus, every *Rayleigh quotient* $(Hx, x)/(x, x)$ equals some value (Hu, u) of the quadratic form at a point u on the unit sphere $\|u\| = 1$. Conversely, if $\|u\| = 1$ then $(Hu, u) = (Hu, u)/(u, u)$. The maxima (7) and (3) are, therefore, identical.

EXAMPLE 1. Let

$$H = \begin{bmatrix} 4 & 3i \\ -3i & 2 \end{bmatrix} \tag{9}$$

Observe that $H = H^*$. The eigenvalues satisfy the equation $\det(\lambda I - H) = \lambda^2 - 6\lambda - 1 = 0$. Therefore

$$\lambda_1 = 3 + \sqrt{10}, \qquad \lambda_2 = 3 - \sqrt{10} \tag{10}$$

According to Rayleigh's principle, for all complex x_1 and x_2 except $0, 0$,

$$\frac{4|x_1|^2 + 3i\bar{x}_1 x_2 - 3i\bar{x}_2 x_1 + 2|x_2|^2}{|x_1|^2 + |x_2|^2} \leqslant 3 + \sqrt{10} \tag{11}$$

Equality is attained when x_1 and x_2 are the components of an eigenvector belonging to the eigenvalue λ_1.

EXAMPLE 2. Suppose that A is *not* Hermitian but has real eigenvalues $\lambda_1 \geqslant \lambda_2 \geqslant \cdots \geqslant \lambda_n$. Does Rayleigh's principle still hold? Let

$$A = \begin{bmatrix} 1, & 94 \\ 0, & 2 \end{bmatrix}$$

Then $\lambda_1 = 2$ and $\lambda_1 = 1$. But

$$\frac{(Ax, x)}{(x, x)} = \frac{x_1^2 + 94x_1 x_2 + 2x_2^2}{x_1^2 + x_2^2} = \frac{97}{2} > \lambda_1$$

if $x_1 = x_2 = 1$. *Rayleigh's principle applies only to Hermitian matrices.*

Having determined the maximum eigenvalue λ_1 of a Hermitian matrix as the maximum of (Hu, u) for $\|u\| = 1$, how can we find the lower eigenvalues $\lambda_2 \geqslant \cdots \geqslant \lambda_n$? Each of these numbers is a value of (Hu, u) for $\|u\| = 1$ *and* u perpendicular to the eigenvectors belonging to the larger eigenvalues. Thus, for $i \geqslant 2$, $\lambda_i = (Hu, u)$ when $u = u^i$, a unit vector orthogonal to $u^1, \ldots, u^{i-1}$.

Theorem 2. *Let* $\lambda_1 \geqslant \lambda_2 \geqslant \cdots \geqslant \lambda_n$ *be the eigenvalues of a Hermitian matrix* H. *For* $i \geqslant 2$, *let* $u^1, \ldots, u^{i-1}$ *be mutually orthogonal unit eigenvectors belonging to* $\lambda_1, \ldots, \lambda_{i-1}$. *Then*

$$\lambda_i = \max (Hu, u)$$
$$\| u \| = 1 \tag{12}$$
$$(u, u^1) = \cdots = (u, u^{i-1}) = 0$$

and the maximum is achieved when u *is an eigenvector belonging to* λ_i.

Proof. Let $u^1, \ldots, u^n$ be a complete set of eigenvectors:

$$Hu^j = \lambda_j u^j, \qquad (u^j, u^k) = \delta_{jk} \quad (j, k = 1, \ldots, n) \tag{13}$$

For any u in E^n we may use the basis $u^1, \ldots, u^n$ for a representation

$$u = c_1 u^1 + \cdots + c_{i-1} u^{i-1} + c_i u^i + \cdots + c_n u^n \tag{14}$$

We then have

$$\| u \| = \sum_{j=1}^{n} | c_j |^2, \qquad c_k = (u, u^k) \quad (\text{for } k = 1, \ldots, n) \tag{15}$$

The constraints in the maximum problem (12) are

$$1 = \sum | c_j |^2, \qquad c_k = 0 \quad (k = 1, \ldots, i-1) \tag{16}$$

Then

$$
\begin{aligned}
(Hu, u) &= (\sum_{j=i}^{n} c_j \lambda_j u^j, \sum_{k=i}^{n} c_k u^k) \\
&= \sum_{j=i}^{n} \sum_{k=i}^{n} \lambda_j c_j \bar{c}_k (u^j, u^k)
\end{aligned} \tag{17}
$$

But $(u^j, u^k) = \delta_{jk}$. Therefore (17) becomes

$$
\begin{aligned}
(Hu, u) &= \lambda_i | c_i |^2 + \lambda_{i+1} | c_{i+1} |^2 + \cdots + \lambda_n | c_n |^2 \\
&\leqslant \lambda_i (| c_i |^2 + \cdots + | c_n |^2) = \lambda_i
\end{aligned} \tag{18}
$$

Equality holds if $c_i = 1$ and all other $c_j = 0$, i.e., if $u = u^i$. If $\lambda_i = \cdots = \lambda_r > \lambda_{r+1} \geqslant \cdots \geqslant \lambda_n$, equality in (18) holds *only* if

$$| c_i |^2 + \cdots + | c_r |^2 = 1, \qquad c_j = 0 \quad (\text{for } j > r) \tag{19}$$

Even if $r > i$, an optimal vector

$$u = c_i u^i + \cdots + c_r u^r$$

is an eigenvector belonging to the multiple eigenvalue λ_i, and u is orthogonal to $u^1, \ldots, u^{i-1}$.

PROBLEMS

1. If λ_n is the least eigenvalue of a Hermitian matrix, H, show that

$$\lambda_n = \min_{x \neq 0} \frac{(Hx, x)}{(x, x)}$$

2. Let a Hermitian matrix H have eigenvalues $\lambda_1 \geqslant \cdots \geqslant \lambda_n$, with associated unit orthogonal eigenvectors $u^1, \ldots, u^n$. For $1 \leqslant k < n$ show that $\lambda_k = \min (Hu, u)$ for all unit vectors u which are orthogonal to u^{k+1}, $\ldots, u^n$; and show that the minimum is achieved for $u = u^k$.

3. Let N be any $n \times n$ matrix with n unit orthogonal eigenvectors $u^1, \ldots, u^n$. Show that, for $\|u\| = 1$, the complex variable (Nu, u) achieves its maximum absolute value when u is an eigenvector of N belonging to an eigenvalue of maximum absolute value.

4. Let K and M be Hermitian matrices, and let M be positive definite. Let the vectors $c^1, \ldots, c^n$ and the real numbers $\lambda_1 \geqslant \cdots \geqslant \lambda_n$ satisfy

$$Kc^j = \lambda_j Mc^j, \qquad (Mc^j, c^k) = \delta_{jk}$$

(Refer to Section 4.8, Theorem 2). Prove that

$$\lambda_1 = \max_{x \neq 0} \frac{(Kx, x)}{(Mx, x)}$$

Show that the maximum is achieved when $x = c^1$.

5. In the notation of Problem 4, prove that for $k > 1$

$$\lambda_k = \max \frac{(Kx, x)}{(Mx, x)}$$

for all vectors x such that

$$x \neq 0 \quad \text{and} \quad (Mx, c^1) = \cdots = (Mx, c^{k-1}) = 0$$

Show that the maximum is achieved when $x = c^k$.

6. Let A be a *non*-Hermitian matrix with eigenvalues λ_j. Show that all λ_j satisfy

$$\min_{\|u\|=1} |(Au, u)| \leqslant |\lambda_j| \leqslant \max_{\|u\|=1} |(Au, u)|$$

7. Let H be the matrix

$$H = \begin{bmatrix} -2 & 7 & 1 \\ 7 & 5 & -3 \\ 1 & -3 & 4 \end{bmatrix}$$

If H has the eigenvalues $\lambda_1 \leqslant \lambda_2 \geqslant \lambda_3$, find a numerical lower bound for λ_1 by Rayleigh's principle. Find a numerical upper bound for λ_3. Use several trial vectors.

6.3 THE COURANT MINIMAX THEOREM

The Rayleigh principle for the second eigenvalue, λ_2, of a Hermitian matrix, H, states that

$$\lambda_2 = \max_{\substack{||u||=1 \\ (u,u^1)=0}} (Hu, u) \tag{1}$$

where u^1 is an eigenvector belonging to the greatest eigenvalue, λ_1. Thus, the Rayleigh principle does not give an independent characterization of λ_2; the maximum problem for λ_2 is stated in terms of an unknown eigenvector belonging to λ_1.

Courant found a characterization of λ_2 which does not explicitly depend upon u^1. For an arbitrary vector v^1 we may define a quantity

$$\phi(v^1) = \max_{\substack{||u||=1 \\ (u,v^1)=0}} (Hu, u) \tag{2}$$

This maximum is a *function* of the given vector v^1. As v^1 ranges over E^n, the function $\phi(v^1)$ takes various real values; Courant's principle states that λ_2 is the *least* of these values:

$$\lambda_2 = \min_{v^1} \phi(v^1) \tag{3}$$

In other words, $\phi(v^1)$ is minimized when $v^1 = u^1$.

EXAMPLE 1. Let

$$(Hu, u) = 3u_1^2 + 2u_2^2 + u_3^2$$

Since $H = \mathrm{diag}\,(3, 2, 1)$ is a *real* Hermitian matrix, we may restrict u to the class of *real* vectors. The matrix H has eigenvalues $\lambda_1 = 3$, $\lambda_2 = 2$, $\lambda_3 = 1$. Corresponding eigenvectors are $u^1 = e^1 = \mathrm{col}\,(1, 0, 0)$, $u^2 = e^2$, $u^3 = e^3$. Rayleigh's principle for λ_2 is

$$\lambda_2 = \max_{\substack{u_1^2+u_2^2+u_3^2=1 \\ (u,e^1)=0}} (3u_1^2 + 2u_2^2 + u_3^2) \tag{4}$$

But $(u, e^1) = u_1$. Therefore,

$$\lambda_2 = \max_{u_2^2+u_3^2=1} (2u_2^2 + u_3^2) = 2$$

To use Courant's principle, we must minimize

$$\phi(v^1) = \max_{\substack{u_1^2+u_2^2+u_3^2=1 \\ (u,\,v^1)=0}} (3u_1^2 + 2u_2^2 + u_3^2) \tag{5}$$

We have $\phi(0) = \lambda_1 = 3$. If $v^1 \neq 0$, then $\phi(v^1)$ is the largest value of (Hu, u) on the unit circle which is the intersection of the unit sphere with the plane through the origin perpendicular to v^1. To minimize the effect of the large coefficient 3 of u_1^2 in (Hu, u), we choose the circle $u_1 = 0$, $u_2^2 = u_3^2 = 1$ to obtain $\lambda_2 = 2 = \phi(e^1) = \min \phi(v^1)$.

Theorem. *Let* $\lambda_1 \geqslant \cdots \geqslant \lambda_n$ *be the eigenvalues of an* n × n *Hermitian matrix* H. *Then for* i < n

$$\lambda_{i+1} = \min_{v^1,\dots,v^i} \left[\max_{\substack{||u||=1 \\ (u,\,v^1)=\cdots=(u,\,v^i)=0}} (Hu, u) \right] \tag{6}$$

Proof. Define the function

$$\phi(v^1, \dots, v^i) = \max_{\substack{||u||=1 \\ (u,\,v^1)=\cdots=(u,\,v^i)=0}} (Hu, u) \tag{7}$$

The function ϕ exists because it is the maximum of a continuous function on a compact set. According to Rayleigh's principle, if $u^1, \dots, u^n$ are mutually orthogonal unit eigenvectors belonging to $\lambda_1, \dots, \lambda_n$,

$$\lambda_{i+1} = \phi(u^1, \dots, u^i) \tag{8}$$

Let $v^1, \dots, v^i$ be given. We will find an admissible vector u for which $(Hu, u) \geqslant \lambda_{i+1}$. Consider all vectors u^0 of the form

$$u^0 = c_1 u^1 + \cdots + c_i u^i + c_{i+1} u^{i+1} \tag{9}$$

The conditions

$$(u^0, v^k) = \sum_{j=1}^{i+1} c_j(u^j, v^k) = 0 \qquad (k = 1, \dots, i) \tag{10}$$

take the form of i linear homogeneous equations in $i + 1$ unknowns c_1, $\dots, c_{i+1}$. Since there are more unknowns than equations, the homogeneous system (10) has a solution $c_j = \lambda \gamma_j$ with not all $\gamma_j = 0$ and with λ arbitrary. By letting $\lambda = (\sum |\gamma_j|^2)^{-1/2}$ we obtain a solution c_j of (10) for which $\sum |c_j|^2 = 1$. Then the vector $u^0 = \sum c_j u^j$ satisfies all the constraints in the maximum problem (7). Therefore, the *maximum* value ϕ satisfies the inequality

$$\phi(v^1, \dots, v^i) \geqslant (Hu^0, u^0) \tag{11}$$

But

$$(Hu^0, u^0) = \left(\sum_{j=1}^{i+1} c_j \lambda_j u^j, \sum_{k=1}^{i+1} c_k u^k \right)$$

$$= \sum_{j=1}^{i+1} |c_j|^2 \lambda_j \geqslant \lambda_{i+1} \sum |c_j|^2 = \lambda_{i+1} \tag{12}$$

We have just shown that $\phi(v^1, \ldots, v^i) \geqslant \lambda_{i+1}$ for any set of vectors $v^1, \ldots, v^i$. But (8) shows that equality is attained when $v^1 = u^1, \ldots, v^i = u^i$. Therefore, λ_{i+1} is precisely the minimum of ϕ, as the theorem asserts.

EXAMPLE 2. Courant's principle for λ_3 implies that

$$1 = \min_{v^1, v^2} \left[\max_{\substack{||u||=1 \\ (u,v^1)=(u,v^2)=0}} (3u_1^2 + 2u_2^2 + u_3^2) \right] \tag{13}$$

This is, indeed, evident because

$$\phi(e^1, e^2) = \max_{\substack{||u||=1 \\ (u,e^1)=(u,e^2)=0}} (3u_1^2 + 2u_2^2 + u_3^2) = \max_{u_3^2=1} u_3^2 = 1$$

while, for *any* unit vector u, the weighted average $3u_1^2 + 2u_2^2 + 1 \cdot u_3^2$ is $\geqslant 1$.

PROBLEMS

1. Let A be a Hermitian matrix with eigenvalues $\alpha_1 \geqslant \cdots \geqslant \alpha_n$. Let B be a Hermitian matrix with eigenvalues $\beta_1 \geqslant \cdots \geqslant \beta_n$. Suppose that

$$(Au, u) - \epsilon \leqslant (Bu, u) \leqslant (Au, u) + \epsilon \qquad (\text{for all } ||u|| = 1)$$

Using Rayleigh's principle, prove that

$$\alpha_1 - \epsilon \leqslant \beta_1 \leqslant \alpha_1 + \epsilon$$

By applying Rayleigh's principle for the lower eigenvalues, can you conclude that $\alpha_2 - \epsilon \leqslant \beta_2 \leqslant \alpha_2 + \epsilon$? Why not?

2. Under the conditions of Problem 1, use Courant's principle to conclude that

$$\alpha_j - \epsilon \leqslant \beta_j \leqslant \alpha_j + \epsilon \qquad (j = 2, \ldots, n)$$

3. Let A, B, and C be Hermitian matrices, with eigenvalues $\alpha_j, \beta_j, \gamma_j$. Let $A = B + \epsilon C$. Assume that B and C are independent of ϵ. Show that, for each $j = 1, \ldots, n$,

$$\alpha_j = \beta_j + O(\epsilon) \qquad (\text{as } \epsilon \to 0)$$

4. In Problem 3, if A and B are not assumed to be Hermitian, show by a counterexample that the conclusion is false.

5. Let A, B, and P be Hermitian matrices. Let P be positive definite, and let $A = B + P$. If $\alpha_1 > \cdots > \alpha_n$ and $\beta_1 > \cdots > \beta_n$ are the eigenvalues of A and of B, show that $\alpha_1 > \beta_1, \ldots, \alpha_n > \beta_n$.

6.4 THE INCLUSION PRINCIPLE

In the analysis of large systems the following result is often useful:

Theorem 1. *Let* $A = (a_{ij})$ *be an* $n \times n$ *Hermitian matrix, with* $n > 1$. *Let* B *be the* $(n-1) \times (n-1)$ *Hermitian matrix formed by deleting the last row and the last column of* A. *Let* $\alpha_1 \geqslant \cdots \geqslant \alpha_n$ *be the eigenvalues of* A, *and let* $\beta_1 \geqslant \cdots \geqslant \beta_{n-1}$ *be the eigenvalues of* B. *Then,*

$$\alpha_1 \geqslant \beta_1 \geqslant \alpha_2 \geqslant \beta_2 \geqslant \cdots \geqslant \alpha_{n-1} \geqslant \beta_{n-1} \geqslant \alpha_n \tag{1}$$

EXAMPLE 1. Let

$$A = \begin{bmatrix} 1 & 2+i \\ 2-i & 3 \end{bmatrix}, \qquad B = \begin{bmatrix} 1 \end{bmatrix}$$

The eigenvalues $\alpha_1 \geqslant \alpha_2$ of A satisfy the equation

$$\alpha^2 - 4\alpha - 2 = 0$$

Therefore,

$$\alpha_1 = 2 + \sqrt{6}, \qquad \alpha_2 = 2 - \sqrt{6}$$

But $\beta_1 = 1$. Therefore, $\alpha_1 \geqslant \beta_1 \geqslant \alpha_2$.

Proof of the Theorem. This is one of the many applications of the minimax principle. First we make a simple observation: The quadratic form (By, y) equals the quadratic form (Ax, x) if $(x, e^n) = x_n = 0$ and if $x_i = y_i (i = 1, \ldots, n-1)$. For then

$$(By, y) = \sum_{i=1}^{n-1} \sum_{j=1}^{n-1} b_{ij} y_j \bar{y}_i$$

$$= \sum_{i=1}^{n-1} \sum_{j=1}^{n-1} a_{ij} x_j \bar{x}_i = \sum_{i=1}^{n} \sum_{j=1}^{n} a_{ij} x_j \bar{x}_i = (Ax, x) \tag{2}$$

Let us show that $\alpha_i \geqslant \beta_i$ if $i < n$. For any $v^1, \ldots, v^{i-1}$ in E^n we have

$$\max_{\substack{||x||=1 \\ x \perp v^1, \ldots, v^{i-1}}} (Ax, x) \geqslant \max_{\substack{||x||=1 \\ x \perp v^1, \ldots, v^{i-1}, e^n}} (Ax, x) \tag{3}$$

By the notation $x \perp v^j$ we mean $(x, v^j) = 0$. The inequality (3) holds because the requirement $x \perp e^n$, on the right-hand side of (3), places an extra restriction on x. Thus, if the tallest blue-eyed man in a class is six feet tall, the tallest man with blue eyes *and* brown hair cannot be more than six feet tall.

We will use the notation $x \longrightarrow y$ to mean that y is formed from x by deleting the last component of x. For example,

$$\max_{\substack{||x||=1 \\ x \perp v^1, \ldots, v^{i-1}, e^n}} (Ax, x) = \max_{\substack{||y||=1 \\ y \perp w^1, \ldots, w^{i-1}}} (By, y) \tag{4}$$

if $v^j \longrightarrow w^j (j = 1, \ldots, i-1)$. In fact,

$$|| x || = 1 \quad \text{and} \quad x \perp v^1, \ldots, v^{i-1}, e^n$$

if *and only if* the truncated vectors $y, w^1, \ldots, w^{i-1}$ satisfy

$$|| y || = 1 \quad \text{and} \quad y \perp w^1, \ldots, w^{i-1}$$

Given the correspondences $v^j \longrightarrow w^j$, both sides of the equation (4) are *functions* of the vectors $v^1, \ldots, v^{i-1}$. Identical functions have the same minimum. Therefore,

$$\min_{v^1, \ldots, v^{i-1}} \left[\max_{\substack{||x||=1 \\ x \perp v^1, \ldots, v^{i-1}, e^n}} (Ax, x) \right]$$
$$= \min_{w^1, \ldots, w^{i-1}} \left[\max_{\substack{||y||=1 \\ y \perp w^1, \ldots, w^{i-1}}} (By, y) \right] = \beta_i \tag{5}$$

Of course, if $i = 1$, no vectors v or w appear, and we replace (5) by

$$\max_{\substack{||x||=1 \\ x \perp e^n}} (Ax, x) = \max_{||y||=1} (By, y) = \beta_1 \tag{6}$$

The inequality (3) states that one function of $v^1, \ldots, v^{i-1}$ is always equal to or greater than another function of $v^1, \ldots, v^{i-1}$. The minima of these two functions must satisfy the same inequality. For example, $\cos \theta + 3 \geqslant \sin \theta$ implies that $2 \geqslant -1$. By Courant's theorem, the minimum of the left-hand side of (3) is α_i. In (5) we showed that the minimum of the right-hand side of (3) is β_i. Therefore, $\alpha_i \geqslant \beta_i$.

It remains to show that $\beta_i \geqslant \alpha_{i+1}$. In (5) we showed that

$$\beta_i = \min_{v^1, \ldots, v^{i-1}} \phi(v^1, \ldots, v^{i-1}, e^n) \tag{7}$$

where we define

$$\phi(v^1, \ldots, v^{i-1}, v^i) = \max_{\substack{||x||=1 \\ x \perp v^1, \ldots, v^{i-1}, v^i}} (Ax, x) \tag{8}$$

But Courant's theorem states that

$$\min_{v^1,\ldots,v^{i-1},v^i} \phi(v^1, \ldots, v^{i-1}, v^i) = \alpha_{i+1} \qquad (9)$$

In the minimization (7) we fix $v^i = e^n$; in the minimization (9) we do not prescribe v^i, and there are more admissible candidates to minimize ϕ. Therefore, the minimum β_1 in (7) is $\geqslant$ the minimum α_{i+1} in (9). This completes the proof.

PROBLEMS

1. Let

$$A = \begin{bmatrix} 1 & 2 & 3 \\ 2 & 4 & 5 \\ 3 & 5 & 6 \end{bmatrix}$$

According to the inclusion principle, what inequalities must the eigenvalues of A satisfy?

2. Let A be an $n \times n$ Hermitian matrix. Let B be the Hermitian matrix formed by deleting row k and column k from A. Show that the eigenvalues of A and the eigenvalues of B satisfy the inequalities in formula (1).

3. Let A be an $n \times n$ Hermitian matrix. Let B be the Hermitian matrix formed by deleting the last two rows and the last two columns of A. If A has eigenvalues $\alpha_1 \geqslant \cdots \geqslant \alpha_n$, and if B has eigenvalues $\beta_1 \geqslant \cdots \geqslant \beta_{n-2}$, show that

$$\alpha_i \geqslant \beta_i \geqslant \alpha_{i+2} \qquad (i = 1, \ldots, n-2)$$

4. Let A be an $n \times n$ Hermitian matrix. Let U be any $n \times n$ unitary matrix. Let B be the Hermitian matrix formed by deleting the last row and the last column of U^*AU. Show that the eigenvalues of A and the eigenvalues of B satisfy the inequalities in formula (1). By a suitable choice of U, deduce the result of Problem 2.

5. Let A be a real, symmetric $n \times n$ positive-definite matrix. Let c be any nonzero column vector with n real components. Let E be the ellipsoid $(Ax, x) = 1$. Let E' be the ellipsoid which is the intersection of E with the plane $(x, c) = 0$. If the principal axes of E and of E' have lengths $l_1 \geqslant \cdots \geqslant l_n$ and lengths $l'_1 \geqslant \cdots \geqslant l'_{n-1}$, show that $l_j \geqslant l'_j \geqslant l_{j+1}$ $(j = 1, \ldots, n-1)$. (First prove the result if $c = e^n$. Then, by suitable rigid motion $x' = Ux$, prove the result for arbitrary $c \neq 0$.)

6. In the notation of Section 4.8, consider the mass-spring system $M\ddot{x} + Kx = 0$. Let the fundamental frequencies of vibration be $w_1 \geqslant \cdots \geqslant w_n$. If the component x_n is constrained to be 0, a reduced system results with fundamental frequencies $w'_1 \geqslant \cdots \geqslant w'_{n-1}$. Show that $w_j \geqslant w'_j \geqslant w_{j+1}$ $(j = 1, \ldots, n-1)$. (First develop a Courant principle

$$\lambda_{k+1} = \min_{v^1, \ldots, v^k} \left[\begin{array}{l} \max\ (Ku, u) \\ {\scriptstyle (Mu,\, u)\, =\, 1} \\ {\scriptstyle (Mu,\, v^j)\, =\, 0 \quad (j\, =\, 1,\, \ldots,\, k)} \end{array} \right]$$

for the generalized eigenvalue problem $Kx = \lambda\, Mx$.)

6.5 A DETERMINANT CRITERION FOR POSITIVE DEFINITENESS

We now give another application of the inclusion principle:

Theorem 1. *Let* $H = (h_{ij})$ *be an* $n \times n$ *Hermitian matrix. Then* H *is positive definite if and only if*

$$h_{11} > 0, \quad \begin{vmatrix} h_{11} & h_{12} \\ h_{21} & h_{22} \end{vmatrix} > 0, \ldots, \quad \begin{vmatrix} h_{11} & \cdots & h_{1n} \\ \cdot & \cdots & \cdot \\ h_{n1} & \cdots & h_{nn} \end{vmatrix} > 0 \qquad (1)$$

Proof. Let H_k be the Hermitian matrix formed from the first k rows and the first k columns of H. We will prove by induction that $H = H_n$ is positive definite if and only if $\det H_k > 0$ $(k = 1, \ldots, n)$.

Suppose that H is positive definite. Then all the eigenvalues of H are positive, and the product of the eigenvalues $= \det H$ is positive. But every H_k is positive definite if H is positive definite, since the quadratic form of H_k equals the quadratic form (Hx, x) when $x_{k+1} = \cdots = x_n = 0$. Therefore, $\det H_k > 0$ for all k.

Conversely, suppose that all $\det H_i > 0$ for all $i \leqslant n$. Then $H_1 = (h_{11})$ is positive definite. Supposing that H_k is positive definite for some $k < n$, we will prove that H_{k+1} is positive definite. If $\alpha_1 \geqslant \cdots \geqslant \alpha_{k+1}$ are the eigenvalues of H_{k+1}, and if $\beta_1 \geqslant \cdots \geqslant \beta_k$ are the eigenvalues of H_k, the inclusion principle tells us that

$$\alpha_1 \geqslant \beta_1 \geqslant \alpha_2 \geqslant \beta_2 \geqslant \cdots \geqslant \alpha_k \geqslant \beta_k \geqslant \alpha_{k+1} \qquad (2)$$

But all β_i are positive, since H_k is positive definite. Therefore, all α_i are positive except, perhaps, α_{k+1}. But

$$\alpha_1 \ldots \alpha_k \cdot \alpha_{k+1} = \det H_{k+1} > 0 \qquad (3)$$

Since all the numbers $\alpha_1, \ldots, \alpha_k$, $\det H_{k+1}$ are positive, we conclude that $\alpha_{k+1} > 0$ and that H_{k+1} is positive definite. At the end of the induction, we conclude that $H_n = H$ is positive definite.

In this proof we have used the fact that a Hermitian matrix A is positive definite if and only if its eigenvalues λ_i are positive. The reader will recall that this is so because

$$(Ax, x) = \sum \lambda_j |c_j|^2 \qquad (\text{if } x = \sum c_j u^j)$$

where $u^1, \ldots, u^n$ are orthogonal unit eigenvectors of A.

PROBLEMS

1. For which values of μ is the matrix

$$\begin{bmatrix} 1 & 2 & 3 \\ 2 & \mu & 4 \\ 3 & 4 & 5 \end{bmatrix}$$

positive definite?

2. For which values of μ is the matrix

$$\begin{bmatrix} 1 & 2 & 4 \\ 2 & 3 & 5 \\ 4 & 5 & \mu \end{bmatrix}$$

positive definite?

3. Let H be an $n \times n$ Hermitian matrix. Let H_k' be formed from the *last* k rows and the *last* k columns of H. Show that H is positive definite if and only if $\det H_k' > 0$ $(k = 1, \ldots, n)$.

6.6 DETERMINANTS AS VOLUMES; HADAMARD'S INEQUALITY

In some applications, for example, in the Fredholm Theory of integral equations, we need to estimate the absolute value of a determinant. Let $A = (a_{ij})$ be an $n \times n$ matrix with columns $a^1, \ldots, a^n$. Let $\| x \| = (\sum |x_i|^2)^{1/2}$, as usual, represent the length of a vector x in E^n. Hadamard proved:

Theorem 1

$$|\det A| \leqslant \| a^1 \| \, \| a^2 \| \cdots \| a^n \| \tag{1}$$

with equality if and only if some $a^j = 0$ *or all* $(a^j, a^k) = 0$ *when* $j \neq k$.

EXAMPLE 1

$$\left| \det \begin{bmatrix} -1 & 2 \\ 3 & 4 \end{bmatrix} \right| = 10 < \sqrt{1^2 + 3^2} \, \sqrt{2^2 + 4^2}$$

EXAMPLE 2. For all real angles θ and $\alpha_1 \geqslant 0$, $\alpha_2 \geqslant 0$

$$\left| \det \begin{bmatrix} \alpha_1 \cos \theta, & \alpha_2 \sin \theta \\ \alpha_1 \sin \theta, & \alpha_2 \cos \theta \end{bmatrix} \right| = \alpha_1 \alpha_2$$

EXAMPLE 3

$$\left| \det \begin{bmatrix} 1 + i, & 2 - i \\ 3, & 4 \end{bmatrix} \right|$$
$$= |-2 + 7i| = \sqrt{53} < \sqrt{|1 + i|^2 + 3^2} \sqrt{|2 - i|^2 + 4^2} = 5\sqrt{11}$$

Hadamard's Inequality has a very simple geometrical interpretation. In the real vector space of two or three dimensions, $|\det A|$ equals the area or volume of the parallelogram or parallelepiped whose sides are the columns of the matrix A. In two dimensions, Hadamard's Inequality states that *the parallelogram with sides* a^1 *and* a^2 *has area* equal to or less than *the area* $\|a^1\| \cdot \|a^2\|$ *of the rectangle whose sides have the same lengths.* In three dimensions, the volume of a parallelepiped with sides that have given lengths is maximized if the angles at the vertices are all 90 degrees.

Proof of the Theorem. Let $\alpha_j = \|a^j\|$ ($j = 1, \ldots, n$). We may assume all $\alpha_j > 0$ because, if any $\alpha_j = 0$, both sides of (1) are zero. We now state a *maximum problem: Find an* n × n *matrix* B, *whose columns* b^j *have given positive lengths* α_j, *for which* $|\det B|$ *is maximized.* This problem surely has a solution, since $|\det B|$ is a continuous function of the n^2 variables b_{ij} defined on the compact set $\sum_{(i)} |b_{ij}|^2 = \alpha_j^2 (j = 1, \ldots, n)$.

Assume that B solves the maximum problem. Expand det B by column j; if $C = (c_{ij})$ is the matrix of signed cofactors of B, then

$$\det B = b_{1j}c_{1j} + b_{2j}c_{2j} + \cdots + b_{nj}c_{nj} \tag{2}$$

We know that $|\det B| \geqslant \alpha_1 \ldots \alpha_n > 0$ because the diagonal matrix diag $(\alpha_1, \ldots, \alpha_n)$ is one competitor in the maximum problem.

In Section (4.4) we proved that, if x and y are $\neq 0$,

$$|(x, y)| \leqslant \|x\| \|y\| \tag{3}$$

with equality if and only if x is some scalar multiple of y. Apply this result to the nonzero vectors

$$x = \text{col} (b_{1j}, \ldots, b_{nj}), \qquad y = \text{col} (\bar{c}_{1j}, \ldots, \bar{c}_{nj}) \tag{4}$$

We find

$$|\det B| \leqslant \alpha_j \|y\| \tag{5}$$

with equality *only* if the jth column of B has the form

$$b^j = \mu_j \overline{c^j} \qquad (\mu_j = \text{some scalar}) \tag{6}$$

where c^j is the jth column of the cofactor matrix. Since B solves the maximum problem, we *must* have the form (6). Otherwise $|\det B|$ could be increased by replacing b^j by the vector $\mu_j \overline{c^j}$, where $\mu_j = \alpha_j / \|c^j\|$. (Keep in mind that the jth column c^j of the cofactor matrix remains constant if the jth column b^j is varied.)

From the form (6) we shall conclude that the columns of B are orthogonal. If $k \neq j$ we have

$$(b^k, b^j) = (b^k, \mu_j \overline{c^j}) = \overline{\mu_j} \sum_{i=1}^{n} b_{ik} c_{ij} \tag{7}$$

But the sum in (7) is the expansion by column j of the determinant of the matrix formed from B by replacing column j by a duplicate of column k. Since a matrix with two identical columns has determinant zero, we have $(b^k, b^j) = 0$ if $k \neq j$.

Since B has orthogonal columns with lengths α_j, we may compute

$$
\begin{aligned}
|\det B|^2 &= (\det B^*)(\det B) \\
&= \det (B^*B) = \det [(b^j, b^i)] \qquad (i, j = 1, \ldots, n) \\
&= \det [\operatorname{diag} (\alpha_1^2, \alpha_2^2, \ldots, \alpha_n^2)] = \prod_{j=1}^{n} \alpha_j^2
\end{aligned} \tag{8}
$$

But $|\det A| \leqslant |\det B|$ because B solves the maximum problem. Therefore, $|\det A| \leqslant \prod \alpha_j$. Equality holds only if A is another solution of the maximum problem. By the reasoning in the preceding paragraph, a matrix which solves the maximum problem must have orthogonal columns. This completes the proof of Hadamard's Theorem.

Why are determinants equal, in absolute value, to volumes? For two reasons: (i) The equality

$$|\det A| = \text{volume generated by columns } a^1, \ldots, a^n \tag{9}$$

does hold if the columns are orthogonal or if the columns are linearly dependent; (ii) neither the volume nor the determinant changes if a multiple of a^j is subtracted from $a^k (k \neq j)$. We have already proved (i) in equation (8), which holds for any square matrix with orthogonal columns.

We illustrate (ii) for $n = 3$. Assume that a^1, a^2, a^3 are linearly independent, i.e., they are not all in one plane. The volume $v(a^1, a^2, a^3)$ may be computed as follows.

We begin with the parallelogram P generated by a^1 and a^2 in Figure 6.1. The vector a^2 has a component λa^1 which is a multiple of a^1 and a component

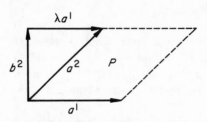

Figure 6.1

b^2 perpendicular to a^1. The area of P equals the area of the rectangle generated by a^1 and the perpendicular component b^2. Therefore,

$$v(a^1, a^2, a^3) = v(a^1, b^2, a^3)$$
$$\text{(with } b^2 = a^2 - \lambda a^1) \quad (10)$$

Similarly, the vector a^3 (not illustrated in Figure 6.1) has a component $\mu a^1 + \nu b^2$ in the plane of P and a component b^3 perpendicular to the plane of P. Since b^3 is the altitude perpendicular to the base parallelogram P, we have

$$v(a^1, b^2, a^3) = v(a^1, b^2, b^3) \quad \text{(with } b^3 = a^3 - \mu a^1 - \nu b^2) \quad (11)$$

But the vectors a^1, b^2, b^3 are orthogonal. If B is the 3×3 matrix with these vectors as columns, we have

$$v(a^1, b^2, b^3) = |\det B| = \|a^1\| \, \|b^2\| \, \|b^3\| \quad (12)$$

Since B arises from A by subtracting multiples of columns from other columns, $\det B = \det A$. This completes the proof of (9) for $n = 3$.

PROBLEMS

1. Obtain a second proof of Hadamard's inequality in the following way. Let the columns of A be the vectors $a^1, \ldots, a^n$. If the columns are independent, $\det A = 0$, so assume that the columns are independent. Form orthogonal vectors $b^1, \ldots, b^n$ successively by the relations

$$a^1 = b^1$$
$$a^2 = b^2 + \lambda_{21} b^1$$
$$a^3 = b^3 + \lambda_{31} b^1 + \lambda_{32} b^2$$
$$\cdot \quad \cdot \quad \cdots$$
$$a^n = b^n + \lambda_{n1} b^1 + \cdots + \lambda_{n, n-1} b^{n-1}$$

   with

$$\lambda_{jk} = (a^j, b^k) / \|b^k\|^2 \quad (j > k)$$

   If B is the matrix with columns $b^1, \ldots, b^n$, show that

$$\det A = \det B$$
$$\|a^j\| \geqslant \|b^j\| \quad (j = 1, \ldots, n)$$
$$|\det B| = \|b^1\| \cdots \|b^n\|$$

2. Let $A = (a_{ij}) \, (i, j = 1, \ldots, n)$. Prove that

$$|\det A|^2 \leqslant \prod_{i=1}^{n} \left(\sum_{j=1}^{n} |a_{ij}|^2 \right)$$

When does equality hold?

3. Let $A = (a_{ij})$ $(i, j = 1, \ldots, n)$. Let $\rho_i > 0$ $(i = 1, \ldots, n)$. Prove that

$$|\det A|^2 \leqslant \prod_{j=1}^{n} \rho_j^{-2} \left(\sum_{i=1}^{n} \rho_i^2 |a_{ij}|^2 \right)$$

When does equality hold?

4. Let $A = (a_{ij})$ $(i, j = 1, \ldots, n)$. Let $\alpha = \max |a_{ij}| > 0$. Prove that

$$|\det A| \leqslant \alpha^n n^{n/2}$$

By discussing the particular matrices

$$H_2 = \begin{bmatrix} 1 & 1 \\ 1 & -1 \end{bmatrix}, \qquad H_4 = \begin{bmatrix} H_2 & H_2 \\ H_2 & -H_2 \end{bmatrix} = \begin{bmatrix} 1 & 1 & 1 & 1 \\ 1 & -1 & 1 & -1 \\ 1 & 1 & -1 & -1 \\ 1 & -1 & -1 & 1 \end{bmatrix}, \ \cdots$$

show that $|\det A| = \alpha^n n^{n/2}$ is possible for indefinitely large values of n.

6.7   WEYL'S INEQUALITIES

Let H be a Hermitian matrix. Suppose that we wish to know the eigenvalues of H, but that we do not know its exact components. We are given a Hermitian matrix, M, whose components are approximations to the components of H. If $M = H + P$, where P is the error matrix, we wish to estimate the differences between the eigenvalues of M and the corresponding eigenvalues of H.

Theorem 1. *Let* $M = H + P$, *where* M, H, *and* P *are Hermitian. Let* M *have eigenvalues* $\mu_1 \geqslant \cdots \geqslant \mu_n$; *let* H *have eigenvalues* $\eta_1 \geqslant \cdots \geqslant \eta_n$; *and let* P *have eigenvalues* $\rho_1 \geqslant \cdots \geqslant \rho_n$. *Then*

$$\mu_i \geqslant \eta_i + \rho_n \quad \text{and} \quad \mu_i \leqslant \eta_i + \rho_1 \quad (i = 1, \ldots, n) \tag{1}$$

In particular, if P *is positive definite, then* $\mu_i > \eta_i$ $(i = 1, \ldots, n)$.

Proof. The minimax theorem states that

$$\mu_i = \min_{v^1, \ldots, v^{i-1}} \left[\max_{\substack{||u||=1 \\ u \perp v^1, \ldots, v^{i-1}}} (Mu, u) \right] \tag{2}$$

But $(Mu, u) = (Hu, u) + (Pu, u)$. By Rayleigh's principle,

$$\max_{||u||=1} (Pu, u) = \rho_1 \tag{3}$$

To find $\min (Pu, u)$, we observe that the eigenvalues of $-P$ are $-\rho_n \geqslant \cdots \geqslant -\rho_1$. The minimum of any function is minus the maximum of minus the function. Therefore, by Rayleigh's principle for the greatest eigenvalue of $-P$,

$$\min_{||u||=1} (Pu, u) = -\max_{||u||=1} [-(Pu, u)] = -(-\rho_n) = \rho_n \tag{4}$$

From (3) and (4) we conclude

$$\rho_n \leqslant (Pu, u) \leqslant \rho_1 \qquad (\text{if } ||\, u\, || = 1) \tag{5}$$

Therefore, if $||\, u\, || = 1$,

$$(Hu, u) + \rho_n \leqslant (Mu, u) \leqslant (Hu, u) + \rho_1 \tag{6}$$

For any given vectors $v^1, \ldots, v^{i-1}$ we conclude

$$\rho_n + \max_{\substack{||u||=1 \\ u \perp v^1, \ldots, v^{i-1}}} (Hu, u) \leqslant \max_{\substack{||u||=1 \\ u \perp v^1, \ldots, v^{i-1}}} (Mu, u) \leqslant \rho_1 + \max_{\substack{||u||=1 \\ u \perp v^1, \ldots, v^{i-1}}} (Hu, u) \tag{7}$$

If some functions satisfy an inequality, their minima satisfy the same inequality. Therefore, the minima, with respect to $v^1, \ldots, v^{i-1}$, of the three functions in (7) satisfy the inequality

$$\rho_n + \eta_i \leqslant \mu_i \leqslant \rho_1 + \eta_i \tag{8}$$

Here we have used the minimax principle for the eigenvalue η_i of H and for the eigenvalue μ_i of M.

If M is near H, are the eigenvalues of M near the eigenvalues of H? Let $M - H = P$. If the eigenvalues of P are $\rho_1 \geqslant \cdots \geqslant \rho_n$, we need only to ask: If P is "small," are its eigenvalues small? Define the *matrix norm*

$$||\, P\, || = \max_{||u||=1} ||\, Pu\, || = \max_{x \neq 0} \frac{||\, Px\, ||}{||\, x\, ||} \tag{9}$$

Letting u be the unit eigenvectors belonging to ρ_1 and ρ_n, we find

$$||\, P\, || \geqslant |\rho_1| \quad \text{and} \quad ||\, P\, || \geqslant |\rho_n| \tag{10}$$

Along with Theorem 1, these inequalities establish Weyl's theorem:

Theorem 2. *Let* M *and* H *be Hermitian. Let* $\mu_1 \geqslant \cdots \geqslant \mu_n$ *be the eigenvalues of* M, *and let* $\eta_1 \geqslant \cdots \geqslant \eta_n$ *be the eigenvalues of* H. *Then*

$$|\mu_i - \eta_i| \leqslant ||\, M - H\, || \qquad (i = 1, \ldots, n) \tag{11}$$

Proof. By Theorem 1, if $P = M - H$,

$$\rho_n \leqslant \mu_i - \eta_i \leqslant \rho_1 \qquad (i = 1, \ldots, n) \tag{12}$$

But (10) implies

$$\rho_1 \leqslant \| P \| \quad \text{and} \quad \rho_n \geqslant -\| P \| \qquad (\text{i.e.,} \ -\rho_n \leqslant \| P \|)$$

This completes the proof.

How can we estimate $\| P \| = \| M - H \|$? From the definition (9) we have

$$\| P \|^2 = \max_{\|u\|=1} \| Pu \|^2 = \max_{\|u\|=1} (Pu, Pu)$$
$$= \max_{\|u\|=1} (P^*Pu, u) \tag{13}$$

But $P^* = P$. By Rayleigh's principle, max $(P^2 u, u)$ is the largest eigenvalue of P^2. Since the eigenvalues of P^2 are $\rho_1^2, \ldots, \rho_n^2$, we conclude that

$$\| P \|^2 = \max (\rho_1^2, \rho_n^2)$$

since $\rho_1 \geqslant \cdots \geqslant \rho_n$, or

$$\| P \| = \max (\rho_1, -\rho_n) \tag{14}$$

ESTIMATE 1

$$\| P \| \leqslant \left(\sum_{i=1}^{n} \sum_{j=1}^{n} |p_{ij}|^2 \right)^{1/2} \tag{15}$$

Proof

$$\| P \|^2 \leqslant \sum_{i=1}^{n} \rho_i^2 = \text{tr } P^2$$
$$= \sum_i \left(\sum_j p_{ij} p_{ji} \right) = \sum_i \sum_j |p_{ij}|^2$$

ESTIMATE 2

$$\| P \| \leqslant \max_i \sum_{j=1}^{n} |p_{ij}| \tag{16}$$

Proof. Let u be an eigenvector of P belonging to $\rho = \rho_1$ or ρ_n. Let $|u_m| = \max |u_j| > 0$. Then

$$\rho u_m = \sum_{j=1}^{n} p_{mj} u_j$$
$$|\rho| |u_m| \leqslant \sum_{j=1}^{n} |p_{mj}| |u_j| \leqslant |u_m| \sum_{j=1}^{n} |p_{mj}| \tag{17}$$

$$|\rho| \leqslant \sum_{j=1}^{n} |p_{mj}| \leqslant \max_i \sum_{j=1}^{n} |p_{ij}| \tag{18}$$

EXAMPLE 1. Suppose that

$$H = \begin{bmatrix} 1.43 & -7.89 \\ -7.89 & 8.36 \end{bmatrix}, \qquad M = \begin{bmatrix} 1.4 & -7.9 \\ -7.9 & 8.4 \end{bmatrix}$$

According to Estimate 2, we have

$$\| M - H \| \leqslant \max (.03 + .01, .01 + .04) = .05$$

Weyl's theorem now gives the inequalities

$$|\mu_1 - \eta_1| \leqslant .05, \qquad |\mu_2 - \eta_2| \leqslant .05$$

for the eigenvalues μ_i of M and the eigenvalues η_i of H. If we use Estimate 1 instead, we find

$$|\mu_i - \eta_i| \leqslant [(.03)^2 + (.01)^2 + (.01)^2 + (.04)^2]^{1/2} = (.01)\sqrt{27}$$

EXAMPLE 2. *Weyl's inequalities do not hold for the class of non-Hermitian matrices.* Let H be replaced by the non-Hermitian matrix

$$A = \begin{bmatrix} 0 & 1 & 0 \\ 0 & 0 & 1 \\ 0 & 0 & 0 \end{bmatrix} \quad \text{and} \quad \text{let } M = \begin{bmatrix} 0 & 1 & 0 \\ 0 & 0 & 1 \\ \epsilon & 0 & 0 \end{bmatrix} \tag{19}$$

where ϵ is a small error of measurement. We find

$$\det (\lambda I - A) = \lambda^3, \qquad \det (\lambda I - M) = \lambda^3 - \epsilon \tag{20}$$

The eigenvalues of A are all zero; the eigenvalues of M are the three cube roots of ϵ. Therefore, for $i = 1, 2, 3$,

$$|\lambda_i(M) - \lambda_i(A)| = |\epsilon|^{1/3} \tag{21}$$

But, if $P = M - A$,

$$\| Px \|^2 = (Px, Px) = |\epsilon|^2 |x_2|^2 \leqslant |\epsilon|^2 \| x \|^2 \tag{22}$$

Therefore, $\| P \| = \| M - A \| = |\epsilon|$, and from (21)

$$|\lambda_i(M) - \lambda_i(A)| = |\epsilon|^{1/3} \gg |\epsilon| = \| M - A \| \tag{23}$$

If the error in measurement is $\epsilon = .001$, the error in the computed eigenvalues is bigger by a factor of 100.

PROBLEMS

1. Suppose that H is a Hermitian matrix, and suppose that some numerical method produces a unitary matrix U for which

$$U^*HU = \begin{bmatrix} 1.02, & -.03, & .01 \\ -.03, & .87, & -.01 \\ .01, & -.01, & 7.23 \end{bmatrix}$$

Estimate the eigenvalues of H.

2. Let M and H be Hermitian matrices, and suppose that $|m_{ij} - h_{ij}| \leqslant \epsilon$. Prove that the eigenvalues of M and of H satisfy:

$$|\mu_i - \eta_i| \leqslant n\epsilon \qquad (i = 1, \ldots, n)$$

3. Is one of the estimates in formulas (15) and (16) always equal to or greater than the other?

4. If $P = P^*$, show that

$$\|P\| \leqslant \max_j \sum_{i=1}^{n} |p_{ij}|$$

6.8 GERSHGORIN'S THEOREM

If A is an $n \times n$ matrix which is strongly weighted along the main diagonal, the following estimate is useful:

Theorem 1. *Every eigenvalue* λ *of an* n $\times$ n *matrix* A *satisfies at least one of the inequalities*

$$|\lambda - a_{ii}| \leqslant \sum_{\substack{j=1 \\ j \neq i}}^{n} |a_{ij}| \qquad (i = 1, \ldots, n) \tag{1}$$

EXAMPLE 1. Let

$$A = \begin{bmatrix} 0 & 1 & -1 \\ 1.3 & 2 & -.7 \\ .5 & .5i & 4i \end{bmatrix} \tag{2}$$

Figure 6.2 shows the three Gershgorin circles; the shaded areas comprise all complex numbers λ satisfying at least one of the inequalities (1).

Proof of Theorem 1. Let u be an eigenvector belonging to λ, and let $|u_m| = \max|u_j|$ for $j = 1, \ldots, n$. Since $(\lambda I - A)u = 0$,

$$(\lambda - a_{mm})u_m + \sum_{j \neq m} (-a_{mj})u_j = 0 \tag{3}$$

Therefore,

$$|\lambda - a_{mm}||u_m| = |\sum_{j \neq m} a_{mj}u_j|$$
$$\leqslant \sum_{j \neq m} |a_{mj}||u_j| \leqslant \sum_{j \neq m} |a_{mj}||u_m| \tag{4}$$

Dividing (4) by $|u_m| > 0$, we find

$$|\lambda - a_{mm}| \leqslant \sum_{j \neq m} |a_{mj}| \tag{5}$$

Therefore, λ lies in the mth Gershgorin circle (1).

Figure 6.2 contains three circles, two of them overlapping. There are two *disjoint components* D_1 and D_2, where D_1 is the upper circle $|\lambda - 4i| \leqslant 1$ and where D_2 is the union of the two lower circles. We will show that D_1 contains 1 eigenvalue of A and that D_2 contains 2 eigenvalues of A.

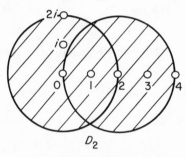

Figure 6.2

Theorem 2. *Let* $D_1, D_2, \ldots, D_k$ *be the disjoint components of the Gershgorin circles* (1). *Let* D_i *be the union of* n_i *of the circles* (1) *(so that* $\sum n_i = n$*). Then* D_i *contains exactly* n_i *eigenvalues of* A.

Proof: This result follows from the fact (proved in Section 6.13) that the eigenvalues of a matrix are continuous functions of the components of the matrix. Define the matrix

$$A(\theta) = \begin{bmatrix} a_{11} & \theta a_{12} & \ldots & \theta a_{1n} \\ \theta a_{21} & a_{22} & \ldots & \theta a_{2n} \\ \cdot & \cdot & \ldots & \cdot \\ \theta a_{n1} & \theta a_{n2} & \ldots & a_{nn} \end{bmatrix} \tag{6}$$

We have

$$A(1) = A, \qquad A(0) = \text{diag}(a_{11}, \ldots, a_{nn}) \tag{7}$$

As θ varies from 1 to 0, the n eigenvalues of A move continuously to a_{11}, $\ldots, a_{nn}$.

We apply Gershgorin's Theorem to each matrix $A(\theta)$ (observe Figure 6.2). As θ shrinks from 1 to 0, the three Gershgorin circles shrink to the points $4i$, 0, and 2. The eigenvalues in D_1 for $\theta = 1$ must move to $4i$ as $\theta \longrightarrow 0$. The eigenvalues in D_2 move either to 0 or to 2 as $\theta \longrightarrow 0$. But in the limit there must be *one* eigenvalue at $4i$, *one* eigenvalue at 0, and *one* eigenvalue at 2. Therefore, D_1 must originally have contained one eigenvalue, and D_2 must have contained two eigenvalues. As the three circles shrink, there is no way in which an eigenvalue originally in D_1 can move *continuously* to any point in D_2. This reasoning, based on the specific example in Figure 6.2, entails no loss of generality, and the theorem is proved.

PROBLEMS

1. If B is an $n \times n$ matrix for which

$$|b_{ii}| > \sum_{\substack{j=1 \\ j \neq i}}^{n} |b_{ij}| \qquad (i = 1, \ldots, n)$$

prove that $\det B \neq 0$.

2. By using Theorem 2, show that the matrix

$$\begin{bmatrix} 9 & 1 & -2 & 1 \\ 0 & 8 & 1 & 1 \\ -1 & 0 & 7 & 0 \\ 1 & 0 & 0 & 1 \end{bmatrix}$$

has at least two real eigenvalues.

3. Let A be an $n \times n$ matrix with real components. Show that the imaginary parts of the eigenvalues of A satisfy

$$|\operatorname{Im} \lambda| \leqslant \max_{i} \sum_{j \neq i} |a_{ij}|$$

4. Let A be an $n \times n$ matrix. Let $\rho_1, \ldots, \rho_n$ be any n positive numbers. Show that every eigenvalue, λ, of A must satisfy at least one of the inequalities

$$|\lambda - a_{ii}| \leqslant \sum_{\substack{j=1 \\ j \neq i}}^{n} (\rho_i/\rho_j) |a_{ij}| \qquad (i = 1, \ldots, n)$$

5. What theorem results if Gershgorin's Theorem is applied to the transpose of A?

6.9 VECTOR NORMS AND THE RELATED MATRIX NORMS

For many purposes we have found it desirable to have a measure of the size of a vector or of a matrix. If λ is a scalar, i.e., a real or complex number, we let $|\lambda|$ represent the familiar absolute value or modulus. Let $x, y, \ldots$

be vectors in the space of vectors with n real components *or* with n real or complex components, where n is a fixed integer $\geqslant 2$. A *norm* of a vector x is often designated by the symbol $\|x\|$, but we shall usually prefer the less cumbersome symbol $|x|$. We should like the norm to have the following properties:

$$|x| \geqslant 0 \qquad \text{(with } |x| = 0 \text{ if and only if } x = 0) \tag{1}$$

$$|\lambda x| = |\lambda||x| \qquad \text{(for any scalar } \lambda) \tag{2}$$

$$|x + y| \leqslant |x| + |y| \qquad \text{(the triangle inequality)} \tag{3}$$

$$|x| \text{ depends continuously on } x. \tag{4}$$

There are positive constants α and β such that

$$\alpha \max_k |x_k| \leqslant |x| \leqslant \beta \max_k |x_k| \qquad \text{(for all } x) \tag{5}$$

We shall call any function $|x|$ of the vector x which has all these properties a *regular vector-norm*.

EXAMPLE 1. The Euclidean norm is

$$|x| = \|x\| = (\sum_{k=1}^{n} |x_k|^2)^{1/2} \tag{6}$$

We shall reserve the symbol $\|x\|$ for this particular norm, which clearly has properties (1) and (2). Property (3) follows from the Schwarz Inequality (Section 4.4) in this way

$$\begin{aligned} \|x + y\|^2 &= (x + y, x + y) = \|x\|^2 + (x, y) + (y, x) + \|y\|^2 \\ &\leqslant \|x\|^2 + 2\|x\|\|y\| + \|y\|^2 = (\|x\| + \|y\|)^2 \end{aligned} \tag{7}$$

Continuity (4) follows from the continuity of $\sqrt{\xi}$ as a function of the scalar $\xi \geqslant 0$. Finally, (5) holds with $\alpha = 1$ and $\beta = \sqrt{n}$.

EXAMPLE 2. If P is positive definite, define

$$|x| = (Px, x)^{1/2} = (\sum_j \sum_k p_{jk} x_k \bar{x}_j)^{1/2} \tag{8}$$

This is the so-called *Riemannian metric*, which is used in differential geometry and in the theory of relativity. For $P = I$ we have the Euclidean norm. The norm (8) clearly has properties (1) and (2). To prove the triangle inequality for this norm, we will first show that

$$(Px, y) \leqslant (Px, x)^{1/2}(Py, y)^{1/2} = |x||y| \tag{9}$$

If P has the eigenvalues $\lambda_k > 0$ and the unit orthogonal eigenvectors u^k, and if

$$x = \sum \xi_k u^k \quad \text{and} \quad y = \sum \eta_k u^k$$

then

$$
\begin{aligned}
(Px, y) &= \sum \lambda_k \xi_k \bar{\eta}_k \\
&= \sum (\sqrt{\lambda_k} \xi_k)(\sqrt{\lambda_k} \bar{\eta}_k) \\
&\leq (\sum_j \lambda_j |\xi_j|^2)^{1/2} (\sum_k \lambda_k |\eta_k|^2)^{1/2} = (Px, x)^{1/2}(Py, y)^{1/2}
\end{aligned}
$$

This proves (9). We can now obtain the triangle inequality:

$$
\begin{aligned}
|x + y|^2 &= [P(x + y), x + y] = (Px, x) + (Px, y) + (Py, x) + (Py, y) \\
&\leq |x|^2 + |x||y| + |y||x| + |y|^2 = (|x| + |y|)^2
\end{aligned}
$$

Continuity (4) is obvious; and (5) holds because, if λ_1 and λ_n are the greatest and least eigenvalues of P, and if $\|x\|$ is the Euclidean norm (6), then

$$\lambda_n^{1/2} \|x\| \leq |x| = (Px, x)^{1/2} \leq \lambda_1^{1/2} \|x\| \tag{10}$$

Since $\max |x_k| \leq \|x\| \leq \sqrt{n} \max |x_k|$, we have (5) with $\alpha = \sqrt{\lambda_n}$ and $\beta = \sqrt{n\lambda_1}$.

EXAMPLE 3. Define

$$|x| = \max_k |x_k|.$$

Here all properties (1)–(5) are obvious.

EXAMPLE 4. Define

$$|x| = \sum_k |x_k| \tag{11}$$

For this norm, as well, properties (1)–(5) are obvious.

The requirements (1)–(5) are *not* independent. We will show in Theorem 1 that every function $|x|$ with the properties (1), (2), (3) necessarily has the property of continuity (4) *and* the property of comparability (5). We call (5) the property of *comparability* because it shows that, if $|x|$ and $|x|'$ are any two regular norms, then the ratio is bounded from above and below:

$$0 < \frac{\alpha'}{\beta} \leq \frac{|x|'}{|x|} \leq \frac{\beta'}{\alpha} < \infty \qquad \text{(for all } x \neq 0) \tag{12}$$

Thus, if $|x|' = \|x\|$, the Euclidean norm of Example 1, and if $|x|$ is the norm of Example 4, we have

$$\frac{1}{n} \leqslant \frac{\|x\|}{|x|} \leqslant \frac{\sqrt{n}}{1}$$

Theorem 1. *Let* $|\mathrm{x}|$ *be any function defined on the* n-*dimensional vector space which has properties* (1), (2), (3). *Then the function* $|\mathrm{x}|$ *also has properties* (4) *and* (5).

Proof. Let

$$e^1 = \begin{bmatrix} 1 \\ 0 \\ \cdot \\ \cdot \\ \cdot \\ 0 \end{bmatrix}, \dots, \quad e^n = \begin{bmatrix} 0 \\ \cdot \\ \cdot \\ \cdot \\ 0 \\ 1 \end{bmatrix}$$

Then, by homogeneity (2) and by repeated application of the triangle inequality (3),

$$|x| = |\sum_{k=1}^{n} x_k e^k| \leqslant \sum_{k=1}^{n} |x_k e^k| = \sum_{k=1}^{n} |x_k||e^k|$$

Therefore,

$$|x| \leqslant \beta \max |x_k| \qquad (\text{if } \beta = \sum_{k=1}^{n} |e^k|) \tag{13}$$

From this inequality we can prove continuity. Let c be a fixed vector. We must show that

$$|c + x| \to |c| \qquad (\text{as } x \to 0) \tag{14}$$

where

$$x \to 0 \text{ means:} \qquad x_1 \to 0, \quad x_2 \to 0, \quad \dots, \quad x_n \to 0. \tag{15}$$

By the triangle inequality

$$|c| = |c + x + (-x)| \leqslant |c + x| + |(-x)| = |c + x| + |x|$$

and also

$$|c + x| \leqslant |c| + |x|$$

Therefore,

$$-|x| \leqslant |c + x| - |c| \leqslant |x| \tag{16}$$

Therefore, to prove continuity (14), we need only to show that $|x| \to 0$ as $x \to 0$; but this is assured by the inequality $|x| \leqslant \beta \max |x_k|$, which we proved in (13).

To complete the proof of comparability (5), we consider the continuous function $|x|$ on the closed, bounded set C of vectors for which $\max |y_k| = 1$. The set C is illustrated in Figure 6.3 for $n = 2$.

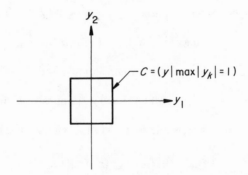

Figure 6.3

In general, C is the boundary of the n-dimensional unit hypercube. Define

$$\alpha = \min |y| \qquad \text{(for } y \text{ on } C) \tag{17}$$

This minimum is achieved at some point y^0 on C. Then $\alpha = |y^0| > 0$ because $y^0 \neq 0$; in fact, $\max |y_k^0| = 1$. We now have $|y| \geqslant \alpha > 0$ for all y on C. For any vector x we may write $x = \mu y$ where $\mu = \max |x_k|$ and y lies on C. Therefore,

$$|x| = |\mu y| = \mu |y| \geqslant \mu \alpha = \alpha \max |x_k| \tag{18}$$

This completes the proof of the theorem.

Given a regular vector-norm, $|x|$, and a fixed $n \times n$ matrix, A, we may measure the "size" of A as the greatest value of the ratio $|Ax|/|x|$ for all $x \neq 0$. Thus, the matrix I has "size" 1, the matrix $-7.3I$ has "size" 7.3, etc. The ratio $|Ax|/|x|$ shows how much the transformation A magnifies the norm of the vector x.

If $|x|$ is a regular vector-norm on the n-dimensional vector space, and if A is an $n \times n$ matrix, we define the *related matrix-norm* as

$$|A| = \max_{x \neq 0} \frac{|Ax|}{|x|} \tag{19}$$

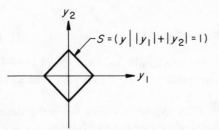

Figure 6.4

For this definition to make sense, we must show that the maximum (19) exists. Let S be the "unit sphere"

$$S = \{y \mid |y| = 1\}$$

relative to the norm $|x|$. For example, if $n = 2$ and $|x|$ is defined as $|x_1| + |x_2|$, the set S is the diamond shape in Figure 6.4.

The set S is bounded because, by comparability (5), for $|y| = 1$

$$\alpha \max |y_k| \leqslant 1 \qquad \text{(with } \alpha > 0\text{)}$$

Moreover, S is closed because $|x|$ is continuous, and

$$y^m \longrightarrow y \quad \text{(with all } |y^m| = 1\text{)} \quad \text{implies} \quad |y| = 1$$

If x is any nonzero vector, we have $x = |x|y$, where y lies on S. Then

$$\frac{|Ax|}{|x|} = \frac{|A(|x|y)|}{|(|x|y)|} = \frac{|x||Ay|}{|x||y|} = |Ay| \tag{20}$$

Therefore, the maximum (19) exists

$$|A| = \max_{x \neq 0} \frac{|Ax|}{|x|} = \max_{|y|=1} |Ay| \tag{21}$$

because the function $|Ay|$ is a continuous function of y defined on the closed, bounded set $S = \{y \mid |y| = 1\}$.

EXAMPLE 5. Let $|x| = \|x\|$, the Euclidean norm of Example 1. The related matrix-norm is

$$\|A\| = \max_{x \neq 0} \frac{\|Ax\|}{\|x\|}$$

But

$$\left(\frac{\|Ax\|}{\|x\|}\right)^2 = \frac{(Ax, Ax)}{(x, x)} = \frac{(A^*Ax, x)}{(x, x)}$$

By Rayleigh's Principle, the maximum value of this quotient is the largest eigenvalue $\lambda_{\max}$ of the positive semidefinite Hermitian matrix A^*A. Taking square roots, we find

$$\|A\| = [\lambda_{\max}(A^*A)]^{1/2} \tag{22}$$

For instance, if

$$A = \begin{bmatrix} 0 & -2 \\ 1 & 0 \end{bmatrix} \quad \text{and} \quad A^*A = \begin{bmatrix} 1 & 0 \\ 0 & 4 \end{bmatrix} \tag{23}$$

then $\lambda_{\max}(A^*A) = 4$, and $\| A \| = \sqrt{4} = 2$.

EXAMPLE 6. Define $| x | = \max_k | x_k |$. Then

$$| A | = \max_{|y|=1} (\max_k | \sum_j a_{kj}y_j |) \tag{24}$$

But, if $\max | y_j | = 1$,

$$\max_k | \sum_j a_{kj}y_j | \leqslant \max_k \sum_j | a_{kj} | \tag{25}$$

Conversely, let m be an index such that

$$\max_k \sum_j | a_{kj} | = \sum_j | a_{mj} |$$

If, for this index m,

$$a_{mj} = | a_{mj} | e^{i\theta_j} \qquad (j = 1, \ldots, n)$$

define the "unit vector" y^0 by

$$y_j^0 = e^{-i\theta_j} \qquad (j = 1, \ldots, n)$$

For this vector y we have

$$\begin{aligned} | Ay^0 | &= \max_k | \sum_j a_{kj}e^{-i\theta_j} | \\ &\geqslant | \sum_j a_{mj}e^{-i\theta_j} | = \sum_j | a_{mj} | \end{aligned} \tag{26}$$

The inequality (25) states that

$$| Ay | \leqslant \max_k \sum_j | a_{kj} | \qquad \text{(for all } | y | = 1)$$

whereas (26) states that, for the particular "unit vector" y^0

$$| Ay^0 | \geqslant \max_k \sum_j | a_{kj} |$$

Therefore,

$$| A | = \max_k \sum_j | a_{kj} | \tag{27}$$

For instance, if

$$A = \begin{bmatrix} -7 & 7 \\ 3 & 9 \end{bmatrix}$$

we have $|A| = 14$ because $|-7| + |7| > |3| + |9|$. The norm (27) is convenient because it can be readily calculated.

The next theorem will show that the matrix norm related to any regular vector norm, has many useful properties.

Theorem 2. *In the n-dimensional space let $|x|$ be any regular vector norm, i.e., any norm satisfying* (1), (2), (3) *and hence* (4) *and* (5). *Let $|A|$ be the related matrix norm* (19) *for* n × n *matrices. Then*

$$|I| = 1 \qquad \text{(for the identity matrix, } I) \tag{i}$$

$$|A| \geqslant 0 \qquad \text{(with } |A| = 0 \text{ if and only if } A = 0) \tag{ii}$$

$$|\lambda A| = |\lambda| |A| \qquad \text{(for all scalars } \lambda) \tag{iii}$$

$$|A + B| \leqslant |A| + |B| \tag{iv}$$

$$|AB| \leqslant |A| |B| \tag{v}$$

$$|Ax| \leqslant |A| |x| \qquad \text{(for all vectors } x) \tag{vi}$$

$$|A| \text{ depends continuously on } A \tag{vii}$$

$$\rho \max_{i,j} |a_{ij}| \leqslant |A| \leqslant \sigma \max_{i,j} |a_{ij}| \qquad \text{(for some positive} \tag{viii}$$

constants ρ, σ which are independent of A)

Proof. Property (i) holds because $|Ix|/|x| = 1$ for all x. We have $|A| \geqslant 0$ because $|A|$ is the maximum of numbers $\geqslant 0$. Since $|0x| = |0| = 0$ for all x, we have $|0| = 0$. Conversely, suppose $|A| = 0$. Then, by the definition (19), $|Ax| = 0$ when x is any one of the basic vectors $e^1, \ldots, e^n$. But this says that $|a^j| = 0$ for all columns a^j of A. But the vector norm $|a^j| = 0$ only if $a^j = 0$; therefore, all columns of A are zero, and A is the zero matrix. This proves (ii).

Property (iii) holds because $|(\lambda A)x| = |\lambda(Ax)| = |\lambda| |Ax|$.

Property (iv) comes from the triangle inequality (3).

Let y^0 be a vector with $|y^0| = 1$ such that, as in (21),

$$|A + B| = |(A + B)y^0|$$

Then

$$|A + B| \leqslant |Ay^0| + |By^0| \leqslant |A| + |B|$$

which proves (iv).

If y^1 satisfies $|y^1| = 1$ and $|AB| = |(AB)y^1|$, then

$$|AB| = |A(By^1)| \leqslant |A||By^1| \leqslant |A||B|$$

which proves (v); here we have used (vi), which is an immediate consequence of the definition. We note parenthetically that $|A|$ *is the* smallest *number* $\theta \geqslant 0$ *for which* $|Ax| \leqslant \theta|x|$ *for all* x.

To prove continuity (vii) and (viii), we make a simple observation: $n \times n$ matrices A may be regarded as vectors $(a_{11}, a_{12}, \ldots, a_{nn})$ in the space of n^2 dimensions. Conversely, every vector z with n^2 components can be written as a matrix A, where $z_1 = a_{11}, z_2 = a_{12}, \ldots, z_{n+1} = a_{21}, \ldots, z_{n^2} = a_{nn}$. Properties (ii), (iii), (iv) show that the matrix norm $|A|$ establishes a *vector* norm with properties (1), (2), (3) on the space of vectors z with n^2 components. Continuity (vii) and comparability (viii) now follow from Theorem 1.

The product inequality. In Theorem 2, which we have just proved, we would like to replace the inequality $|AB| \leqslant |A||B|$ by equality $|AB| = |A||B|$. This would be analogous to the law $|ab| = |a||b|$ which holds for the moduli of complex numbers. Unfortunately, for $n \geqslant 2$ *there is no matrix norm with the properties*

$$|A| > 0 \quad (\text{if } A \neq 0), \qquad |A| = 0 \quad (\text{if } A = 0); \qquad |AB| = |A||B| \quad (28)$$

To see this let $A = B =$ any nonzero matrix whose square is zero, e.g., the matrix with 1 in component 2, 1 and with zeros elsewhere. In two dimensions,

$$A = B = \begin{bmatrix} 0 & 0 \\ 1 & 0 \end{bmatrix}.$$

Then (28) implies $|A| > 0, |B| > 0, |AB| = |A||B| > 0$; but $|AB| = |0| = 0$, which is a contradiction.

Vector norms and convex bodies. We shall show that all norms in a real, finite-dimensional vector space are characterized as follows: Let K be a convex body (i.e., a bounded, closed, convex set) which is symmetric about the origin. By convex we mean that, if x and y lie in K, the whole line segment $(1 - \vartheta)x + \vartheta y$ $(0 < \vartheta < 1)$ lies in K. We call K a *generalized unit sphere*; it will consist of all points x for which $|x| \leqslant 1$. Let $\|z\|$ represent ordinary Euclidean distance. To

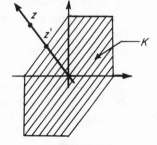

Figure 6.5

find the norm $|z|$ belonging to any vector $z \neq 0$, draw the ray from the origin through the point z, as in Figure 6.5. This ray intersects the boundary of K in a point z'. The norm of z is the ratio

$$|z| \equiv \frac{\|z\|}{\|z'\|} \tag{29}$$

Theorem 3. *Let $|x|$ be a regular vector norm. Let*

$$K = \{x \mid |x| \leqslant 1\} \tag{30}$$

Then K is a closed, bounded, convex set which is symmetric about the origin and in which the origin is an interior point. Further, if z $\neq$ 0, and z' is the boundary point of K on the ray from the origin through z, then $|z|$ is the ratio of the Euclidean lengths $\|z\|$ and $\|z'\|$.

Proof. By continuity (4), K is closed: If $x^k \longrightarrow x$, and if all $|x^k| \leqslant 1$, then $|x| \leqslant 1$. K is bounded by comparability (5): $|x| \leqslant 1$ implies $\max |x_j| \leqslant 1/\alpha$. K is convex because, if $|x| \leqslant 1$ and $|y| \leqslant 1$, then

$$|(1 - \theta)x + \theta y| \leqslant (1 - \theta)|x| + \theta|y| \leqslant 1 \qquad (0 < \theta < 1)$$

Let $z \neq 0$, and let z' be the boundary point on the ray from the origin through z. First we show $|z'| = 1$. We have $|z'| \leqslant 1$ because z' lies in the closed set K. Suppose $|z'| < 1$. Let D_ϵ be the open set of points x for which

$$\max_k |x_k - z_k'| < \epsilon$$

For all x in D_ϵ we have the norm

$$|x| = |z' + (x - z')| \leqslant |z'| + |x - z'|$$
$$\leqslant |z'| + \beta \max_k |x_k - z_k'| < |z'| + \beta\epsilon$$

If we choose $\epsilon = (1 - |z'|)/\beta$, then we have $|x| < 1$ for all x in D_ϵ. Then z' would be an *interior* point of K. This is a contradiction. Therefore, $|z'| = 1$. Since z and z' lie on the same ray, we may write $z = \lambda z'$, where $\lambda > 0$ since $z \neq 0$. By homogeneity (2) we have $|z| = |\lambda||z'| = \lambda$. But $\|z\| = \lambda\|z'\|$. Therefore, $|z| = \lambda = \|z\|/\|z'\|$. K is symmetric since $|z| = |-z|$.

The reader will observe that the Euclidean norms $\|z\|$ and $\|z'\|$ play no special role in the characterization of $|z|$. It is only the scalar $\lambda > 0$ for which $z = \lambda z'$, which is important.

Theorem 4. *Let* K *be a closed, bounded, convex set in the space of* n *dimensions. Let* x = 0 *be an interior point of* K, *and let* K *be symmetric about the origin. We define* $|\,0\,| = 0$, *and if* z $\neq$ 0, *we define* $|\,z\,|$ *by the ratio (29), where* z' *is the boundary point of* K *on the ray from the origin through* z. *Then* $|\,z\,|$ *is a regular vector norm, i.e.,* $|\,z\,|$ *has properties* (1)–(5).

Proof. By Theorem 1, we only need to demonstrate (1), (2), and (3). Properties (1) and (2) are obvious. We must prove the triangle inequality (3). If $x = 0$ or if $y = 0$, (3) is trivial. Assume $x \neq 0$ and $y \neq 0$. Write

$$x = \lambda x', \qquad y = \mu y' \quad (\text{where } \lambda > 0 \text{ and } \mu > 0) \tag{31}$$

and where x' and y' are boundary points of K. Since K is supposed to be convex, the point

$$z = \frac{\lambda x' + \mu y'}{\lambda + \mu} \tag{32}$$

lies *in* K. Therefore, if z' is the boundary point of K on the ray from the origin through z, the point z lies between the origin and z', and $\|z\| \leqslant \|z'\|$ so that

$$|z| = \frac{\|z\|}{\|z'\|} \leqslant 1 \tag{33}$$

But $|z| \leqslant 1$ states, according to (31) and (32),

$$|z| = \frac{|\lambda x' + \mu y'|}{\lambda + \mu} = \frac{|x + y|}{\lambda + \mu} \leqslant 1 \tag{34}$$

Since $\lambda \equiv |x|$ and $\mu \equiv |y|$, the last inequality says:

$$|x + y| \leqslant \lambda + \mu = |x| + |y|$$

This completes the proof.

PROBLEMS

1. Prove that the matrix norm related to $|x| = \sum |x_k|$ is
$$|A| = \max_j \sum_i |a_{ij}|$$

2. If $n = 2$, show that $|x| = 3|x_1| + 5|x_2|$ is a regular vector norm by verifying all properties (1)–(5). Draw the "unit sphere" $K = \{x \,\big|\, |x| \leqslant 1\}$.

3. What is the matrix norm related to the vector norm in the last problem?

4. If $|x|$ is the norm $(Px, x)^{1/2}$, where P is positive definite, express the related matrix norm, $|A|$, in terms of a certain generalized eigenvalue.

5. Define the matrix norm $|A| = \max|a_{ij}|$. If $|x|$ is the vector norm $|x| = \max|x_k|$, which of the properties (i)–(viii) does the norm $|A|$ *not* have?

6. Let K be a closed, bounded, convex set in which the origin is an interior point. Let $z \neq 0$. Show that the ray $\{x \,|\, x = \lambda z, \lambda > 0\}$ intersects the boundary of K in one and *only* one point z'.

7. Suppose that the earth is travelling on a simple Keplerian orbit about the sun. In what regular vector norm, analytically, is the earth travelling on the surface of the "unit sphere"?

8. Let $\rho(A)$ be the maximum of the moduli of the eigenvalues of an $n \times n$ matrix A. If $|A|$ is the matrix norm related to any regular vector norm, show that $\rho(A) \leqslant |A|$.

9. Let H and K be $n \times n$ Hermitian matrices. Define ρ as in the last problem. Prove that $\rho(H + K) \leqslant \rho(H) + \rho(K)$ by identifying ρ with some matrix norm related to a regular vector norm.

10. Let $n \geqslant 2$. Using the method of the last problem, show that there are positive numbers α and β for which

$$\alpha \max_{i,j}|h_{ij}| \leqslant \rho(H) \leqslant \beta \max_{i,j}|h_{ij}|$$

for all $n \times n$ Hermitian matrices H, where α and β are independent of H.

11. If we define

$$|A| = (\sum\sum|a_{ij}|^2)^{1/2}$$

show that $|AB| \leqslant |A||B|$, and show that $|A + B| \leqslant |A| + |B|$.

12. If $|x|$ is a regular vector norm defined on E^n, and if K is any $n \times n$ nonsingular matrix, show that $|x|' \equiv |Kx|$ is also a regular vector norm. Show that $|A|' = |KAK^{-1}|$ is the related matrix-norm.

13. Let A be a given $n \times n$ matrix, and let $\epsilon > 0$. Show that a regular vector norm can be defined on E^n for which the related matrix norm satisfies the inequality $|A| < \rho(A) + \epsilon$. (METHOD: By the result of the last problem, $|x| = \|Kx\|$ is a regular vector norm if K^{-1} exists. If A is similar to a diagonal matrix, Λ, pick K so that $KAK^{-1} = \Lambda$. If A cannot be diagonalized, let $U^*AU = R$, a right-triangular matrix. Now choose an appropriate diagonal matrix D so that DRD^{-1} is "almost" diagonal. Then let $K = UD$.)

6.10 THE CONDITION-NUMBER OF A MATRIX

Let $|x|$ be a vector-norm defined as in the preceding section. For definiteness, the reader may think of

$$|x| = \max_i|x_i| \tag{1}$$

If A is a nonsingular square matrix, we define the *condition-number*

$$\gamma(A) = \max \frac{|Au|}{|Av|} \qquad (\text{for } |u| = |v| = 1) \tag{2}$$

This number has a simple interpretation. Let the unit sphere $|x| = 1$ be mapped by the transformation $y = Ax$ into some surface S. The condition number $\gamma(A)$ is the ratio of the largest to the smallest distances from the origin to points on S. Thus, $\gamma(A) \geqslant 1$. In fact,

$$\gamma(A) \geqslant \left| \frac{\lambda_1(A)}{\lambda_n(A)} \right| \geqslant 1 \tag{3}$$

if $\lambda_1, \ldots, \lambda_n$ are the eigenvalues of A arranged so that $|\lambda_1| \geqslant \cdots \geqslant |\lambda_n|$. This follows from setting u and v equal to eigenvectors belonging to λ_1 and λ_n.

To obtain a convenient representation for $\gamma(A)$, we note from (2) that

$$\gamma(A) = \frac{\max |Au|}{\min |Av|} \qquad (\text{for } |u| = |v| = 1) \tag{4}$$

By the definition given in the preceding section, the matrix-norm $|A|$ related to the vector-norm $|x|$, is

$$|A| = \max |Au| \qquad (\text{for } |u| = 1) \tag{5}$$

For instance, the norm $|A|$ related to the maximum norm (1) was computed in Example 6 of the last section:

$$|A| = \max_i \sum_j |a_{ij}| \tag{6}$$

But what is the *minimum* of $|Av|$ for $|v| = 1$? We have

$$1 = |v| = |A^{-1}(Av)| \leqslant |A^{-1}| |Av|$$

and equality is attained for some vector (Av). Therefore,

$$|A^{-1}|^{-1} = \min |Av| \qquad (\text{for } |v| = 1) \tag{7}$$

From (5) and (7) we now obtain the expression

$$\boxed{\gamma(A) = |A^{-1}| |A|} \tag{8}$$

The condition number comes into many sorts of error analyses. Here we shall give only one example. Suppose that we are solving $Ax = b$, where the data A and b are not known exactly. What is the effect of errors δA and δb on the solution? Let

$$(A + \delta A)(x + \delta x) = b + \delta b \qquad (9)$$

Assume that A and $A + \delta A$ are nonsingular, and that $b \neq 0$. Define the error ratios

$$\alpha = \frac{|\delta A|}{|A|}, \qquad \xi = \frac{|\delta x|}{|x|}, \qquad \beta = \frac{|\delta b|}{|b|} \qquad (10)$$

We will estimate ξ as a function of α and β. Equation (9) yields

$$A\delta x + (\delta A)\delta x = \delta b - (\delta A)x \qquad (11)$$

But

$$|A\delta x + (\delta A)\delta x| \geqslant |A\delta x| - |(\delta A)\delta x|$$
$$\geqslant |A^{-1}|^{-1}|\delta x| - |\delta A||\delta x|$$

whereas

$$|\delta b - (\delta A)x| \leqslant |\delta b| + |\delta A||x|$$

Therefore,

$$|A^{-1}|^{-1}|\delta x| - |\delta A||\delta x| \leqslant |\delta b| + |\delta A||x| \qquad (12)$$

Multiplication by $|A^{-1}|$ and division by $|x|$ yield

$$\xi - |A^{-1}||\delta A|\xi \leqslant |A^{-1}|\frac{|\delta b|}{|x|} + |A^{-1}||\delta A| \qquad (13)$$

To work in the ratios α and β, we write

$$|A^{-1}||\delta A| = |A^{-1}||A|\alpha \qquad (14)$$

and (since $b = Ax$)

$$\frac{|\delta b|}{|x|} = \frac{|\delta b|}{|b|} \cdot \frac{|Ax|}{|x|} = \beta\frac{|Ax|}{|x|} \leqslant \beta|A| $$

Hence

$$|A^{-1}|\frac{|\delta b|}{|x|} \leqslant |A^{-1}||A|\beta \qquad (15)$$

Both identities (14) and (15) contain the condition-number $\gamma = |A^{-1}||A|$! Now (13) yields

$$\xi - \gamma\alpha\xi \leqslant \gamma\beta + \gamma\alpha$$

Assuming that $\gamma\alpha < 1$, we find

$$\xi \leqslant \frac{\gamma}{1 - \gamma\alpha}(\beta + \alpha)$$

or, written out,

$$\boxed{\frac{|\delta x|}{|x|} \leqslant \frac{\gamma(A)}{1 - \gamma(A)(|\delta A|/|A|)}\left(\frac{|\delta b|}{|b|} + \frac{|\delta A|}{|A|}\right)} \qquad (16)$$

PROBLEMS

1. Let

$$A = \begin{bmatrix} 1 & 2 \\ 3 & 4 \end{bmatrix}, \qquad b = \begin{bmatrix} 5 \\ 6 \end{bmatrix}$$

If all of the components of A and b are changed by increments with absolute values $\leqslant .01$, give an upper bound for the increments $|\delta x_1|$ and $|\delta x_2|$ in the components of the solution to $Ax = b$.

2. Let

$$A + \delta A = \begin{bmatrix} 1 & 2 \\ 3 & 4 \end{bmatrix}, \qquad b + \delta b = \begin{bmatrix} 5 \\ 6 \end{bmatrix}$$

Assume that $|\delta A|/|A| \leqslant .01$ and $|\delta b|/|b| \leqslant .01$. Give an upper bound for $|\delta x|/|x|$ if $Ax = b$ and $(A + \delta A)(x + \delta x) = (b + \delta b)$.

3. Let A be Hermitian and positive definite, with eigenvalues $\lambda_1 \geqslant \cdots \geqslant \lambda_n > 0$. Relative to the Euclidean norm, $|x| = (\sum |x_v|^2)^{1/2}$, what is the condition-number of A?

4. Prove that $\gamma(AB) \leqslant \gamma(A)\gamma(B)$.

5.* If $|B|/|A| = \theta < 1$, prove that

$$\gamma(A + B) \leqslant \frac{\gamma(A) + \theta}{1 - \theta}$$

6. Relative to the Euclidean norm, show that $\gamma(UA) = \gamma(AU) = \gamma(A)$ if U is any unitary matrix.

6.11   POSITIVE AND IRREDUCIBLE MATRICES

In the numerical analysis of elliptic partial differential equations,[1] in probability theory, and in physics and chemistry, we encounter matrices $A = (a_{ij})$ with all $a_{ij} \geqslant 0$. In the simplest case, all a_{ij} are positive. The basic theorem of Perron states:

[1] See, for example, R. S. Varga, *Matrix Iterative Analysis.* Englewood Cliffs, N. J.: Prentice-Hall, Inc., 1962.

Theorem 1. *Let* $A = (a_{ij})$ *be an* n × n *matrix with all* $a_{ij} > 0$. *Then* A *has a positive eigenvalue* ρ, *of multiplicity one, with* $\rho > |\lambda_i|$ *for all other eigenvalues* λ_i *of* A. *The eigenvalue* ρ *has an eigenvector* u *all of whose components are positive.*

EXAMPLE 1. If $n = 2$, we have $\det(\lambda I - A) = 0$ for $\lambda = \rho$, where

$$\rho = \tfrac{1}{2}\{a_{11} + a_{22} + [(a_{11} + a_{22})^2 - 4(a_{11}a_{22} - a_{12}a_{21})]^{1/2}\}$$
$$= \tfrac{1}{2}\{a_{11} + a_{22} + [(a_{11} - a_{22})^2 + 4a_{12}a_{21}]^{1/2}\}$$

If all $a_{ij} > 0$, this expression is real and positive.

Proof. By $x > 0$ for a vector x we shall mean that all $x_i > 0$; by $x \geqslant 0$, that all $x_i \geqslant 0$. By $A > 0$ we mean that all $a_{ij} > 0$. If $x \geqslant 0$ but $x \neq 0$, define

$$\phi(x) = \min_{x_i > 0} x_i^{-1} \sum_{j=1}^{n} a_{ij}x_j \tag{1}$$

Thus, ϕ *is the largest number such that* Ax $\geqslant \phi \cdot$x. For instance, if

$$A = \begin{bmatrix} 1 & 2 & 3 \\ 4 & 5 & 6 \\ 7 & 8 & 9 \end{bmatrix} \quad \text{and} \quad x = \begin{bmatrix} 2 \\ 0 \\ 3 \end{bmatrix}$$

then

$$x_1^{-1} \sum_{j=1}^{3} a_{1j}x_j = \frac{11}{2}, \qquad x_3^{-1} \sum_{i=1}^{3} a_{3j}x_j = \frac{41}{3}$$

Therefore, $\phi(x) = \frac{11}{2}$, and $\frac{11}{2}$ is the largest number ν such that $Ax \geqslant \nu x$.

We can consider the problem of maximizing $\phi(x)$ as a function of x. We will show that

$$\rho = \max \phi(x) \qquad (\text{for } x \geqslant 0, x \neq 0) \tag{2}$$

and that the maximum is achieved for $x =$ the eigenvector $u > 0$.

To show that max $\phi(x)$ exists, we will restrict the domain of $\phi(x)$ to a closed, bounded set C on which $\phi(x)$ is continuous. By the definition (1), we see that $\phi(x) = \phi(\mu x)$ for any scalar $\mu > 0$. Therefore, $\phi(x) = \phi(y)$ for the vector $y = \mu x$ such that $\sum y_i = 1$. Since the definition (1) appears to give trouble for small x_i, we will make a further restriction. Since

$$Ay \geqslant \phi y \qquad [\text{where } \phi = \phi(x) = \phi(y)]$$

we find, multiplying the inequality by $A > 0$, that

$$Az \geqslant \phi(x)z \qquad (\text{if } z = Ay)$$

Thus, for any nonzero $x \geqslant 0$, we have

$$\phi(x) \leqslant \phi(z)$$

where z lies in the set

$$C = \{z \,|\, z = Ay, \quad y \geqslant 0, \quad \Sigma\, y_i = 1\} \tag{3}$$

The set C is closed and bounded because it is a continuous map, $z = Ay$, of the closed, bounded set of vectors y for which $y \geqslant 0$ and $\Sigma\, y_i = 1$. The components z_i are bounded away from zero:

$$z_i = \sum_{j=1}^{n} a_{ij} y_j \geqslant \min a_{ij} > 0$$

Therefore, the maximum exists:

$$\rho = \max_{\substack{x \geqslant 0 \\ x \neq 0}} \phi(x) = \max_{z \in C} \phi(z) \tag{4}$$

Let the maximum ρ be attained for $z = u \in C$. Then, since $\rho = \phi(u)$,

$$Au \geqslant \rho u \tag{5}$$

If $Au \neq \rho u$, then the difference $Au - \rho u \geqslant 0$ has at least one positive component. Therefore, since *every* component of A is positive,

$$A(Au - \rho u) > 0$$

In other words,

$$Av > \rho v \qquad \text{if } v = Au > 0$$

This inequality shows that ρ is not the greatest number $\phi = \phi(v)$ such that $Av \geqslant \phi v$. Therefore, $\rho < \phi(v)$, and $\rho < \max \phi(x)$. This contradiction shows that (5) should read

$$Au = \rho u \tag{6}$$

The number $\rho > 0$ is, therefore, an eigenvalue of A. For any other real or complex eigenvalue λ we have $\lambda c = Ac$, with $c \neq 0$, and

$$|\lambda|\,|c_i| = |\sum_j a_{ij} c_j| \leqslant \sum_j a_{ij}\,|c_j| \qquad (i = 1, \ldots, n) \tag{7}$$

In other words, $|\lambda|\,x \leqslant Ax$ if x is the vector with components $x_j = |c_j| \geqslant 0$. Therefore,

$$|\lambda| \leqslant \phi(x) \leqslant \rho$$

If for any index i in (7) we have the strict inequality

$$|\lambda|\,x_i < \sum_j a_{ij}x_j$$

then $Ax - |\lambda|\,x \geqslant 0$, but multiplication by $A > 0$ yields

$$Ay - |\lambda|\,y > 0 \qquad (\text{if } y = Ax)$$

Then $|\lambda| < \phi(y) \leqslant \rho$. Therefore, $|\lambda| = \rho$ only if equality holds for all i in (7). Since all a_{ij} are positive,

$$\left|\sum_j a_{ij}c_j\right| = \sum_j a_{ij}|c_j|$$

only if the complex components c_j have the same argument:

$$c_j = |c_j|\,e^{i\theta} \qquad (j = 1, \ldots, n)$$

where θ is independent of j. Then $\lambda c = Ac$ implies

$$\lambda\,|c_i| = \sum_j a_{ij}|c_j| \qquad (i = 1, \ldots, n)$$

Division by any $|c_i| \neq 0$ yields $\lambda > 0$, and therefore $\lambda = \rho$. Therefore, if $\lambda \neq \rho$, and if λ is an eigenvalue of A, $|\lambda| < \rho$.

It remains only to show that the eigenvalue ρ is not a multiple eigenvalue. If $\Delta(\lambda) = \det(\lambda I - A)$, we must prove that the derivative $\Delta'(\rho) \neq 0$. Since ρ is the largest root of $\Delta(\lambda) = 0$, the derivative $\Delta'(\lambda)$ is positive for $\lambda > \rho$. We will show that $\Delta'(\rho) > 0$.

Differentiation of the characteristic determinant gives

$$\Delta'(\rho) = \sum_{k=1}^{n} \Delta_k(\rho) \tag{8}$$

where $\Delta_k(\lambda)$ is the characteristic determinant of the matrix A_k formed by deleting row k and column k from A. For example,

$$\frac{d}{d\lambda}\begin{vmatrix} \lambda - a_{11} & -a_{12} & -a_{13} \\ -a_{21} & \lambda - a_{22} & -a_{23} \\ -a_{31} & -a_{32} & \lambda - a_{33} \end{vmatrix} = \begin{vmatrix} \lambda - a_{22}, & -a_{23} \\ -a_{32}, & \lambda - a_{33} \end{vmatrix} + \cdots$$

$$= \Delta_1(\lambda) + \Delta_2(\lambda) + \Delta_3(\lambda)$$

The identity (8) was proved in Section 1.8.

We will prove all $\Delta_k(\rho) > 0$. Consider $\Delta_1(\lambda) = \det(\lambda I - A_1)$. The matrix A_1 has positive components. By what we have already shown, A_1 has a positive eigenvalue ρ_1 of maximum modulus, and there is a positive eigenvector u^1. Let the $n-1$ components of u^1 be called $u_2, u_3, \ldots, u_n$.

The equation $A_1 u^1 = \rho_1 u^1$ states

$$\sum_{j=2}^{n} a_{ij} u_j = \rho_1 u_i \qquad (i = 2, \ldots, n) \tag{9}$$

Define the n-component vector x by setting $x_1 = 0$ and $x_i = u_i$ for $i \geqslant 2$. Then

$$\sum_{j=1}^{n} a_{ij} x_j \geqslant \rho_1 x_i \qquad (i = 1, 2, \ldots, n) \tag{10}$$

with $>$ for $i = 1$, and with $=$ for $i \geqslant 2$. Since

$$Ax - \rho_1 x \geqslant 0 \quad \text{but} \quad Ax - \rho_1 x \neq 0 \tag{11}$$

multiplication of (11) by $A > 0$ gives

$$Av > \rho_1 v \qquad (\text{if } v = Ax > 0) \tag{12}$$

This inequality shows that $\rho_1 < \phi(v)$. Since $\phi(v) \leqslant \rho$ for all $v > 0$, we conclude that $\rho_1 < \rho$. Since ρ_1 is the greatest positive root of $\Delta_1(\lambda) = 0$, we have $\Delta_1(\rho) > 0$. Similarly, $\Delta_k(\rho) > 0$ for $k > 1$. Therefore, $\Delta'(\rho) = \sum \Delta_k(\rho) > 0$, and we conclude that ρ has multiplicity one as an eigenvalue of A.

Irreducible matrices. Suppose that we do not have all $a_{ij} > 0$, but only $a_{ij} \geqslant 0$. Under a certain natural assumption, there is still a positive eigenvalue of maximum modulus.

We shall say that the $n \times n$ matrix A is *irreducible* if, for all pairs of indices $p \neq q$, either $a_{pq} \neq 0$ or there is some set of indices $i_1, \ldots, i_r$ such that

$$a_{p i_1} \neq 0, \qquad a_{i_1 i_2} \neq 0, \ldots, a_{i_{r-1}, i_r} \neq 0, \qquad a_{i_r q} \neq 0$$

where the indices $p, i_1, \ldots, i_r, q$ are all different. (Thus, $r \leqslant n - 2$). For example, if a_{ij}^{-1} is the resistance between two nodes, i and j, in an electrical network, the matrix A is irreducible if there is a chain of resistors connecting every pair of nodes, p and q. If A is not irreducible, the corresponding resistance network consists of two or more unconnected parts.

EXAMPLE 2. The matrix

$$A = \begin{bmatrix} 0 & 1 & 0 & 0 \\ 0 & 0 & 1 & 0 \\ 0 & 0 & 0 & 1 \\ 1 & 0 & 0 & 0 \end{bmatrix}$$

is irreducible, and $A \geqslant 0$. The eigenvalues of A are $1, i, -1, -i$. There is a positive eigenvalue of maximum modulus, but the positive eigenvalue is not the only eigenvalue of maximum modulus.

Theorem 2. *Let* A *be an* n × n *irreducible matrix with all* $a_{ij} \geqslant 0$. *If* $\lambda_1, \ldots, \lambda_n$ *are the eigenvalues of* A, *let* $\rho = \max |\lambda_v|$. *Then* ρ *is an eigenvalue of* A. *The eigenvalue* ρ *has multiplicity one, and there is associated with* ρ *an eigenvector* u *all of whose components are positive.*

Proof. First we will prove that

$$(I + A)^{n-1} > 0 \tag{13}$$

Consider the matrices $A, A^2, \ldots, A^{n-1}$. Let $p \neq q$. The matrix A has a component a_{pq}. The matrix A^2 has a component $\sum_{(i)} a_{pi} a_{iq}$, which is positive if any single term $a_{pi} a_{iq}$ is positive. The matrix A^{r+1} has a component

$$\sum_{i_1, \ldots, i_r} a_{p i_1} a_{i_1 i_2} \cdots a_{i_{r-1} i_r} a_{i_r q}$$

which is positive if any of its terms are positive. But the hypotheses of non-negativity and of irreducibility imply that at least one of the terms

$$a_{pq}, a_{p i_1} \cdots a_{i_r q} \qquad (r \leqslant n - 2)$$

is positive. Therefore, the p, q-component of the sum

$$\sum_{v=0}^{n-1} \binom{n-1}{v} A^v \tag{14}$$

is positive. (In fact, the p, q-component of any sum $\sum \alpha_v A^v$ with positive coefficients, would be positive.) The diagonal terms of the sum (14) are also positive because the first term in the sum is I. Since the sum (14) equals $(I + A)^{n-1}$, the assertion (13) is proved.

If $x \geqslant 0$ but $x \neq 0$, we again define

$$\phi(x) = \min_{x_i > 0} x_i^{-1} \sum_{j=1}^{n} a_{ij} x_j \tag{15}$$

The number $\phi(x)$ is the largest positive number ϕ such that $Ax \geqslant \phi \cdot x$. We will show that $\phi(x)$ attains a maximum value. If $x \geqslant 0$ and $x \neq 0$, define $y = x / \sum x_i$. By the homogeneity of the expression $\phi(x)$, we have $\phi(x) = \phi(y)$. As x ranges over all non-negative, nonzero vectors, y ranges over the bounded, closed set

$$C_1 = \{y \mid \text{all } y_i \geqslant 0 \quad \text{and} \quad \sum y_i = 1\}$$

It is not clear that $\phi(y)$ is continuous on C_1, since the factor y_i^{-1} may become infinite in the expression $y_i^{-1} \sum a_{ij}y_j$. We bypass this difficulty by defining the closed, bounded set of *positive* vectors

$$C = \{z \mid z = (I + A)^{n-1}y, \qquad y \text{ in } C_1\}$$

All components z_i of a vector z in C are bounded away from zero. In fact, if α is the smallest component of the positive matrix $(I + A)^{n-1}$, we have all $z_i \geqslant \alpha > 0$. For every y in C_1, we have

$$Ay \geqslant \phi(y)y \tag{16}$$

Multiplying the inequality (16) by the positive matrix $(I + A)^{n-1}$, we find

$$Az \geqslant \phi(y)z \qquad [\text{if } z = (I + A)^{n-1}y] \tag{17}$$

Since $\phi(z)$ is the greatest number ϕ such that $Az \geqslant \phi \cdot z$, the inequality (17) implies that $\phi(z) \geqslant \phi(y)$.

For any vector $x \geqslant 0$, with $x \neq 0$, we set up the correspondence $x \longrightarrow y \longrightarrow z$. Then

$$\phi(x) = \phi(y) \leqslant \phi(z) \tag{18}$$

But the function $\phi(z)$ is *continuous* on the closed, bounded set of positive vectors, C. Therefore, we have the existence of the maximum value of $\phi(z)$ for all z in C. If the maximum is attained for $z = u$, the relation (18) implies

$$\max_{\substack{x \geqslant 0 \\ x \neq 0}} \phi(x) = \phi(u) \tag{19}$$

We will show that $\phi(u)$ is an eigenvalue of A, and that u is an eigenvector. We have

$$(A - \phi(u)I)u \geqslant 0 \tag{20}$$

Unless equality holds in (20), multiplication by $(I + A)^{n-1}$ yields

$$(A - \phi(u)I)v > 0 \qquad [\text{if } v = (I + A)^{n-1}u] \tag{21}$$

But $Av > \phi(u)v$ implies $\phi(u) < \phi(v)$, which contradicts the maximum property (19). Therefore, equality holds in (20).

$$Au = \phi(u)u \tag{22}$$

If λ is any other eigenvalue of A, let $c \neq 0$, and

$$\lambda c_i = \sum_{j=1}^{n} a_{ij}c_j \qquad (i = 1, \ldots, n)$$

Then

$$|\lambda||c_i| = |\sum_{j=1}^{n} a_{ij}c_j| \leqslant \sum_{j=1}^{n} a_{ij}|c_j| \qquad (23)$$

Since some a_{ij} may be zero, we cannot conclude that equality in (23) holds *only* if all c_j have the same argument. But we do have

$$|\lambda| \leqslant \min_{x_i>0} x_i^{-1} \sum_{j=1}^{n} a_{ij}x_j \equiv \phi(x) \qquad (\text{if } x_j = |c_j|)$$

Therefore,

$$|\lambda| \leqslant \max \phi(x) = \phi(u)$$

Thus, $\phi(u) = \rho \equiv \max|\lambda_v(A)|$.

We have proved that ρ is an eigenvalue of A, and it remains only to show that ρ is a *simple* eigenvalue. If $\rho = \lambda_1, \lambda_2, \ldots, \lambda_n$ are the eigenvalues of A, then the eigenvalues of the *positive* matrix $(I + A)^{n-1}$ are

$$(1 + \rho)^{n-1}, (1 + \lambda_2)^{n-1}, \ldots, (1 + \lambda_n)^{n-1}$$

But

$$(1 + \rho)^{n-1} \geqslant |(1 + \lambda_v)^{n-1}| \qquad (v = 2, \ldots, n)$$

Theorem 1, applied to the positive matrix $(I + A)^{n-1}$, implies that $(1 + \rho)^{n-1}$ is a simple eigenvalue of $(I + A)^{n-1}$. Therefore, ρ is a simple eigenvalue of A, and the proof is complete.

PROBLEMS

1. Let $c_1, \ldots, c_n$ be complex numbers. Let $a_{i1}, \ldots, a_{in}$ be positive. Prove that

$$|\sum_j a_{ij}c_j| = \sum_j a_{ij}|c_j|$$

only if, for some argument θ independent of j,

$$c_j = |c_j|e^{i\theta} \qquad (j = 1, \ldots, n)$$

2. Let

$$A = (a_{ij}), \qquad A^+ = (|a_{ij}|) \qquad (i, j = 1, \ldots, n).$$

Let $\rho(A)$ be the maximum of the absolute values of the eigenvalues of A, and let $\rho(A^+)$ be defined similarly for A^+. Prove that $\rho(A) \leqslant \rho(A^+)$.

3. Let

$$A = \begin{bmatrix} 0 & 1 & 2 \\ 1 & 3 & 4 \\ 2 & 4 & 5 \end{bmatrix}, \qquad x = \begin{bmatrix} 1 \\ 2 \\ 3 \end{bmatrix}$$

Using x, find a lower bound for $\rho(A)$.

4.* Let $A > 0$. For any $x \geqslant 0$, with $x \neq 0$, define

$$\psi(x) = \max_{x_i > 0} x_i^{-1} \sum_{j=1}^{n} a_{ij}x_j$$

Prove that the minimum value of $\psi(x)$ exists and equals $\rho(A)$.

5. Using Theorem 1 and the result of Problem 4, show that, if $A > 0$,

$$\min_{x_i > 0} x_i^{-1} \sum_{j=1}^{n} a_{ij}x_j \leqslant \rho(A) \leqslant \max_{x_i > 0} x_i^{-1} \sum_{j=1}^{n} a_{ij}x_j$$

for all nonzero $x \geqslant 0$. Apply this result to obtain a two-sided inequality for $\rho(A)$ in Problem 3.

6.* Let A be an irreducible $n \times n$ matrix for which

$$|a_{ii}| \geqslant \sum_{\substack{j=1 \\ j \neq i}}^{n} |a_{ij}| \qquad (i = 1, \ldots, n)$$

Prove that $\det A \neq 0$ if the $>$ sign holds for at least one i.

7. Prove that the $n \times n$ matrix A is reducible, i.e., not irreducible, if and only if there is a proper subset S of the integers $1, \ldots, n$ such that every system of equations $Ax = b$ contains the smaller system of equations

$$\sum_{q \in S} a_{pq}x_q = b_p \qquad (p \in S)$$

For example, if A is the reducible matrix

$$A = \begin{bmatrix} -7 & 0 & 3 \\ 2 & 1 & 9 \\ -4 & 0 & 6 \end{bmatrix}$$

every system $Ax = b$ contains the smaller system

$$-7x_1 + 3x_3 = b_1$$
$$-4x_1 + 6x_3 = b_3$$

In this example, $S = \{1, 3\}$.

8. A permutation matrix P is a matrix such that $Px = y$ rearranges the components of x. Thus, the rearrangement $y_1 = x_2$, $y_2 = x_3$, $y_3 = x_1$ is accomplished by

$$Px = \begin{bmatrix} 0 & 1 & 0 \\ 0 & 0 & 1 \\ 1 & 0 & 0 \end{bmatrix} \begin{bmatrix} x_1 \\ x_2 \\ x_3 \end{bmatrix} = \begin{bmatrix} y_1 \\ y_2 \\ y_3 \end{bmatrix} = y$$

A permutation matrix is unitary; its columns consist of a rearrangement of the columns of the identity matrix. Using the result of Problem 7, show that an $n \times n$ matrix A is reducible if and only if there is a permutation matrix P such that PAP^T has the form

$$PAP^T = \left[\begin{array}{c|c} B & 0 \\ \hline C & D \end{array} \right]$$

where B is an $m \times m$ matrix with $1 \leqslant m \leqslant n - 1$. What is the matrix P for the example in Problem 7?

9. Let A be a Markov matrix: The component $a_{ij} > 0$ represents the probability of transition from state i to state j. Thus, $\sum_{(j)} a_{ij} = 1$ for all i. Prove that A has the eigenvalue $\lambda_1 = 1$ with multiplicity one, and that $|\lambda_v| < 1$ for all other eigenvalues of A. Deduce the same conclusions for A^T. Prove that there is a row-vector $u^T > 0$, with $\sum u_i = 1$, for which $u^T A = u^T$.

10.* In the notation of Problem 9, let $x_1 \geqslant 0, \ldots, x_n \geqslant 0$ and let $\sum x_i = 1$. (The component x_i represents the initial probability of state i). Prove that

$$(x_1, \ldots, x_n) A^k \longrightarrow (u_1, \ldots, u_n) \qquad (\text{as } k \longrightarrow \infty)$$

[Develop $x = \text{col} (x_1, \ldots, x_n)$ in principal vectors of A^T. The number u_i gives the probability of state i after infinitely many transitions.]

11.* In Problem 2, show that $\rho(A) = \rho(A^+)$ if and only if the components $a_{\mu\nu}$ have the form

$$a_{\mu\nu} = e^{i(\theta_\mu - \theta_\nu)} |a_{\mu\nu}| \qquad (\mu, \nu = 1, \ldots, n)$$

6.12 PERTURBATIONS OF THE SPECTRUM

Let A be an $n \times n$ matrix with eigenvalues $\lambda_1, \ldots, \lambda_n$ and with corresponding eigenvectors $u^1, \ldots, u^n$. A small change δA in the matrix produces changes $\delta\lambda_i$ in the eigenvalues and changes δu^i in the eigenvectors. The purpose of this section is to show approximately how the eigenvalues and the eigenvectors change as the matrix changes. We shall treat only the easiest case, in which the eigenvalues λ_i are distinct.

According to Section 4.1, the eigenvectors u^j are linearly independent and are unique, except for nonzero scalar multiples αu^j. We have $Au^j = \lambda_j u^j$ and

$$(A + \delta A)(u^j + \delta u^j) = (\lambda_j + \delta\lambda_j)(u^j + \delta u^j) \tag{1}$$

In this equation we consider

$$A, \delta A, u^j, \lambda_j \text{ known;} \qquad \delta u^j, \delta\lambda_j \text{ unknown} \tag{2}$$

We must be careful how we define δu^j. If $\delta A = 0$, then $\delta \lambda_j = 0$ ($j = 1$, $\ldots, n$); but the perturbation equation (1) is satisfied by any δu^j which is a multiple of u^j. To insure $\delta u^j = 0$ if $\delta A = 0$, we shall normalize the perturbed eigenvector by the assumption that, in the expansion

$$u^j + \delta u^j = \sum_{k=1}^{n} (\ \ )u^k$$

the coefficient ( ) of u^j remains equal to 1 when A is replaced by $A + \delta A$. In other words, we shall require expansions

$$\delta u^j = \sum_{k=1}^{n} \epsilon_{jk} u^k \qquad (\text{with } \epsilon_{kk} = 0) \tag{3}$$

The unknowns are now $\delta \lambda_j$ and the coefficients ϵ_{jk} for $j \neq k$.

If the components of the matrix δA are very small, equation (1) becomes, to first order,

$$Au^j + A\delta u^j + (\delta A)u^j = \lambda_j u^j + \lambda_j \delta u^j + (\delta \lambda_j)u^j \tag{4}$$

where the neglected terms, $(\delta A)\ \delta u^j$ and $(\delta \lambda_j)\ \delta u^j$ are of second order. Since $Au^j = \lambda_j u^j$, equation (4) yields

$$A\delta u^j + (\delta A)u^j = \lambda_j \delta u^j + (\delta \lambda_j)u^j \tag{5}$$

To compute the unknowns δu^j and $\delta \lambda_j$ we will use the *principle of biorthogonality*:

Let $u^1, \ldots, u^n$ be eigenvectors corresponding to the eigenvalues $\lambda_1, \ldots, \lambda_n$ of an $n \times n$ matrix A. Assume $\lambda_i \neq \lambda_j$ for $i \neq j$. Let $v^1, \ldots, v^n$ be eigenvectors corresponding to the eigenvalues $\bar{\lambda}_1, \ldots, \bar{\lambda}_n$ of A^*. Then

$$(u^i, v^i) \neq 0, \qquad (u^i, v^j) = 0 \quad (\text{for } i \neq j) \tag{6}$$

This generalizes the orthogonality which holds for the eigenvectors $u^i = v^i$ of Hermitian matrices $A = A^*$. To prove (6), we first observe that

$$\det (\bar{\lambda}_i I - A^*) = \det (\bar{\lambda}_i I - \overline{A^T})$$

But this is the complex conjugate of

$$\det (\lambda_i I - A^T) = \det (\lambda_i I - A)^T = \det (\lambda_i I - A) = 0$$

Thus, A^* does have the n distinct eigenvalues $\bar{\lambda}_1, \ldots, \bar{\lambda}_n$.

For $i \neq j$ we write

$$Au^i = \lambda_i u^i; \qquad A^*v^j = \bar{\lambda}_j v^j$$

Taking inner products, we find

$$(Au^i, v^j) = (\lambda_i u^i, v^j); \qquad (u^i, A^*v^j) = (u^i, \bar{\lambda}_j v^j)$$

Since $(Au, v) = (u, A^*v)$ for all u and v, we have

$$(\lambda_i u^i, v^j) = (u^i, \bar{\lambda}_j v^j)$$

or

$$\lambda_i(u^i, v^j) = \lambda_j(u^i, v^j)$$

Since $\lambda_i \neq \lambda_j$, we conclude that $(u^i, v^j) = 0$.

The inequality $(u^i, v^i) \neq 0$ now follows because, if u^i were orthogonal to *all* the v's, then a representation $u^i = \sum(\quad)v^k$ would yield $(u^i, u^i) = 0$, and hence $u^i = 0$.

To solve equation (5) for $\delta\lambda_j$ and δu^j, we will use the eigenvectors v^1, $\ldots, v^n$ of A^*. By the normalization (3), the perturbation δu^j is a combination of u^k for $k \neq j$. Therefore, $(\delta u^j, v^j) = 0$. Now (5) yields

$$(A\delta u^j, v^j) + [(\delta A)u^j, v^j] = 0 + (\delta\lambda_j)(u^j, v^j) \tag{7}$$

But

$$(A\delta u^j, v^j) = (\delta u^j, A^*v^j) = (\delta u^j, \bar{\lambda}_j v^j) = 0$$

Therefore, since $(u^j, v^j) \neq 0$,

$$\boxed{\delta\lambda_j = \frac{((\delta A)u^j, v^j)}{(u^j, v^j)}} \qquad (j = 1, \ldots, n) \tag{8}$$

To find δu^j take the inner product of equation (5) with v^k for $k \neq j$:

$$(A\delta u^j, v^k) + [(\delta A)u^j, v^k] = \lambda_j(\delta u^j, v^k) + 0$$

Since $(A\delta u^j, v^k) = (\delta u^j, A^*v^k) = (\delta u^j, \bar{\lambda}_k v^k) = \lambda_k(\delta u^j, v^k)$,

$$\lambda_k(\delta u^j, v^k) + [(\delta A)u^j, v^k] = \lambda_j(\delta u^j, v^k) \tag{9}$$

But the normalization (3) gives

$$(\delta u^j, v^k) = \epsilon_{jk}(u^k, v^k) \tag{10}$$

Equations (9) and (10) now give the required coefficients

$$\boxed{\epsilon_{jk} = \frac{((\delta A)u^j, v^k)}{(\lambda_j - \lambda_k)(u^k, v^k)}} \qquad (j \neq k) \tag{11}$$

EXAMPLE. Let $A = \text{diag}(\lambda_1, \ldots, \lambda_n)$, where $\lambda_i \neq \lambda_j$ for $i \neq j$. Let $(\delta A) = \epsilon B$, where $B = (b_{ij})$ and ϵ is a small parameter. In this case, we may take

$$u^j = v^j = e^j = \text{col}(0, \ldots, 1, \ldots, 0)$$

for the eigenvectors of A and of A^*. Formula (8) now yields

$$\delta \lambda_j = (\epsilon B e^j, e^j) = \epsilon b_{jj}$$

Formula (11) gives

$$\epsilon_{jk} = \frac{(\epsilon B e^j, e^k)}{\lambda_j - \lambda_k} = \frac{\epsilon b_{kj}}{\lambda_j - \lambda_k} \qquad (j \neq k)$$

Now (3) gives

$$\delta u^j = \epsilon \sum_{\substack{k=1 \\ k \neq j}}^{n} b_{kj}(\lambda_j - \lambda_k)^{-1} e^k$$

In other words, δu^j is the vector whose jth component is 0 and whose kth component $(k \neq j)$ is $\epsilon b_{kj}/(\lambda_j - \lambda_k)$.

PROBLEMS

1. Verify the principle of biorthogonality for the matrix

$$A = \begin{bmatrix} 1 & 2 \\ 3 & 4 \end{bmatrix}$$

2. Let A be defined as in Problem 1. If

$$A + \delta A = \begin{bmatrix} 1.001, & 1.999 \\ 3.002, & 3.999 \end{bmatrix}$$

compute the variations $\delta \lambda_1$, $\delta \lambda_2$, δu^1, δu^2.

3* Let A_0 be an $n \times n$ matrix with distinct eigenvalues $\lambda_{10}, \ldots, \lambda_{n0}$ and corresponding eigenvectors $u^{10}, \ldots, u^{n0}$. Let $v^{10}, \ldots, v^{n0}$ be eigenvectors corresponding to the eigenvalues $\bar{\lambda}_{10}, \ldots, \bar{\lambda}_{n0}$ of A_0^*. For small $|\epsilon|$ let

$$A = A_0 + \epsilon A_1 + \epsilon^2 A_2 + \cdots$$

For $j = 1, \ldots, n$, let A have the eigenvalues and eigenvectors

$$\lambda_j = \lambda_{j0} + \epsilon \lambda_{j1} + \epsilon^2 \lambda_{j2} + \cdots$$
$$u^j = u^{j0} + \epsilon u^{j1} + \epsilon^2 u^{j2} + \cdots$$

Normalize u^j by the requirement

$$(u^{jk}, v^{j0}) = 0 \qquad (\text{for } k \geqslant 1)$$

Devise a recursive scheme for computing the quantities

$$\lambda_{j1}, u^{j1}; \lambda_{j2}, u^{j2}; \lambda_{j3}, u^{j3}; \ldots$$

4. For small $|\epsilon|$ let

$$A = \begin{bmatrix} 1 & 1 \\ \epsilon & 1 \end{bmatrix}$$

Does A have an eigenvalue which can be developed in a convergent power series of the form

$$\lambda_1 = 1 + \epsilon\lambda_{11} + \epsilon^2\lambda_{12} + \epsilon^3\lambda_{13} + \cdots$$

5.* Let $A(\epsilon)$ be an $n \times n$ matrix whose components are analytic functions of ϵ in the neighborhood of $\epsilon = 0$. Let $A(0)$ have distinct eigenvalues $\lambda_{10}, \ldots, \lambda_{n0}$. Let

$$\phi(\lambda, \epsilon) = \det [\lambda I - A(\epsilon)]$$

If

$$\phi(\lambda, \epsilon) = \lambda^n + c_1(\epsilon)\lambda^{n-1} + c_2(\epsilon)^{n-2} + \cdots + c_n(\epsilon)$$

are the coefficients $c_1(\epsilon), \ldots, c_n(\epsilon)$ analytic functions of ϵ? Using Cauchy-integral representations

$$\lambda_j(\epsilon) = \frac{1}{2\pi i} \int_{|\lambda - \lambda_{j0}|=\delta} \lambda\phi'(\lambda, \epsilon)[\phi(\lambda, \epsilon)]^{-1} \, d\lambda$$

show that $A(\epsilon)$ has distinct eigenvalues which are analytic functions of ϵ in the neighborhood of $\epsilon = 0$.

6.* Using the assumptions in Problem 5, show that the function $\lambda_j(\epsilon)$ is the solution of the analytic differential equation

$$\frac{d\lambda}{d\epsilon} = -\frac{c_1'(\epsilon)\lambda^{n-1} + c_2'(\epsilon)\lambda^{n-2} + \cdots + c_n'(\epsilon)}{n\lambda^{n-1} + (n-1)c_1(\epsilon)\lambda^{n-2} + \cdots + c_{n-1}(\epsilon)}$$

which satisfies the initial condition $\lambda(0) = \lambda_{j0}$.

7.* Let $A(\epsilon)$ be an $n \times n$ matrix whose components are analytic functions of ϵ. For $\epsilon = 0$ let A have the simple eigenvalue λ_0, and let

$$A(0)u^0 = \lambda_0 u^0, \qquad A(0)v^0 = \bar{\lambda}_0 v^0 \quad (u^0 \neq 0, \, v^0 \neq 0)$$

For ϵ in the neighborhood of zero, let $\lambda(\epsilon)$ be a simple eigenvalue of A, where $\lambda(\epsilon)$ is analytic and $\lambda(0) = \lambda_0$. For ϵ near zero show that the equations

$$A(\epsilon)u(\epsilon) = \lambda(\epsilon)u(\epsilon); \qquad [v^0, u(\epsilon)] = (v^0, u^0)$$

determine a *unique* vector $u(\epsilon)$ with *analytic* components, and with $u(0) = u^0$. {Show that rank $[A(\epsilon) - \lambda(\epsilon)I] = n - 1$, and show that the row-vector $(v^0)^*$ is *not* a linear combination of the rows of $A(\epsilon) - \lambda(\epsilon)I$. Hence, show that $u(\epsilon)$ is the solution of an equation $B(\epsilon)u(\epsilon) = c$, where $B(\epsilon)$ is an $n \times n$ nonsingular matrix formed from $n - 1$ rows of $A(\epsilon) - \lambda(\epsilon)I$ and the row $(v^0)^*$}.

6.13 CONTINUOUS DEPENDENCE OF EIGENVALUES ON MATRICES

A frequently used but seldom proved fact in matrix theory is that the eigenvalues $\lambda_1, \ldots, \lambda_n$ of a matrix $B = (b_{ij})$ depend continuously on the coefficients $b_{11}, b_{12}, \ldots, b_{nn}$.

Theorem 1. *Let* $\mu_1, \ldots, \mu_s$ *be the different eigenvalues of an* $n \times n$ *matrix* $A = (a_{ij})$. *Let the eigenvalue* μ_j *have multiplicity* m_j, *where* $\sum m_j = n$. *Then for all sufficiently small* $\epsilon > 0$ *there is a number* $\delta = \delta(\epsilon) > 0$ *such that, if* $|b_{ij} - a_{ij}| \leqslant \delta$ *for* $i, j = 1, \ldots, n$, *then the matrix* $B = (b_{ij})$ *has exactly* m_j *eigenvalues in the circle* $|\lambda - \mu_j| < \epsilon$ *for each* $j = 1, \ldots, s$.

EXAMPLE 1. Let $n = 8$. Suppose $s = 4$, $m_1 = 3$, $m_2 = 2$, $m_3 = 2$, $m_4 = 1$. In other words, an 8×8 matrix A has the different eigenvalues $\mu_1, \mu_2, \mu_3, \mu_4$ with multiplicities 3, 2, 2, 1. Draw the four circles of radius $\epsilon > 0$ about the roots μ_i, as in Figure 6.6. The theorem states that, if ϵ is less than some critical value $\epsilon_0 > 0$, then there is a number $\delta > 0$ such that, if $|b_{ij} - a_{ij}| < \delta$ $(i, j = 1, \ldots, 8)$, then B has three eigen-

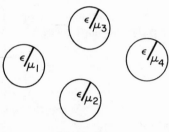

Figure 6.6

values in the first circle (counted by their multiplicities), two eigenvalues in the second circle, two in the third, and one in the last.

Proof of the Theorem. The proof uses the theory of functions of a complex variable. Let B be a variable $n \times n$ matrix. Define

$$\phi(\lambda, B) = \det(\lambda I - B) \tag{1}$$

Let

$$\epsilon_0 = \tfrac{1}{2} \min |\mu_i - \mu_j| \qquad (\text{for } 1 \leqslant i < j \leqslant s) \tag{2}$$

Choose any positive $\epsilon < \epsilon_0$. Then the circles

$$C_j: |\lambda - \mu_j| = \epsilon \qquad (j = 1, \ldots, s) \tag{3}$$

are nonintersecting. Define

$$\rho_j = \min |\phi(\lambda, A)| \qquad (\text{for } \lambda \text{ on } C_j) \tag{4}$$

All ρ_j are positive because the roots of $\phi(\lambda, A) = 0$ are the centers of the circles. The minima (4) are defined because $\phi(\lambda, A)$ depends continuously on λ.

Because the determinant $\phi(\lambda, B)$ depends continuously on all $1 + n^2$ variables $\lambda, b_{11}, \ldots, b_{nn}$, there is some $\delta > 0$ such that

$$\phi(\lambda, B) \neq 0 \qquad [\text{for } \lambda \text{ on any } C_j \ (j = 1, \ldots, s)] \tag{5}$$

if $|b_{ij} - a_{ij}| \leqslant \delta$ for all $i, j = 1, \ldots, n$. Now consider the integral

$$n_j(B) = \frac{1}{2\pi i} \int_{C_j} \frac{\phi'(\lambda, B)}{\phi(\lambda, B)} \, d\lambda \tag{6}$$

This is the integral which counts the number n_j of roots λ of the equation $\phi(\lambda, B) = 0$ which lie inside the circle C_j. For instance, we are given that

$$n_j(A) = m_j \qquad (j = 1, \ldots, s) \tag{7}$$

By (5) the integrand in (6) is a continuous function of $\lambda, b_{11}, \ldots, b_{nn}$ in the closed set

$$|\lambda - \mu_j| = \epsilon, \qquad |b_{ij} - a_{ij}| \leqslant \delta \quad (i, j = 1, \ldots, n) \tag{8}$$

Therefore, the integral $n_j(B)$ is a continuous function of the b_{ij} satisfying $|b_{ij} - a_{ij}| \leqslant \delta$. Since the integral cannot jump continuously from one integer to another, we must have

$$n_j(B) = n_j(A) = m_j \qquad (j = 1, \ldots, s) \tag{9}$$

for all matrices B with $|b_{ij} - a_{ij}| \leqslant \delta$ $(i, j = 1, \ldots, n)$. This completes the proof.

The reader will recognize that this is not really a theorem about matrices, but about polynomials. Since the coefficients of the characteristic polynomial $\phi(\lambda, B)$ depend continuously on the variables $b_{11}, \ldots, b_{nn}$, it was only necessary to prove that the roots of a polynomial depend continuously on the coefficients of the polynomial.

PROBLEMS

1. By a trivial modification of the preceding proof, show that the roots of the equation $\lambda^n + c_1\lambda^{n-1} + \cdots + c_{n-1}\lambda + c_n = 0$ depend continuously on the complex variables $c_1, \ldots c_n$.

2. Let an $n \times n$ matrix A have distinct eigenvalues $\lambda_1, \ldots, \lambda_n$. Let B be a matrix whose coefficients $b_{ij}(\epsilon)$ are analytic functions of ϵ for $|\epsilon| < \rho$, with $b_{ij}(0) = a_{ij}$. Prove that, for sufficiently small $|\epsilon|$, B has distinct eigenvalues $\mu_1(\epsilon), \ldots, \mu_n(\epsilon)$ which are analytic functions of ϵ such that $\mu_j(0) = \lambda_j$. (See Problem 5, Section 6.11.)

3. Let $B(\theta)$ be a real $n \times n$ matrix depending continuously on a parameter θ. Suppose that for $\theta = 0$ the matrix has n distinct real eigenvalues, but that for $\theta = 1$ the matrix has some complex, nonreal eigenvalues. Show that $B(\theta)$ cannot have distinct eigenvalues for all θ in the range $0 < \theta < 1$.

7 NUMERICAL METHODS

7.1 INTRODUCTION

The preceding chapters have presented an introduction to the *theory* of matrices. Computational procedures are surprisingly different from theory. For example, suppose that we wish to obtain a *numerical* solution for a given set of 50 linear equations in 50 unknowns.

$$\sum_{j=1}^{50} a_{ij}x_j = b_i \qquad (i = 1, \ldots, 50) \tag{1}$$

Shall we use Cramer's rule? Each x_i is expressed as the quotient of two 50×50 determinants. Expanding the denominator, det A, by the first row, we find

$$\det A = a_{11} \det A_{11} - a_{12} \det A_{12} + \cdots - a_{1,50} \det A_{1,50} \tag{2}$$

Each cofactor $\pm \det A_{1j}$ is a 49×49 determinant. If the cofactors are known, formula (2) exhibits 50 multiplications. But the 49×49 cofactors must be expanded, and so on. The complete expansion of det A, therefore, requires $50 \times 49 \times 48 \times \cdots \times 2 \times 1$ multiplications. This process would take *years* on a modern electronic computer.

There *is* a better way. A 50×50 system (1) can be solved in *seconds*, as this chapter will show.

Why, then, should one have bothered to learn the theory? Theory is understanding. Numerical methods, themselves, cannot be understood or applied effectively without the underlying theory. And for applications we want, most of all, insight. We want qualitative information, which no amount of blind computation can provide. For example, the theory of the Jordan form shows that a linear system of differential equations $x' = Ax$ may have solutions whose components behave like $t \sin \omega t$ as $t \rightarrow \infty$. Computation would never reveal this. We shall even show that the Jordan form is numerically unstable; for most matrices whose eigenvectors do not form a basis, the Jordan form cannot be computed by *any* method because of rounding error.

The literature on matrix computations is enormous. This book is not a survey, but a text. We shall study not all methods, but only a few of the best. For certain particular classes of matrices there are better techniques. But the methods presented here are among the fastest and the most reliable for the great bulk of problems to be met in practice.

7.2   THE METHOD OF ELIMINATION

We wish to solve a system of equations $Ax = b$ where $A = (a_{ij})$ is an $n \times n$ matrix. *If* A *is a triangular matrix with all* $a_{ii} \neq 0$, *the system can be solved by recursion.* Suppose $a_{ij} = 0$ if $i > j$. We first solve the last equation for x_n, then the next-to-the-last equation for x_{n-1}, etc.

EXAMPLE 1. To solve

$$\begin{aligned} x_1 + x_2 + x_3 &= 6 \\ 4x_2 - x_3 &= 5 \\ -2x_3 &= -6 \end{aligned} \qquad (1)$$

we compute, successively,

$$\begin{aligned} x_3 &= 3 \\ x_2 &= \frac{5 + x_3}{4} = \frac{5 + 3}{4} = 2 \\ x_1 &= 6 - x_2 - x_3 = 6 - 2 - 3 = 1 \end{aligned} \qquad (2)$$

If A *is not a triangular matrix, we transform* A *into a triangular matrix by operations which preserve the solution* x.

EXAMPLE 2. To solve

$$\begin{aligned} 4x_2 - x_3 &= 5 \\ x_1 + x_2 + x_3 &= 6 \\ 2x_1 - 2x_2 + x_3 &= 1 \end{aligned} \qquad (3)$$

first interchange the first two equations.

$$x_1 + x_2 + x_3 = 6$$
$$4x_2 - x_3 = 5 \qquad (4)$$
$$2x_1 - 2x_2 + x_3 = 1$$

Then subtract twice the first equation from the last equation.

$$x_1 + x_2 + x_3 = 6$$
$$4x_2 - x_3 = 5 \qquad (5)$$
$$-4x_2 - x_3 = -11$$

If we now add the second equation to the third equation, we obtain the triangular system in Example 1.

The reduction of a system of equations to triangular form can be accomplished by matrix manipulations. It is not necessary to write the letters x_1, x_2, etc.

EXAMPLE 3. To solve the system $Ax = b$ in Example 2, write the 3×4 augmented matrix $[A, b]$

$$[A, b] = \begin{bmatrix} 0 & 4 & -1 & 5 \\ 1 & 1 & 1 & 6 \\ 2 & -2 & 1 & 1 \end{bmatrix} \qquad (3')$$

We use this matrix to *represent* the system $Ax = b$. First interchange the first two rows.

$$\begin{bmatrix} 1 & 1 & 1 & 6 \\ 0 & 4 & -1 & 5 \\ 2 & -2 & 1 & 1 \end{bmatrix} \qquad (4')$$

Subtract twice the first row from the last row.

$$\begin{bmatrix} 1 & 1 & 1 & 6 \\ 0 & 4 & -1 & 5 \\ 0 & -4 & -1 & -11 \end{bmatrix} \qquad (5')$$

If we now add the second row to the third row, we obtain

$$\begin{bmatrix} 1 & 1 & 1 & 6 \\ 0 & 4 & -1 & 5 \\ 0 & 0 & -2 & -6 \end{bmatrix} \qquad (1')$$

which is the augmented matrix $[T, c]$ representing the triangular system $Tx = c$ in Example 1.

In Example 2 we used two operations: (a) interchanging two rows and (b) adding a multiple of one row to another. *If a rectangular matrix* X *can be transformed into a matrix* Y *by a succession of these operations, we shall write* $X \sim Y$. Evidently, $X \sim Y$ implies $Y \sim X$; and $\{X \sim Y$ and $Y \sim Z\}$ implies $X \sim Z$; and $X \sim X$.

Theorem 1. *Let* A *be an* n $\times$ n *matrix. Then* A $\sim$ T *for some triangular matrix* T, *with* $t_{ij} = 0$ *for* i $>$ j. *Moreover,*

$$\det A = (-1)^R t_{11} t_{22} \ldots t_{nn} \tag{6}$$

where R *is the number of row-interchanges used in transforming* A *into* T.

Proof. Note that we do not assume $\det A \neq 0$. The theorem is obvious for $n = 1$, with $A = T = a_{11}$. If $n > 1$, we look at the first column of A. If some element in the first column is nonzero, we can, if necessary, perform a row-interchange to obtain a matrix with a nonzero element in the 1, 1 position. Now, subtracting multiples of the first row from the other rows, we obtain

$$A \sim \begin{bmatrix} t_{11} & t_{12} & \cdots & t_{1n} \\ 0 & & & \\ \cdot & & A' & \\ \cdot & & & \\ 0 & & & \end{bmatrix} \tag{7}$$

where A' is an $(n - 1) \times (n - 1)$ matrix. If the first column of A is zero, A already has the form of the right-hand side of (7), with $t_{11} = 0$.

By induction, $A' \sim$ some triangular matrix, say

$$A' \sim (t_{ij}) \qquad (i, j = 2, \ldots, n) \quad (\text{with } t_{ij} = 0 \text{ for } i > j)$$

Therefore, as (7) shows, $A \sim (t_{ij})$ $(i, j = 1, \ldots, n)$. The formula (6) for $\det A$ follows because each row-interchange reverses the sign of the determinant.

Theorem 2. *Let* A *be an* n $\times$ n *matrix. Let* B *be an* n $\times$ k *matrix. Then there is a triangular matrix* T *such that* [A, B] $\sim$ [T, C], *where the systems* AX = B *and* TX = C *have the same solution or solutions* X, *unless both systems have no solution.*

Proof. By Theorem 1 there is a triangular matrix T such that $A \sim T$. The transformation of A into T is achieved by a sequence of (a) row-interchanges and (b) additions of multiples of rows to other rows. If the same sequence of operations is performed on the $n \times (n + k)$ matrix $[A, B]$, we obtain an $n \times k$ matrix C for which $[A, B] \sim [T, C]$. The systems $AX = B$ and $TX = C$ have the same solution or solutions X because every operation (a) corresponds to interchanging two equations, and every operation (b) corresponds to adding a multiple of one equation to another equation.

In Example 2, B was a vector. *To compute the inverse* of A *if* det A $\neq 0$, *we let* B $=$ I because then we are solving the equation $AX = I$. If all $t_{ii} \neq 0$, the triangular system $TX = C$, where C is an $n \times k$ matrix, is solved by solving the equation $Tx^j = c^j$ for each column-vector x^j $(j = 1, \ldots, k)$ by recursion, as in Example 1.

COUNT OF OPERATIONS

To determine the speed of computation we need to know how many calculations of various sorts are made. Consider the reduction $[A, B] \sim [T, C]$, where A is an $n \times n$ matrix and B is an $n \times k$ matrix. Let

$$M_n = \text{the number of multiplications or divisions}$$
$$A_n = \text{the number of additions or subtractions} \tag{8}$$

Evidently, $M_1 = 0$ and $A_1 = 0$ for any $k \geqslant 1$, since a 1×1 matrix A is already triangular. If $n > 1$, consider the first column reduction. If the first column of A is not zero, usually a row-interchange is made to bring the element of largest absolute value in the first column into the 1, 1 position. Again call the new matrix $[A, B]$. We must now subtract a multiple of the row

$$a_{11}a_{12} \ldots a_{1n}b_{11} \ldots b_{1k}$$

from each row

$$a_{i1}a_{i2} \ldots a_{in}b_{i1} \ldots b_{ik} \qquad (i = 2, \ldots, n)$$

to produce a row of the form

$$0a'_{i2} \ldots a'_{in}b'_{i1} \ldots b'_{ik} \qquad (i = 2, \ldots, n) \tag{9}$$

Explicitly, if $r_i = a_{i1}/a_{11}$,

$$\begin{aligned} a'_{ij} &= a_{ij} - r_i a_{1j} \qquad (j = 2, \ldots, n) \\ b'_{ij} &= b_{ij} - r_i b_{1j} \qquad (j = 1, \ldots, k) \end{aligned} \tag{10}$$

There is one division to produce r_i. Formula (10) requires $n - 1 + k$ multiplications and an equal number of subtractions. Since $n - 1$ rows

(9) are formed, the first column reduction can be achieved with

$$(1 + n - 1 + k)(n - 1) \text{ divisions or multiplications}$$
$$\text{and } (n - 1 + k)(n - 1) \text{ subtractions} \tag{11}$$

The first column now has zeros below the 1, 1 position. We now have to reduce the $(n - 1) \times (n - 1 + k)$ matrix below the first row and to the right of the first column. From formula (11) we obtain the recursion

$$\left.\begin{array}{l} M_n = (n + k)(n - 1) + M_{n-1} \\ A_n = (n - 1 + k)(n - 1) + A_{n-1} \end{array}\right\} \quad (n \geqslant 2) \tag{12}$$

Therefore, since $M_1 = A_1 = 0$, we have for $n \geqslant 2$

$$M_n = (2 + k)\cdot 1 + (3 + k)\cdot 2 + \cdots + (n + k)(n - 1)$$
$$A_n = (1 + k)\cdot 1 + (2 + k)\cdot 2 + \cdots + (n - 1 + k)(n - 1) \tag{13}$$

One readily verifies by induction:

$$\sum_{s=1}^{n-1} s = \tfrac{1}{2}(n - 1)n; \qquad \sum_{s=1}^{n-1} s^2 = \tfrac{1}{6}(n - 1)n(2n - 1)$$

Therefore, since $M_n = \sum\limits_{s=1}^{n-1} (1 + k + s)s$ and $A_n = \sum\limits_{s=1}^{n-1} (k + s)s$,

$$M_n = (1 + k)\cdot\tfrac{1}{2}(n - 1)n + \tfrac{1}{6}(n - 1)n(2n - 1)$$
$$A_n = k\cdot\tfrac{1}{2}(n - 1)n + \tfrac{1}{6}(n - 1)n(2n - 1) \tag{14}$$

Now we will count the number m_n of multiplications or divisions and the number a_n of additions or subtractions needed to solve the triangular system $TX = C$. Assume all $t_{ii} \neq 0$. Let $n \geqslant 2$. Suppose that we have already solved for $x_{nj}, x_{n-1,j}, \ldots, x_{2,j}$ for each column $j = 1, \ldots, k$. Only x_{1j} $(j = 1, \ldots, k)$ remain to be calculated. So far, m_{n-1} and a_{n-1} operations have been used, since the triangular system *below* the first equation of $TX = C$ has been solved. Now

$$x_{1j} = \frac{c_{1j} - t_{12}x_{2j} - \cdots - t_{1n}x_{nj}}{t_{11}} \tag{15}$$

For each $j = 1, \ldots, k$ formula (15) requires $n - 1$ multiplications, one division, and $n - 1$ subtractions. Therefore, for $n \geqslant 2$,

$$m_n = (n - 1 + 1)k + m_{n-1}, \qquad a_n = (n - 1)k + a_{n-1} \tag{16}$$

Since $m_1 = k$ and $a_1 = 0$, we have

$$m_n = k + 2k + 3k + \cdots + nk = \tfrac{1}{2}n(n+1)k$$
$$a_n = 0 + k + 2k + \cdots + (n-1)k = \tfrac{1}{2}(n-1)nk \tag{17}$$

The next theorem summarizes our results:

Theorem 3. *Let* A *be an* n $\times$ n *matrix with* det A $\neq 0$. *If* B *is an* n $\times$ k *matrix, then the equation* AX $=$ B *can be solved by the method of elimination with*

$$\mu_n = n^2k + \tfrac{1}{3}(n-1)n(n+1) \qquad multiplications\ or\ divisions \tag{18}$$

and

$$\alpha_n = n(n-1)k + \tfrac{1}{6}(n-1)n(2n-1) \qquad additions\ or\ subtractions \tag{19}$$

Proof. From (14) and (17) we find (18) as the sum $M_n + m_n$, and we find (19) as the sum $A_n + a_n$.

Observe that μ_n and α_n are each less than $n^2k + n^3/3$. For large n, if $k = 1$, μ_n and α_n are approximately $n^3/3$. If $k = n$, μ_n and α_n are approximately $4n^3/3$.

In the preceding discussion we reduced the original system $AX = B$ to a triangular system $TX = C$. The next example will show that, if all $t_{ii} \neq 0$, the triangular system can be solved by matrix manipulations. For this purpose we use one additional operation: (c) dividing (or multiplying) a row by a nonzero scalar. This corresponds to dividing (or multiplying) equations by a nonzero scalar.

EXAMPLE 4. We will solve the triangular system

$$\begin{bmatrix} 1 & 1 & 1 \\ 0 & 4 & -1 \\ 0 & 0 & -2 \end{bmatrix} \begin{bmatrix} x_{11} & x_{12} \\ x_{21} & x_{22} \\ x_{31} & x_{32} \end{bmatrix} = \begin{bmatrix} 6 & 2 \\ 5 & -9 \\ -6 & -2 \end{bmatrix} \tag{20}$$

First we write down the augmented matrix $[T, C]$:

$$[T, C] = \begin{bmatrix} 1 & 1 & 1 & 6 & 2 \\ 0 & 4 & -1 & 5 & -9 \\ 0 & 0 & -2 & -6 & -2 \end{bmatrix} \tag{21}$$

By the elementary row-operations (a), (b), and (c) we will reduce this matrix to the form $[I, R]$. In other words, we will reduce the system $TX = C$ to the system $IX = R$, which will give the solution $X = R$. Division of the last row by $t_{33} = -2$ yields

$$\begin{bmatrix} 1 & 1 & 1 & 6 & 2 \\ 0 & 4 & -1 & 5 & -9 \\ 0 & 0 & 1 & 3 & 1 \end{bmatrix}$$

We now add appropriate multiples of the last row to the other rows to obtain

$$\begin{bmatrix} 1 & 1 & 0 & 3 & 1 \\ 0 & 4 & 0 & 8 & -8 \\ 0 & 0 & 1 & 3 & 1 \end{bmatrix}$$

Then we divide the second row by $t_{22} = 4$. (In computer programming, we take care not to waste time dividing elements which we know already equal zero.) We obtain

$$\begin{bmatrix} 1 & 1 & 0 & 3 & 1 \\ 0 & 1 & 0 & 2 & -2 \\ 0 & 0 & 1 & 3 & 1 \end{bmatrix}$$

Subtraction of the second row from the upper row yields

$$\begin{bmatrix} 1 & 0 & 0 & 1 & 3 \\ 0 & 1 & 0 & 2 & -2 \\ 0 & 0 & 1 & 3 & 1 \end{bmatrix} = [I, R] \tag{22}$$

Thus, we have found the solution

$$X = \begin{bmatrix} x_{11} & x_{12} \\ x_{21} & x_{22} \\ x_{31} & x_{32} \end{bmatrix} = \begin{bmatrix} 1 & 3 \\ 2 & -2 \\ 3 & 1 \end{bmatrix}$$

PIVOTAL STRATEGY

In practical digital computation, it is important to reduce cumulative rounding error. The following procedure has been found useful. In the reduction to triangular form, to produce zeros below the diagonal in a certain column, we first look for an element of maximum absolute value on or below the diagonal in that column. If this so-called "pivotal element" lies below the diagonal, we first perform a row-interchange to bring the pivotal element onto the diagonal. Then we subtract multiples of the pivotal row to produce zeros below the diagonal in the pivotal column. For example, to reduce the second column of the matrix

$$
\begin{matrix}
25 & 13 & 6 & -7 \\
0 & 4 & 3 & 1 \\
0 & \boxed{-10} & 1 & 2 \\
0 & 1 & 4 & 2
\end{matrix}
$$

we first recognize the pivotal element -10. We interchange rows to obtain

$$
\begin{matrix}
25 & 13 & 6 & -7 \\
0 & -10 & 1 & 2 \\
0 & 4 & 3 & 1 \\
0 & 1 & 4 & 2
\end{matrix}
$$

We now subtract multiples of the pivotal row to obtain

$$
\begin{matrix}
25 & 13 & 6 & -7 \\
0 & -10 & 1 & 2 \\
0 & 0 & 3.4 & 1.8 \\
0 & 0 & 4.1 & 2.2
\end{matrix}
$$

Note that the multipliers used (in this case .4 and .1) lie between -1 and $+1$, since the pivotal element has maximum absolute value. In our example, the next pivotal element will be 4.1 because $|4.1| > |3.4|$.

PROBLEMS

1.* In the matrix-form of the solution of triangular systems, as illustrated by Example 4, verify the recursion formulas (16) for the numbers of operations, m_n and a_n.

2. Solve $AX = B$ if

$$
[A, B] = \begin{bmatrix}
0 & 2 & -1 & 1 & -3 \\
-3 & 1 & 4 & 2 & 27 \\
1 & 6 & -5 & 2 & -22
\end{bmatrix}
$$

3. Find the inverse of the matrix A in Problem 2. (Here we are solving $AX = I$. Begin by writing the augmented matrix $[A, I]$.)

4. By reduction to a triangular matrix T, calculate the determinant of the matrix

$$A = \begin{bmatrix} 0 & 1 & -1 & 2 \\ 3 & 0 & -4 & 1 \\ 5 & -7 & 1 & 2 \\ -3 & 1 & 2 & 9 \end{bmatrix}$$

Use only the elementary operations (a) and (b) to form T.

5.* If A is an $n \times n$ matrix with det $A \neq 0$, and if C is an $n \times n$ matrix, Theorem 3 shows that $AX = C$ can be solved by the method of elimination with about $\frac{4}{3}n^3$ multiplications. Show that, in the particular case $C = I$, this number may be reduced to n^3. Thus, *the inverse matrix can be formed with only* n³ *multiplications.*

7.3 FACTORIZATION BY TRIANGULAR MATRICES

In the preceding section we described a form of the method of elimination which applies to any system $Ax = b$ in which det $A \neq 0$. For a wide class of matrices it is possible to solve $Ax = b$ by the factorization $A = LR$, where L and R have the forms

$$L = \begin{bmatrix} 1 & 0 & 0 & \cdots & 0 \\ l_{21} & 1 & 0 & \cdots & 0 \\ l_{31} & l_{32} & 1 & \cdots & 0 \\ \cdot & \cdot & \cdot & \cdots & \cdot \\ l_{n1} & l_{n2} & l_{n3} & \cdots & 1 \end{bmatrix}, \quad R = \begin{bmatrix} r_{11} & r_{12} & r_{13} \cdot r_{1n} \\ 0 & r_{22} & r_{23} \cdot r_{2n} \\ 0 & 0 & r_{33} \cdot r_{3n} \\ \cdot & \cdot & \cdot & \cdots & \cdot \\ 0 & 0 & 0 \cdot r_{nn} \end{bmatrix} \quad \text{(all } r_{ii} \neq 0)$$

$$\tag{1}$$

This factorization is not always possible; but, when it is possible, it yields a faster solution of $Ax = b$ than the more general method of the preceding section. The solution is faster because there are no row-interchanges. We shall give a count of operations in Section 7.4.

EXAMPLE 1. The factorization

$$A = \begin{bmatrix} 0 & 1 \\ 1 & 0 \end{bmatrix} = \begin{bmatrix} 1 & 0 \\ l_{21} & 1 \end{bmatrix} \begin{bmatrix} r_{11} & r_{12} \\ 0 & r_{22} \end{bmatrix} = LR \tag{2}$$

is impossible because (2) implies $r_{11} = 0$. Hence, det $R = 0$. But we must have $-1 = \det A = (\det L)(\det R) = r_{11}r_{22}$.

If $A = LR$, where all diagonal elements $r_{ii} \neq 0$, the system $Ax = b$ is readily solvable. Since L is triangular with nonzero diagonal elements, we may solve $L(Rx) = b$ for $c = Rx$ by recursion. Then $Rx = c$ is solved by recursion for x.

EXAMPLE 2. Let A have the factorization

$$A = \begin{bmatrix} 3 & -1 \\ -1 & 2 \end{bmatrix} = \begin{bmatrix} 1 & 0 \\ -\frac{1}{3} & 1 \end{bmatrix} \begin{bmatrix} 3 & -1 \\ 0 & \frac{5}{3} \end{bmatrix} = LR \qquad (3)$$

To solve $Ax = b = \mathrm{col}\,(1, 3)$ we first solve

$$Lc = \begin{bmatrix} 1 & 0 \\ -\frac{1}{3} & 1 \end{bmatrix} \begin{bmatrix} c_1 \\ c_2 \end{bmatrix} = \begin{bmatrix} 1 \\ 3 \end{bmatrix} = b \qquad (4)$$

We find, successively, $c_1 = 1$, $c_2 = \frac{10}{3}$. We now solve

$$Rx = \begin{bmatrix} 3 & -1 \\ 0 & \frac{5}{3} \end{bmatrix} \begin{bmatrix} x_1 \\ x_2 \end{bmatrix} = \begin{bmatrix} 1 \\ \frac{10}{3} \end{bmatrix} \qquad (5)$$

finding, successively, $x_2 = 2$, $x_1 = 1$.

Theorem 1. *Let* A *be an* $n \times n$ *matrix. Then* A *has a factorization* A = LR *where* L *is left-triangular with* 1's *on the diagonal, and where* R *is right-triangular with nonzero diagonal elements, if and only if*

$$a_{11} \neq 0, \quad \begin{vmatrix} a_{11} & a_{12} \\ a_{21} & a_{22} \end{vmatrix} \neq 0, \ldots, \quad \begin{vmatrix} a_{11} & & a_{1n} \\ \cdot & \cdots & \cdot \\ a_{n1} & & a_{nn} \end{vmatrix} \neq 0 \qquad (6)$$

Moreover, the factorization A = LR, *if it is possible, is unique.*

In particular, if A is positive definite, there is a factorization $A = LR$, since all the determinants in (6) are positive, as we showed in Section 6.5. If A is not Hermitian, the proof will show that the components of L and of R are computed in this order: row 1 of R, column 1 of L; row 2 of R, column 2 of L; etc. There is a simplification if A is Hermitian.

Proof of the Theorem. First we prove the uniqueness. Let $r_{(i)}$ denote the ith row of R, and l^j denote the jth column of L, with similar conventions for the rows and columns of A. If $A = LR$, where L and R have the forms (1), then the rows of the product are

$$a_{(1)} = r_{(1)}, \qquad a_{(2)} = l_{21}r_{(1)} + r_{(2)}, \ldots, \qquad a_{(n)} = \sum_{k=1}^{n-1} l_{nk}r_{(k)} + r_{(n)} \qquad (7)$$

The columns of $A = LR$, excepting the last, are

$$a^1 = r_{11}l^1, \qquad a^2 = r_{12}l^1 + r_{22}l^2, \ldots,$$
$$a^{n-1} = \sum_{k=1}^{n-2} r_{k,n-1}l^k + r_{n-1,n-1}l^{n-1} \tag{8}$$

Since all $r_{jj} \neq 0$ in (1), we may solve (7) and (8) recursively:

$$\begin{aligned}
r_{(1)} &= a_{(1)} & &\text{by (7)} \\
l^1 &= r_{11}^{-1}a^1 & &\text{by (8)} \\
r_{(2)} &= a_{(2)} - l_{21}r_{(1)} & &\text{by (7)} \\
l^2 &= r_{22}^{-1}(a^2 - r_{12}l^1) & &\text{by (8)}
\end{aligned} \tag{9}$$

and so on, until at last we solve for $r_{(n-1)}$, l^{n-1}, and $r_{(n)}$. The last column of L is known $= \mathrm{col}\,(0, \ldots, 0, 1)$.

Explicitly, $r_{(i)}$ is given by (7) as

$$r_{ij} = a_{ij} - \sum_{k=1}^{i-1} l_{ik}r_{kj} \qquad (j = i, \ldots, n) \tag{10}$$

whereas l^j is given by (8) as

$$l_{ij} = r_{jj}^{-1}\left(a_{ij} - \sum_{k=1}^{j-1} r_{kj}l_{ik}\right) \qquad (i = j + 1, \ldots, n) \tag{11}$$

Here we use the summation convention $\sum_{k=1}^{0} = 0$.

Now we will show that a factorization $A = LR$, with L and R of the forms (1), is possible *only if* the subdeterminants (6) are nonzero. We observe that $A = LR$ implies

$$[a_{11}] = [1]\,[r_{11}], \qquad \begin{bmatrix} a_{11} & a_{12} \\ a_{21} & a_{22} \end{bmatrix} = \begin{bmatrix} 1 & 0 \\ l_{21} & 1 \end{bmatrix}\begin{bmatrix} r_{11} & r_{12} \\ 0 & r_{22} \end{bmatrix}, \ldots, A = LR \tag{12}$$

Taking determinants, we find

$$a_{11} = r_{11}, \qquad \begin{vmatrix} a_{11} & a_{12} \\ a_{21} & a_{22} \end{vmatrix} = r_{11}r_{22}, \ldots, \det A = r_{11}r_{22}\ldots r_{nn} \tag{13}$$

Since (1) assumes all $r_{ii} \neq 0$, we must have all subdeterminants (6) nonzero.

Finally, we will show that a factorization $A = LR$ is possible *if* the inequalities (6) hold. It is sufficient to show that there exist numbers r_{ij} $(i \leqslant j)$ and l_{ij} $(i > j)$ satisfying (10) and (11). We satisfy (10) for $i = 1$ by defining $r_{1j} = a_{1j}$ $(j = 1, \ldots, n)$. Since $r_{11} = a_{11} \neq 0$, we may define

l_{i1} from (11) with $j = 1$. By induction, suppose that we have satisfied (10) for $i < m$ and (11) for $j < m$, where $1 < m \leqslant n$. We now satisfy (10) for $i = m$ by defining

$$r_{mj} = a_{mj} - \sum_{k=1}^{m-1} l_{mk} r_{kj} \qquad (j = m, \ldots, n) \tag{14}$$

To show that $r_{mm} \neq 0$, we use (10) for $i = 1, \ldots, m$ and (11) for $j = 1$, $\ldots, m - 1$ to write the matrix identity

$$\begin{bmatrix} 1 & 0 & \cdots & 0 & 0 \\ l_{21} & 1 & \cdots & 0 & 0 \\ \cdot & \cdot & \cdots & \cdot & \cdot \\ l_{m1} & l_{m2} & \cdots & l_{m,m-1} & 1 \end{bmatrix} \begin{bmatrix} r_{11} & r_{12} & \cdots & r_{1m} \\ 0 & r_{22} & \cdots & r_{2m} \\ \cdot & \cdot & \cdots & \cdot \\ 0 & 0 & \cdots & r_{mm} \end{bmatrix} = (a_{ij})_{i,j=1,\ldots,m} \tag{15}$$

Taking determinants, we find

$$1 \cdot 1 \cdots 1 \cdot r_{11} r_{22} \cdots r_{mm} = \det (a_{ij})_{i,j=1,\ldots,m} \tag{16}$$

Since the determinant on the right is nonzero by assumption (6), we conclude that $r_{mm} \neq 0$. Therefore, (11) may be satisfied for $j = m$, and the inductive proof is complete.

EXAMPLE 3. To obtain the factorization which was given in (3), write

$$\begin{bmatrix} 3 & -1 \\ -1 & 2 \end{bmatrix} = \begin{bmatrix} 1 & 0 \\ l_{21} & 1 \end{bmatrix} \begin{bmatrix} r_{11} & r_{12} \\ 0 & r_{22} \end{bmatrix} \tag{17}$$

Equations (10) for $i = 1$ are

$$r_{11} = 3, \qquad r_{12} = -1$$

Equation (11) for $j = 1$ is: $l_{21} = 3^{-1}(-1)$. Finally, equation (10) for $i = 2$ is: $r_{22} = 2 - (-\frac{1}{3})(-1) = \frac{5}{3}$. Note that

$$3 = r_{11}, \qquad \begin{vmatrix} 3 & -1 \\ -1 & 2 \end{vmatrix} = r_{11} r_{22} = 3(\tfrac{5}{3})$$

SIMPLIFICATION FOR HERMITIAN MATRICES

If A is Hermitian, there is a simple relation between L and R. Let $A = A^*$, and suppose that the subdeterminants (6) are nonzero. Then $A = LR$ implies $A = A^* = R^* L^*$. But R^* is left-triangular, and L^* is right-triangular. By the uniqueness of the factorization $A = LR$, we could conclude that $R^* = L$ and $L^* = R$ if the diagonal elements r_{ii} were all 1's. If some $r_{ii} \neq 1$, define $D = \text{diag}(r_{11}, \ldots, r_{nn})$. Then $R = DR^1$, where $r_{ij} = r_{ii}r_{ij}^1$ $(i, j = 1, \ldots, n)$. Hence, all $r_{ii}^1 = 1$. We now have

$$LR = A = A^* = R^*L^* = (DR^1)^*L^* = (R^1)^*(D^*L^*) \tag{18}$$

Since R^1 has 1's on the diagonal, we conclude by uniqueness:

$$(R^1)^* = L, \qquad D^*L^* = R \tag{19}$$

Further, $D^* = D$, since $\bar{r}_{11}, \ldots$ are the diagonal elements of D^*L^*, whereas $r_{11}, \ldots$ are the diagonal elements of R.

In practice, we use (19) to simplify the computation of L. We have $L = (R^1)^* = (D^{-1}R)^* = R^*D^{-1}$, or

$$l_{ij} = \frac{\bar{r}_{ji}}{r_{jj}} \qquad (i = j + 1, \ldots, n) \tag{20}$$

For Hermitian A, this formula replaces the longer formula (11). In (20) the jth column of L is given directly from the jth row of R.

For certain applications in mathematical statistics it is desirable to construct a factorization

$$A = TT^* \tag{21}$$

of a *positive definite* Hermitian matrix A, where T is left-triangular. To do this, we first factor $A = LR$, as above. The elements r_{ii}, being the quotients of principal minor determinants of A, are positive. Since A is Hermitian, $L = R^*D^{-1}$, as in (20). Now we have $A = (R^*D^{-1})R$. But

$$D^{-1} = [\text{diag}(r_{11}^{-1/2}, r_{22}^{-1/2}, \ldots, r_{nn}^{-1/2})]^2 \equiv P^2 \tag{22}$$

Therefore, $A = TT^*$, where $T = R^*P$, i.e.,

$$t_{ij} = \frac{r_{ji}}{\sqrt{r_{jj}}} \qquad (i \geqslant j) \tag{23}$$

In particular, $t_{ii} = \sqrt{r_{ii}}$.

The components t_{ij} can be computed directly. From the identity $A = TT^*$, we find

$$a_{jj} = \sum_{k=1}^{j} |t_{jk}|^2$$

$$a_{ij} = \sum_{k=1}^{j} t_{ik}\bar{t}_{jk} \qquad (i > j)$$

Therefore, we may compute the t_{ij} in the order $t_{11}, \ldots, t_{n1}$; $t_{22}, \ldots, t_{n2}$; $\ldots$; t_{nn} from the recursion formulas

$$t_{jj} = \left(a_{jj} - \sum_{k=1}^{j-1} |t_{jk}|^2\right)^{1/2} \tag{24}$$

$$t_{ij} = t_{jj}^{-1}\left(a_{ij} - \sum_{k=1}^{j-1} t_{ik}\bar{t}_{jk}\right) \qquad (i = j+1, \ldots, n) \tag{25}$$

PROBLEMS

1. Find the components l_{ij}, r_{ij} in the factorization

$$\begin{bmatrix} 1 & 0 & 7 \\ 3 & 2 & 0 \\ 1 & 1 & 1 \end{bmatrix} = \begin{bmatrix} 1 & 0 & 0 \\ l_{21} & 1 & 0 \\ l_{31} & l_{32} & 1 \end{bmatrix} \begin{bmatrix} r_{11} & r_{12} & r_{13} \\ 0 & r_{22} & r_{23} \\ 0 & 0 & r_{33} \end{bmatrix}$$

2. Find the components r_{ij} in the factorization

$$\begin{bmatrix} -3 & 1 & 1 \\ 1 & 4 & -2 \\ 1 & -2 & 5 \end{bmatrix} = \begin{bmatrix} 1 & 0 & 0 \\ l_{21} & 1 & 0 \\ l_{31} & l_{32} & 1 \end{bmatrix} \begin{bmatrix} r_{11} & r_{12} & r_{13} \\ 0 & r_{22} & r_{23} \\ 0 & 0 & r_{33} \end{bmatrix}$$

Verify the identity $l_{ij} = r_{ji}/r_{jj}$ with $i > j$.

3. Find the components t_{ij} in the factorization

$$\begin{bmatrix} 3 & -1 & 1 \\ -1 & 4 & -2 \\ 1 & -2 & 5 \end{bmatrix} = \begin{bmatrix} t_{11} & 0 & 0 \\ t_{21} & t_{22} & 0 \\ t_{31} & t_{32} & t_{33} \end{bmatrix} \begin{bmatrix} t_{11} & t_{21} & t_{31} \\ 0 & t_{22} & t_{32} \\ 0 & 0 & t_{33} \end{bmatrix}$$

Require all $t_{jj} > 0$.

4.* Prove that, if A is only positive *semi*definite, the factorization $A = TT^*$ is still possible, with $t_{ij} = 0$ for $j > i$, and $t_{ii} \geqslant 0$. [This result can be proved algebraically. It can also be proved analytically: Replace A by $A + \epsilon I$ with $\epsilon > 0$. Now $A + \epsilon I = T(\epsilon)T^*(\epsilon)$. Why? But $\sum \sum |t_{jk}(\epsilon)|^2 = \sum (a_{jj} + \epsilon)$. Why? Let $\epsilon \to 0$ and pick a convergent subsequence of the bounded matrices $T(\epsilon)$.]

7.4 DIRECT SOLUTION OF LARGE SYSTEMS OF LINEAR EQUATIONS

In structural engineering, in numerical analysis, and in many other fields, we encounter large systems of equations $Ax = b$ in which A is a band-matrix, i.e., a matrix whose nonzero components are near the main diagonal. Let $A = (a_{ij})$ be an $n \times n$ matrix. *We say that* A *has bandwidth* w *if* $a_{ij} = 0$ *whenever* $|i - j| \geqslant$ w. Thus, a diagonal matrix has bandwidth $w = 1$; a full matrix has $w = n$; tridiagonal matrix has $w = 2$.

EXAMPLE 1. Let a rectangular structure be given with base > height. For purposes of analysis we place a grid of 40 points on this rectangle, as in Figure 7.1. If the nodes are numbered in some way from 1 to 40, a symmetric matrix $A = (a_{ij})$ is defined, from engineering considerations, in which $a_{ij} \neq 0$ whenever node i and node j are adjacent.

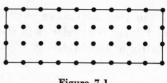

Figure 7.1

To number the nodes as in Figure 7.2

```
4   8   12   ·   40
3   7   11   ·   39
2   6   10   ·   38
1   5    9   ·   37
```

Figure 7.2

produces a matrix A with bandwidth $w = 5$, since nodes i and j are neighbors only if $|i - j| < 5$. For example, node $i = 6$ has the neighbors $j = 2, 5, 10$, and 7.

If the grid in Figure 7.1 is numbered by rows, as in Figure 7.3,

```
31   32   33   ...   40
21   22   23   ...   30
11   12   13   ...   20
 1    2    3   ...   10
```

Figure 7.3

the bandwidth $w = 11$ results. For example, node $i = 12$ has the neighbors $j = 11, 2, 13, 22$, for which $|i - j| < 11$.

EXAMPLE 2. Consider the ring structure in Figure 7.4(a). The nodes are to be numbered from 1 to 6. A matrix $A = (a_{ij})$ will be defined, from physical considerations, with $a_{ij} \neq 0$ when nodes i and j are neighbors. The natural ordering in Figure 7.4(b) gives a 6×6 matrix A with bandwidth $w = 6$, since nodes 1 and 6 are neighbors. However, the ordering in Figure 7.4(c) reduces the bandwidth to $w = 3$.

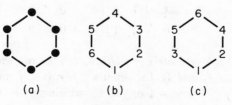

(a)   (b)   (c)

Figure 7.4

In this section we shall discuss the factorization $A = LR$, where L and R are triangular as in the preceding section, and where A is an $n \times n$ matrix of bandwidth w. We shall suppose

$$a_{11} \neq 0, \quad \begin{vmatrix} a_{11} & a_{12} \\ a_{21} & a_{22} \end{vmatrix} \neq 0, \ldots, \det A \neq 0 \tag{1}$$

According to the last section, these inequalities guarantee the existence and uniqueness of the matrices L and R.

Formulas (10), (11), and (20) of the last section are:

$$r_{ij} = a_{ij} - \sum_{k=1}^{i-1} l_{ik} r_{kj} \qquad (j = i, \ldots, n) \tag{2}$$

$$l_{ij} = r_{jj}^{-1} \left(a_{ij} - \sum_{k=1}^{j-1} r_{kj} l_{ik} \right) \qquad (i = j+1, \ldots, n) \tag{3}$$

$$l_{ij} = \frac{\bar{r}_{ji}}{r_{jj}} \quad \text{if} \quad A = A^* \qquad (i = j+1, \ldots, n) \tag{4}$$

The last formula replaces the one above it if A is Hermitian.

We now assert that *the triangular matrices* R *and* L *have bandwidth* w:

$$r_{ij} = 0 \quad (\text{if } j \geq i + w); \qquad l_{ij} = 0 \quad (\text{if } i \geq j + w) \tag{5}$$

Since $r_{1j} = a_{1j}$ and $l_{i1} = a_{i1}/r_{11}$, the assertion is evident for the first row of R and for the first column of L. For the other rows of R and for the other columns of L, the assertion follows by induction from (2) and (3).

EXAMPLE 3. In the following factorization A is positive definite, $n = 4$, and $w = 2$.

$$A = \begin{bmatrix} 2 & -1 & 0 & 0 \\ -1 & 2 & -1 & 0 \\ 0 & -1 & 2 & -1 \\ 0 & 0 & -1 & 2 \end{bmatrix}$$

$$= \begin{bmatrix} 1 & 0 & 0 & 0 \\ -\frac{1}{2} & 1 & 0 & 0 \\ 0 & -\frac{2}{3} & 1 & 0 \\ 0 & 0 & -\frac{3}{4} & 1 \end{bmatrix} \begin{bmatrix} 2 & -1 & 0 & 0 \\ 0 & \frac{3}{2} & -1 & 0 \\ 0 & 0 & \frac{4}{3} & -1 \\ 0 & 0 & 0 & \frac{5}{4} \end{bmatrix} = LR \tag{6}$$

If A *is an* n $\times$ n *band-matrix of width* w $<$ n, *we can shorten the calculations* (2), (3), (4) *for* R *and* L. In formula (2), $r_{ij}(i \leq j)$ needs to be computed only for $j \leq i + w - 1$ or $j \leq n$, whichever is smaller. In the summation (2) we have $k < i \leqslant j$, and the number r_{kj} vanishes unless $k \geqslant j - w + 1$. Therefore, (2) becomes

$$r_{ij} = a_{ij} - \sum_{k=\max (1, j-w+1)}^{i-1} l_{ik} r_{kj} \qquad [j = i, \ldots, \min (i + w - 1, n)] \qquad (2')$$

In particular, as we will show,

$$r_{ij} = a_{ij} \quad (\text{if } i = 1 \quad \text{or if} \quad j = i + w - 1)$$

If $i = 1$, the upper limit of the summation (2') is $i - 1 = 0$. If $j = i + w - 1$, the lower limit, $\max (1, j - w + 1)$, equals i, which is greater than the upper limit, $i - 1$. In either case the sum $\sum$ equals zero.

In formula (3), l_{ij} $(i > j)$ needs to be computed only for $i \leqslant j + w - 1$ or $i \leqslant n$, whichever is smaller. In the summation (3) we have $k < j < i$, and the number l_{ik} vanishes unless $k \geqslant i - w + 1$. Therefore, (3) and (4) become

$$l_{ij} = r_{jj}^{-1} (a_{ij} - \sum_{k=\max (1, i-w+1)}^{j-1} r_{kj} l_{ik}) \qquad [i = j + 1, \ldots, \min (j + w - 1, n)] \tag{3'}$$

$$l_{ij} = \frac{\bar{r}_{ji}}{r_{jj}} \qquad (\text{if } A = A^*) \quad \text{and} \quad [i = j + 1, \ldots, \min (j + w - 1, n)] \tag{4'}$$

In particular,

$$l_{ij} = r_{jj}^{-1} a_{ij} \qquad (\text{if } i = j + w - 1)$$

for then the lower limit of the summation (3') is $j >$ the upper limit, $j - 1$.

COUNT OF OPERATIONS

It is not a trivial problem to count the number of operations used in the factorization $A = LR$ of a band-matrix A. The difficulty lies in the cumbersome forms of the limits in the summations (2') and (3'). We shall count the total number μ of multiplications and divisions.

We shall find, for an $n \times n$ non-Hermitian matrix A of bandwidth w,

$$\boxed{\mu = \tfrac{1}{3} w(w - 1)(3n - 2w + 1)} \tag{7}$$

If A is Hermitian, μ is reduced to

$$\boxed{\mu = \tfrac{1}{6}(w - 1)[3(w + 2)n - 2w(w + 1)] \qquad (\text{if } A = A^*)} \tag{8}$$

The number of additions and subtractions is substantially the same.

To calculate μ we shall use a trick of combinatorial analysis. Let L^1 and R^1 be the special matrices defined as follows:

$$l_{ij}^1 = \begin{cases} 1 \text{ (if } j \leqslant i \leqslant j + w - 1) \\ 0 \text{ (otherwise)} \end{cases}$$

$$r_{ij}^1 = \begin{cases} 1 \text{ (if } i \leqslant j \leqslant i + w - 1) \\ 0 \text{ (otherwise)} \end{cases} \tag{9}$$

For example, if $n = 4$ and $w = 2$,

$$L^1 = \begin{bmatrix} 1 & 0 & 0 & 0 \\ 1 & 1 & 0 & 0 \\ 0 & 1 & 1 & 0 \\ 0 & 0 & 1 & 1 \end{bmatrix}, \quad R^1 = \begin{bmatrix} 1 & 1 & 0 & 0 \\ 0 & 1 & 1 & 0 \\ 0 & 0 & 1 & 1 \\ 0 & 0 & 0 & 1 \end{bmatrix} \tag{10}$$

Let $A^1 = L^1 R^1$. This special matrix A^1 will count the number μ for us.

Applied to the matrix A^1, formula (2') becomes

$$r_{ij}^1 = 1 = a_{ij}^1 - \sum_{k=\max(1, j-w+1)}^{i-1} 1 \qquad [j = i, \ldots, \min(i + w - 1, n)] \tag{11}$$

The summation in (11) counts 1 for each multiplication used in the general calculation (2') of r_{ij}. Therefore, by (11), the number of multiplications in the calculation of r_{ij} equals $a_{ij}^1 - 1$. For example, if $n = 4$ and $w = 2$,

$$A^1 = \begin{bmatrix} 1 & 1 & 0 & 0 \\ 1 & 2 & 1 & 0 \\ 0 & 1 & ② & 1 \\ 0 & 0 & 1 & 2 \end{bmatrix} \tag{12}$$

The circled 2 in (12) shows that the general calculation of r_{33} requires $a_{33}^1 - 1 = 2 - 1 = 1$ multiplication. Indeed, this is correct because the limits in the summation (2') for r_{33} are $k = \max(1, j - w + 1) = \max(1, 3 - 2 + 1) = 2$, and $k = i - 1 = 3 - 1 = 2$, so that the summation does contain exactly one multiplication $l_{ik} r_{kj}$.

Observe that A^1 is an $n \times n$ matrix of bandwidth w. Therefore, the total number of multiplications used to form R equals

$$\sum_{i \leqslant j \leqslant i+w-1} (a_{ij}^1 - 1) = \sum_{i \leqslant j} a_{ij}^1 - \tau \tag{13}$$

where τ is the number of calculated r_{ij}. Equivalently, τ is the number of

1's in R^1. The example (10) illustrates that

$$\tau = \underbrace{w + w + \cdots + w +}_{n - w + 1 \text{ times}} (w - 1) + (w - 2) + \cdots + 1 \qquad (14)$$

Thus,

$$\tau = (n - w + 1)w + \tfrac{1}{2}w(w - 1) \qquad (15)$$

The matrix A^1 is symmetric because L^1 is the transpose of R^1. Therefore,

$$\sum_{i=1}^{n} \sum_{j=1}^{n} a_{ij}^1 = 2 \sum_{i \leqslant j} a_{ij}^1 - \sum_{i=1}^{n} a_{ii}^1 \qquad (16)$$

From this identity we can compute the sum (13). First we observe, from the product form $A^1 = L^1 R^1$,

$$a_{11}^1 = 1, \quad a_{22}^1 = 2, \ldots, a_{w-1,w-1}^1 = w - 1, \quad a_{ii}^1 = w \qquad (\text{for } i \geqslant w)$$

Therefore, by (15),

$$\sum_{i=1}^{n} a_{ii}^1 = \tfrac{1}{2}w(w - 1) + (n - w + 1)w = \tau \qquad (17)$$

Let $u = \text{col}\,(1, 1, \ldots, 1)$. Then we have the quadratic form

$$\sum_{i=1}^{n} \sum_{j=1}^{n} a_{ij}^1 = u^T A^1 u \qquad (18)$$

But

$$
\begin{aligned}
u^T A^1 u = u^T L^1 R^1 u = u^T (R^1)^T R^1 u \\
= (R^1 u)^T (R^1 u) = \| R^1 u \|^2
\end{aligned}
\qquad (19)$$

Now

$$R^1 u = \text{col}\,(\underbrace{w, w, \ldots, w}_{n - w + 1 \text{ times}}, w - 1, w - 2, \ldots, 1) \qquad (20)$$

Therefore, the square of the length equals

$$\| R^1 u \|^2 = (n - w + 1)w^2 + (w - 1)^2 + (w - 2)^2 + \cdots + 1^2$$

or

$$\sum_{i=1}^{n} \sum_{j=1}^{n} a_{ij}^1 = (n - w + 1)w^2 + \tfrac{1}{6}(w - 1)w(2w - 1) \qquad (21)$$

From (16), (17), and (21) we compute

$$\sum_{i \leqslant j} a_{ij}^1 = \tfrac{1}{2}[(n - w + 1)w^2 + \tfrac{1}{6}(w - 1)w(2w - 1) + \tau] \qquad (22)$$

If A is non-Hermitian, formula (3') is used to compute L. Applied to L^1, R^1, and A^1, (3') gives

$$l_{ij}^1 = 1 = a_{ij}^1 - \sum_{k=\max(1, i-w+1)}^{j-1} 1 \qquad [i = j + 1, \ldots, \min(j + w - 1, n)] \qquad (23)$$

The summation in (23) counts 1 for each multiplication used in (3'); therefore, the number of multiplications is $a_{ij}^1 - 1$. Formula (3') also contains a division by r_{jj}. Therefore, a_{ij}^1 counts the multiplications and the division used to compute l_{ij}. Since $l_{ij} = a_{ij}^1 = 0$ when $i \geqslant j + w$, the total number of multiplications and divisions used to compute L is $\sum a_{ij}^1$ summed for $i > j$. Since A^1 is symmetric,

$$\sum_{j>i} a_{ij}^1 = \tfrac{1}{2}(\sum_{i=1}^{n} \sum_{j=1}^{n} a_{ij}^1 - \sum_{i=1}^{n} a_{ii}^1) \qquad (24)$$
$$= \tfrac{1}{2}[(n - w + 1)w^2 + \tfrac{1}{6}(w - 1)w(2w - 1) - \tau]$$

When the contribution (24) from L is added to the contribution (13) from R, we find, by (22) and (15),

$$\mu = (n - w + 1)w^2 + \tfrac{1}{6}(w - 1)w(2w - 1) - (n - w + 1)w \qquad (25)$$
$$- \tfrac{1}{2}w(w - 1)$$

Algebraic simplification gives the required formula (7).

If A is Hermitian, the calculation (4') of l_{ij} just consists of one division. The contribution to μ from L is then just

$$1 + 2 + \cdots + (w - 1) + (n - w)(w - 1) = \tau - n \qquad (26)$$

Adding this to the contribution (13) from R, we find

$$\mu = \sum_{i \leqslant j} a_{ij}^1 - n \qquad (\text{if } A = A^*)$$

The identities (22) and (15) now yield

$$\mu = \tfrac{1}{2}[(n - w + 1)w^2 + \tfrac{1}{6}(w - 1)w(2w - 1) + (n - w + 1)w$$
$$+ \tfrac{1}{2}w(w - 1)] - n$$

which reduces algebraically to (8).

To solve $LRx = b$ requires some additional number μ' of multiplications and divisions. Solving $Lc = b$ for c requires

$$1 + 2 + \cdots + (w - 1) + (n - w)(w - 1) \tag{27}$$

multiplications. Solving $Rx = c$ for x requires

$$1 + 2 + \cdots + w + (n - w)w \tag{28}$$

multiplications and divisions. The sum of (27) and (28) is

$$\boxed{\mu' = (2w - 1)n - w(w - 1)} \tag{29}$$

The total number of multiplications required to solve $Ax = b$ is $\mu + \mu'$.

PROBLEMS

1. Consider electrical network of resistors and one battery in Figure 7.5.

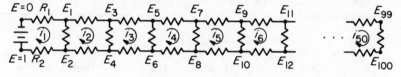

Figure 7.5

If there is a resistor between nodes i and j, call the resistance $R_{ij} = R_{ji}$. Suppose that equations were written for the unknown voltages $E_1, \ldots, E_{100}$. For example, the equation at node 5 is

$$\frac{E_5 - E_3}{R_{53}} + \frac{E_5 - E_6}{R_{56}} + \frac{E_5 - E_7}{R_{57}} = 0$$

The equation at node 2 is

$$\frac{E_2 - 1}{R_2} + \frac{E_2 - E_1}{R_{21}} + \frac{E_2 - E_4}{R_{24}} = 0$$

Suppose that the equations in matrix-vector form are $Ax = b$, where $x = \text{col}\,(E_1, \ldots, E_{100})$. The vector b is nonzero; what are its components? The 100×100 matrix A is a band-matrix; what is its bandwidth, w? What are the components in the 84th row of A?

2. Show that the matrix A in Problem 1 is symmetric. Show that the quadratic form of A equals

$$(Ax, x) = \frac{E_1^2}{R_1} + \frac{E_2^2}{R_2} + \frac{1}{2} \sum_{i=1}^{100} \sum_{j=1}^{100} \frac{(E_i - E_j)^2}{R_{ij}}$$

where $R_{ij}^{-1} \equiv 0$ if there is no resistor between nodes i and j. Conclude that A is positive definite. (HINT: The quadratic form of A is

$$(Ax, x) = \frac{E_1^2}{R_1} + \frac{E_2^2}{R_2} + \sum_i \sum_j \frac{E_i - E_j}{R_{ij}} E_i$$

Reverse the indices i and j. Add the two expressions for (Ax, x), and divide by 2. Use the symmetry of R_{ij}.)

3. Why can the matrix A in Problem 1 be factored in the form $A = LR$? How many multiplications, μ, are needed for this factorization? What is the total number of multiplications, $\mu + \mu'$, needed to solve for the unknown potentials $E_1, \ldots, E_{100}$?

4. A full 100×100 matrix requires 10,000 computer-storage locations. How many computer-storage locations are required to store the symmetric band-matrix A in Problem 1?

5. Suppose that the voltages in Problem 1 were renamed as follows: On the upper row, call the unknown voltages $V_1, V_2, \ldots, V_{50}$; on the lower row, call the unknown voltages $V_{51}, V_{52}, \ldots, V_{100}$. If a matrix-vector equation is written for the renamed voltages, what is the bandwidth of the matrix?

6. Define the *mesh* currents $i_1, i_2, \ldots, i_{50}$ as indicated in Figure 7.5. The current between nodes 1 and 3 is i_2. The net current between nodes 5 and 6 is the difference $i_3 - i_4$. The equations for the mesh currents are

$$R_1 i_1 + R_{12}(i_1 - i_2) + R_2 i_1 = 1 \quad \text{(first loop)}$$
$$R_{21}(i_2 - i_1) + R_{13} i_2 + R_{34}(i_2 - i_3) + R_{42} i_2 = 0 \quad \text{(second loop)}$$
$$R_{43}(i_3 - i_2) + R_{35} i_3 + R_{56}(i_3 - i_4) + R_{64} i_3 = 0 \quad \text{(third loop)}$$

etc. If these equations are written in matrix-vector form, $Ax = b$, show that A is a 50×50, *tridiagonal* ($w = 2$) matrix.

7. Show that the matrix A in Problem 6 is symmetric and positive definite.

8. How many multiplications, $\mu + \mu'$, are needed to solve for the mesh currents in Problem 6? Problems 1, 5, and 6 present three different mathematical formulations of the same physical problem. Which of these formulations is the best for computation?

9. *The continued fractions related to a triadiagonal matrix:* Let

$$A = \begin{bmatrix} b_1 & c_1 & 0 & 0 \\ a_1 & b_2 & c_2 & 0 \\ 0 & a_2 & b_3 & c_3 \\ 0 & 0 & a_3 & b_4 \end{bmatrix}$$

and assume

$$b_1 \neq 0, \quad \begin{vmatrix} b_1 & c_1 \\ a_1 & b_2 \end{vmatrix} \neq 0, \ldots, \det A \neq 0$$

Show that

$$A = \begin{bmatrix} 1 & 0 & 0 & 0 \\ \dfrac{a_1}{r_1} & 1 & 0 & 0 \\ 0 & \dfrac{a_2}{r_2} & 1 & 0 \\ 0 & 0 & \dfrac{a_3}{r_3} & 1 \end{bmatrix} \begin{bmatrix} r_1 & c_1 & 0 & 0 \\ 0 & r_2 & c_2 & 0 \\ 0 & 0 & r_3 & c_3 \\ 0 & 0 & 0 & r_4 \end{bmatrix}$$

where the unknowns $r_1, \ldots, r_4$ are given by

$$r_1 = b_1, \qquad r_{i+1} = b_{i+1} - \frac{a_i c_i}{r_i} \quad (i \geqslant 1)$$

Replace 4 by n and generalize this result.

10. In the factorization discussed in Problem 9, if A is Hermitian and positive definite, show that

$$0 < r_k \leqslant b_k \qquad (k = 1, \ldots, n)$$

11.* In Problem 10, show that all $r_k \geqslant$ the smallest eigenvalue of A. [Use the inclusion theorem, Section 6.4, and the identity $r_1 \ldots r_\nu = \det (a_{ij})(i, j = 1, \ldots, \nu)$, Section 7.3.]

7.5 REDUCTION OF ROUNDING ERROR

Digital computers do not do arithmetic exactly. A number stored in a digital computer has only a certain number of significant figures. For example, the number may be stored in binary, floating-point form as

$$x = 2^5 \, (.10011001) \tag{1}$$

This number has an exponent $e = 5$, and it has $s = 8$ significant figures, called "bits" in the binary form. The numerical value of x is

$$x = 32 \left(\tfrac{1}{2} + \tfrac{0}{4} + \tfrac{0}{8} + \tfrac{1}{16} + \tfrac{1}{32} + \tfrac{0}{64} + \tfrac{0}{128} + \tfrac{1}{256} \right) \tag{2}$$

If only s significant figures are conserved, computation produces rounding error. For example, if

$$y = 2^{-1}(.10101011) \tag{3}$$

The number $x + y$ is computed as follows:

$$\begin{aligned} x + y &= 2^5(.10011001) \\ &\quad + 2^5(.00000010101011) \\ &= 2^5(.10011011101011) \end{aligned} \tag{4}$$

If z is the computed value of the sum in single precision, with $s = 8$, we write

$$z \stackrel{1}{=} 2^5(.10011100) \tag{5}$$

The number equal to z results from rounding the precise sum (4) to 8 significant bits; in this case we round up, since the first neglected bit is a 1.

We shall use the notation $x \stackrel{1}{=} \ldots$ to mean that x is the computed value of ... if the computation is performed (by some prescribed algorithm) in single precision. If the computation is performed in double precision, we shall write $x \stackrel{2}{=} \ldots$. If s significant bits are used in single precision, then $2s$ bits are used in double precision; in current practice, $s = 27$ or some greater number. The sign "$=$" shall designate exact equality.

EXAMPLE 1. Let $s = 3$. Let

$$
\begin{aligned}
x &= 2^6(.101) = 64\left(\frac{1}{2} + 0 + \frac{1}{8}\right) \\
y &= 2^2(.111) = 4\left(\frac{1}{2} + \frac{1}{4} + \frac{1}{8}\right)
\end{aligned}
\tag{6}
$$

Let

$$u = x + y, \quad v \stackrel{1}{=} x + y \text{ and } w \stackrel{2}{=} x + y$$

Since $y = 2^6(.0000111)$, we have

$$
\begin{aligned}
u &= 2^6(.1010111) \\
v &= 2^6(.101) \\
w &= 2^6(.101100)
\end{aligned}
\tag{7}
$$

Observe that the true sum u is rounded down to produce v, since the first neglected bit is 0; u is rounded up to produce w, since the first neglected bit is 1.

Rounding error in matrix computations is discussed at length in a book by J. H. Wilkinson.[1] Here we shall only present two simple suggestions and give one crude analysis. Our arguments will be not mathematically rigorous, but only suggestive.

The first suggestion is to *accumulate inner products in double precision* before rounding to single precision. Whenever an expression $x_1y_1 + \cdots + x_ky_k$ has to be computed, there is a great gain in accuracy if

$$x_1y_1; \; x_1y_1 + x_2y_2; \; x_1y_1 + x_2y_2 + x_3y_3; \; \ldots$$

[1] J. H. Wilkinson, *Rounding Errors in Algebraic Processes*. Englewood Cliffs, N.J.: Prentice-Hall, Inc., 1963.

are successively computed in double precision. The final value is then rounded to s significant bits, and the computation proceeds. Of course, if there are time and memory enough to perform the whole computation in double precision, so much the better.

The second suggestion is more elaborate. Suppose that we have solved a large system of equations $Ax = b$ in single precision by some algorithm, say that of the preceding section. If the computed solution is called c, we write

$$c \overset{1}{=} A^{-1}b \tag{8}$$

To assess the error, we compute the residual vector $b - Ac$ in double precision, obtaining

$$e \overset{2}{=} b - Ac \tag{9}$$

We now try to diminish the residual $b - Ac$ by computing

$$d \overset{1}{=} A^{-1}e \tag{10}$$

and by forming the new vector

$$y \overset{2}{=} c + d \tag{11}$$

The vector y *is usually an improved value for* A^{-1}b; in other words, we assert that usually

$$|y - A^{-1}b| < |c - A^{-1}b| \tag{12}$$

if $|\ \ |$ is some convenient norm (see Section 6.9). The assertion (12) is motivated as follows: If e were the exact value of the residual, $b - Ac$, and if d were exactly $A^{-1}e$, then we should have

$$Ay = (Ac) + (Ad) = (b - e) + (e) = b$$

The objection, of course, is that we have used a single-precision solution (10) to correct a single-precision solution (8). This objection is usually not valid because c equals $A^{-1}b$ apart from an error which is usually a small fraction of b in norm. The vector e practically equals $b - Ac$ because e is computed in double precision. From (10), the vector d equals $A^{-1}e$ apart from an error which is a small fraction of e, and therefore a *very* small fraction of b. Thus, d has less absolute error than c does, and it makes sense to add d as a correction to c.

Now we will make the reasoning in the preceding paragraph more precise. Refer to the computational equations (8)–(11). We shall estimate the errors $c - A^{-1}b$ and $y - A^{-1}b$. The error $c - A^{-1}b$ can often be estimated by some inequality

$$|c - A^{-1}b| \leqslant \alpha |A^{-1}||b| \cdot 2^{-s} \tag{13}$$

where $|A^{-1}|$ is the norm of A^{-1}, $|b|$ is the norm of b, s is the number of significant bits in single-precision computation, and α is some not-too-large constant depending only on the prescribed solution algorithm and on the number n of components in the vector b. Similarly, for the error in the double-precision computation (9), we write

$$|e - (b - Ac)| \leqslant \beta(|b| + |A||c|) \cdot 2^{-2s} \tag{14}$$

where β is some constant like α. Following (13), we write for the error in the single-precision solution (10)

$$|d - A^{-1}e| \leqslant \alpha |A^{-1}||e| \cdot 2^{-s} \tag{15}$$

Finally, from (11) we write

$$|y - (c + d)| \leqslant \gamma(|c| + |d|) \cdot 2^{-2s} \tag{16}$$

where γ is some constant like α and β.

We can estimate $y - A^{-1}b$ from the preceding inequalities.

$$y - A^{-1}b = [y - (c + d)] + [d - A^{-1}e] + A^{-1}[e - (b - Ac)] \tag{17}$$

Therefore,

$$\begin{aligned}|y - A^{-1}b| \leqslant \gamma(|c| + |d|)2^{-2s} + \alpha |A^{-1}||e| \cdot 2^{-s} \\ + |A^{-1}|\beta(|b| + |A||c|) \cdot 2^{-2s}\end{aligned} \tag{18}$$

The quantities b and A are given; we must estimate $|c|$, $|d|$, and $|e|$. From (13),

$$|c| \leqslant |A^{-1}b| + \alpha |A^{-1}||b|2^{-s} \leqslant (1 + \alpha 2^{-s})|A^{-1}||b| \equiv \rho_c \tag{19}$$

From (14), (13), and (19) we find

$$\begin{aligned}|e| \leqslant |b - Ac| + \beta(|b| + |A||c|)2^{-2s} \\ |e| \leqslant |A|\alpha |A^{-1}||b|2^{-s} + \beta(|b| + |A|\rho_c)2^{-2s} \equiv \rho_e 2^{-s}\end{aligned} \tag{20}$$

Now (15) gives

$$|d| \leqslant |A^{-1}e| + \alpha |A^{-1}||e|2^{-s} \leqslant (1 + \alpha 2^{-s})|A^{-1}|\rho_e 2^{-s} \equiv \rho_d 2^{-s} \tag{21}$$

As just defined, the numbers ρ_c, ρ_e, ρ_d are of moderate size unless $|b|$, $|A|$, or $|A^{-1}|$ is large. Regarding s as a parameter, we may say that c is of order 1, while e and d are of order 2^{-s}. From (18) we now find

$$|y - A^{-1}b| \leqslant \gamma(\rho_c + \rho_d 2^{-s}) 2^{-2s} + \alpha |A^{-1}| (\rho_e 2^{-s}) 2^{-s}$$
$$+ |A^{-1}| \beta (|b| + |A| \rho_c) \cdot 2^{-2s} \equiv \rho \cdot 2^{-2s} \tag{22}$$

Thus, as a function of s, the original error $c - A^{-1}b$ is of order 2^{-s}; but the new error $y - A^{-1}b$ is of order 2^{-2s}. For further analysis, one could put the right-hand side of (22) in an explicit form by evaluating the constants ρ_c, ρ_e, and ρ_d from the definitions (19), (20), (21).

PROBLEMS

1. Let x_1 and x_2 be two binary numbers

$$x_1 = (2^m)(.a_1 a_2 a_3 a_4), \qquad x_2 = (2^n)(.b_1 b_2 b_3 b_4)$$

Here we have $s = 4$ significant bits. Assume $m \geqslant n$, and assume $a_1 = b_1 = 1$. Form the single precision sum or difference

$$y \stackrel{1}{=} x_1 \pm x_2$$

Let there be rounding up or rounding down, depending upon whether the first neglected bit is a 1 or a 0. Let $z = x_1 \pm x_2$. Show that

$$|z - y| \leqslant 2^{m-s-1} \leqslant 2^{-s} x_1$$

Deduce that y can be written in the form

$$y = x_1(1 + \epsilon_1) \pm x_2(1 + \epsilon_2)$$

where $|\epsilon_1| \leqslant 2^{-s}$ and $|\epsilon_2| \leqslant 2^{-s}$.

2. Let x_1 and x_2 be defined as in Problem 1. Let

$$y \stackrel{1}{=} x_1 \cdot x_2$$

Show that $y = x_1 x_2 (1 + \epsilon)$, where $|\epsilon| < 2^{-s}$.

7.6 THE GAUSS-SEIDEL AND OTHER ITERATIVE METHODS

To solve large systems of equations $Ax = b$, particularly those occurring in the numerical analysis of partial differential equations, we may use an iterative method. Beginning with an initial guess x^0, we compute an improved guess x^1. From x^1 we obtain an improved guess x^2, etc. The method converges if, for every initial guess x^0, the vectors $x^1, x^2, \ldots$ tend to the true solution x.

The simplest iterative method is the Gauss-Seidel method. For notational simplicity we shall write $u = x^k$ and $v = x^{k+1}$; the manner of forming x^{k+1} from x^k is independent of k. The first guess x^0 is chosen in any convenient manner, e.g., $x^0 = 0$ or $x^0 =$ some vector which appears to approximate the desired solution x.

If all $a_{ii} \neq 0$, for $n = 3$ the system $Ax = b$ may be written in the form

$$
\begin{aligned}
x_1 &= a_{11}^{-1}(b_1 && - a_{12}x_2 - a_{13}x_3) \\
x_2 &= a_{22}^{-1}(b_2 - a_{21}x_1 && - a_{23}x_3) \\
x_3 &= a_{33}^{-1}(b_3 - a_{31}x_1 - a_{32}x_2 &&)
\end{aligned} \tag{1}
$$

The equations (1) suggest the following scheme for obtaining an improved guess v from a given guess u:

$$
\begin{aligned}
v_1 &= a_{11}^{-1}(b_1 && - a_{12}u_2 - a_{13}u_3) \\
v_2 &= a_{22}^{-1}(b_2 - a_{21}v_1 && - a_{23}u_3) \\
v_3 &= a_{33}^{-1}(b_3 - a_{31}v_1 - a_{32}v_2 &&)
\end{aligned} \tag{2}
$$

Observe that, after a component v_i has been computed, it is used in all subsequent equations. Thus, v_1 appears on the right-hand sides of the last two equations; v_2 appears on the right-hand side of the last equation. For general n the scheme is

$$
v_i = a_{ii}^{-1}(b_i - \sum_{j<i} a_{ij}v_j - \sum_{j>i} a_{ij}u_j) \qquad (i = 1, \ldots, n) \tag{3}
$$

Thus, for $k = 0, 1, 2, \ldots$ we define an infinite sequence of vectors $x^1, x^2, \ldots$ by the scheme

$$
x_i^{(k+1)} = a_{ii}^{-1}(b_i - \sum_{j<i} a_{ij}x_j^{(k+1)} - \sum_{j>i} a_{ij}x_j^{(k)}) \qquad (i = 1, \ldots, n) \tag{4}
$$

We assume $\det A \neq 0$ and all $a_{ii} \neq 0$. We ask whether

$$
x^{(k)} \longrightarrow x = A^{-1}b \qquad (\text{as } k \to \infty) \tag{5}
$$

If the kth error-vector is $d^k = x^k - x$, the limit (5) exists if $d^k \to 0$ as $k \to \infty$. For notational simplicity, let

$$
d = d^k = u - x, \qquad e = d^{k+1} = v - x
$$

Subtracting the equations

$$
x_i = a_{ii}^{-1}(b_i - \sum_{j<i} a_{ij}x_j - \sum_{j>i} a_{ij}x_j) \qquad (i = 1, \ldots, n) \tag{6}
$$

from the equations (3), we find

$$
e_i = a_{ii}^{-1}(-\sum_{j<i} a_{ij}e_j - \sum_{j>i} a_{ij}d_j) \tag{7}
$$

Define the matrices L and R as follows:

$$l_{ij} = \begin{cases} a_{ij} & (\text{if } i \geqslant j) \\ 0 & (\text{if } i < j) \end{cases} \qquad r_{ij} = \begin{cases} 0 & (\text{if } i \geqslant j) \\ a_{ij} & (\text{if } i < j) \end{cases} \tag{8}$$

Thus, $A = L + R$. By (7),

$$\sum_{j \leqslant i} a_{ij} e_j = -\sum_{j > i} a_{ij} d_j \tag{9}$$

In other words, $Le = -Rd$, or

$$e = (-L^{-1}R)d \quad \text{or} \quad d^{k+1} = (-L^{-1}R)d^k \tag{10}$$

Applying (10) repeatedly, we find

$$d^k = (-L^{-1}R)^k d^0 \qquad (k = 0, 1, \dots) \tag{11}$$

On the left-hand side of (11), k is a superscript; on the right-hand side, k is an exponent. We now show:

Theorem 1. *Let* A *be an* $n \times n$ *matrix with* $\det A \neq 0$ *and all* $a_{ii} \neq 0$. *Then the vectors* $x^1, x^2, \dots$ *defined by the Gauss-Seidel method* (4) *converge to the limit* $x = A^{-1}b$ *for every initial guess* x^0 *if and only if all roots* λ *of the equation*

$$\begin{vmatrix} \lambda a_{11} & a_{12} & \cdots & a_{1n} \\ \lambda a_{21} & \lambda a_{22} & \cdots & a_{2n} \\ \cdot & \cdot & \cdots & \cdot \\ \lambda a_{n1} & \lambda a_{n2} & \cdots & \lambda a_{nn} \end{vmatrix} = 0 \tag{12}$$

lie in the unit circle $|\lambda| < 1$.

EXAMPLE 1. For $n = 2$ the equation (12) becomes

$$\lambda^2 a_{11} a_{22} - \lambda a_{12} a_{21} = 0$$

The roots of this equation are $\lambda = 0$ and $\lambda = a_{12}a_{21}/(a_{11}a_{22})$. Thus, for $n = 2$, the Gauss-Seidel method converges for every initial guess if and only if $|a_{12}a_{21}| < |a_{11}a_{22}|$.

Proof of Theorem 1. Equation (11) states

$$x^k - x = (-L^{-1}R)^k(x^0 - x) \tag{13}$$

The vector $x^0 - x$ is arbitrary because x^0 is arbitrary. Letting $M = -L^{-1}R$, we ask when the vectors $M^k d^0$ tend to zero as $k \to \infty$ for every vector d^0.

Clearly, the vectors $M^k d^0$ tend to zero if the matrices M^k tend to the zero matrix. If $M^k \not\rightarrow O$, then some component, say the r, s component, of M^k does not tend to zero. Then if d^0 equals the unit vector e^s, the rth component of the vectors $M^k e^s$ cannot tend to zero. Hence, $x^k \rightarrow x$ *for all* x^0 *if and only if the matrix powers* M^k *tend to* O.

Theorem 3 of Section 4.9 states that $M^k \rightarrow O$ if and only if all eigenvalues λ of M lie in the unit circle $|\lambda| < 1$. But

$$\det(\lambda I - M) = \det(\lambda I + L^{-1}R)$$
$$= \frac{\det(\lambda L + R)}{\det L} \tag{14}$$

Since $\det L$ is the nonzero constant Πa_{ii}, we have $\det(\lambda I - M) = 0$ if and only if $\det(\lambda L + R) = 0$; but this is equation (12), and the proof is complete.

Next we shall present a general theorem of H. B. Keller which implies that *the Gauss-Seidel method converges for every positive-definite Hermitian matrix* A.

Theorem 2. *Let* A *be an* n × n *positive-definite Hermitian matrix. Let* N *be any nonsingular* n × n *matrix for which the Hermitian matrix* N + N* − A *is positive definite. Given an initial vector* x^0, *form* $x^1, x^2, \ldots$ *from the iteration scheme*

$$Nx^{k+1} = b + (N - A)x^k \qquad (k = 0, 1, \ldots) \tag{15}$$

Then, for every x^0, $x^k \rightarrow A^{-1}b$ *as* k → ∞.

In the Gauss-Seidel method (3), we have

$$Lx^{k+1} = b - Rx^k \tag{16}$$

where the matrices L and R are defined in (8). In the notation of (15),

$$N = L, \qquad N - A = -R, \quad \text{and} \quad N + N^* - A = \text{diag}(a_{11}, \ldots, a_{nn}) \tag{17}$$

The diagonal matrix is positive definite because all $a_{ii} > 0$ in positive-definite matrix A. Thus, the hypothesis of Theorem 2 is satisfied.

Proof of Theorem 2. The solution $x = A^{-1}b$ satisfies $Nx = b + (N - A)x$. Subtraction from (15) yields

$$N(x^{k+1} - x) = (N - A)(x^k - x)$$
$$x^{k+1} - x = (I - N^{-1}A)(x^k - x) \tag{18}$$

Therefore,

$$x^k - x = (I - N^{-1}A)^k(x^0 - x) \qquad (k = 0, 1, \ldots) \tag{19}$$

As in the proof of Theorem 1, $x^k \to x$ *for every initial vector* x^0 *if and only if all eigenvalues* λ *of the matrix* $I - N^{-1}A$ *lie in the unit circle* $|\lambda| < 1$.

Let λ be an eigenvalue of $I - N^{-1}A$, and let $u \neq 0$ be an eigenvector. We will show that $|\lambda| < 1$. From $(I - N^{-1}A)u = \lambda u$ we find, after multiplying by N,

$$(1 - \lambda)Nu = Au \tag{20}$$

Taking the inner product of both sides with u, we find

$$(1 - \lambda)(Nu, u) = (Au, u) \tag{21}$$

Since the right-hand side is positive, $\lambda \neq 1$. The conjugate of equation (21) is

$$(1 - \bar{\lambda})(N^*u, u) = (Au, u) \tag{22}$$

because $\overline{(Nu, u)} = (u, Nu) = (N^*u, u)$. Let $\lambda = \alpha + i\beta$. Then (21) and (22) yield

$$\begin{aligned}
(Nu, u) + (N^*u, u) &= [(1 - \lambda)^{-1} + (1 - \bar{\lambda})^{-1}](Au, u) \\
&= \frac{2(1 - \alpha)}{(1 - \alpha)^2 + \beta^2}(Au, u)
\end{aligned} \tag{23}$$

Because $N + N^* - A$ is positive definite, the left-hand side is $> (Au, u)$. Division of (23) by (Au, u) now yields

$$1 < \frac{2(1 - \alpha)}{(1 - \alpha)^2 + \beta^2} \tag{24}$$

$$1 - 2\alpha + \alpha^2 + \beta^2 < 2 - 2\alpha$$

and hence $\alpha^2 + \beta^2 < 1$. Thus, $|\lambda|^2 < 1$, and the proof is complete.

RATE OF CONVERGENCE

In any iterative scheme of the form $Nx^{k+1} = b + (N - A)x^k$, the error $x^k - x$ equals $(I - N^{-1}A)^k$ times the initial error. For simplicity, suppose that the initial error has an expansion

$$x^0 - x = \sum_{j=1}^{n} \xi_j u^j \tag{25}$$

in the eigenvectors u^j of the matrix $T = I - N^{-1}A$. Let T have the eigenvalues λ_j, with $|\lambda_1| > |\lambda_j|$ for $j > 1$. Then

$$x^k - x = T^k(x^0 - x) = \lambda_1^k(\xi_1 u^1 + \sum_{j>1} \xi_j \rho_j^k u^j) \tag{26}$$

where

$$\rho_j^k = \left(\frac{\lambda_j}{\lambda_1}\right)^k \longrightarrow 0 \qquad (\text{as } k \to \infty \quad \text{for } j > 1)$$

Then, if $\xi_1 \neq 0$,

$$x^k - x \cong \lambda_1^k \xi_1 u^1 \qquad (\text{as } k \to \infty) \tag{27}$$

If the norm $|u^1| = 1$, we have the norm of the error

$$|x^k - x| \cong |\lambda_1|^k |\xi_1| \qquad (\text{as } k \to \infty) \tag{28}$$

Thus, *the rate of convergence is determined by the dominant eigenvalue* λ_1.

If $\epsilon > 0$ is very small, the number ν of iterations required so that $|x^\nu - x| \leqslant \epsilon$ is determined approximately by the equation $|\lambda_1|^\nu |\xi_1| = \epsilon$. Therefore,

$$\nu \cong \nu_e \log \frac{|\xi_1|}{\epsilon} \tag{29}$$

where

$$\nu_e = \left(\log \frac{1}{|\lambda_1|}\right)^{-1} \tag{30}$$

The number ν_e is approximately equal to the number of iterations necessary to divide an initial error by the factor $e = 2.718\ldots$, since $|\lambda_1|$ raised to the power ν_e equals $1/e$. The number ν_e depends only on the matrices A and N; ν_e *is a measure of the slowness of the iteration scheme* $Nx^{k+1} = (N - A)x^k + b$. A different scheme, with a measure of slowness ν_e', is twice as slow if $\nu_e' = 2\nu_e$. *The rate of convergence may be defined as* $1/\nu_e = \log(1/|\lambda_1|)$.

The assumption (25) that the initial error $x^0 - x$ can be developed in a series of eigenvectors of T, is not important; nor is it important that T have a single dominant eigenvalue of multiplicity one. An initial error $x^0 - x$ has an expansion

$$x^0 - x = p^1 + p^2 + \cdots + p^s \tag{31}$$

in principal vectors (see Section 5.2) associated with the different eigenvalues $\lambda_1, \lambda_2, \ldots, \lambda_s$ of T. If λ_j has multiplicity m_j, then

$$T^k p^j = (T - \lambda_j I + \lambda_j I)^k p^j$$

$$= \sum_{0 \leqslant \nu < m_j} \binom{k}{\nu} \lambda_j^{k-\nu} (T - \lambda_j I)^\nu p^j \qquad (k \geqslant m_j - 1) \tag{32}$$

The series terminates with $\nu = m_j - 1$ because the principal vector p^j has grade $g \leqslant m_j$. If $g = 0$, then $p^j = 0$. If $g \geqslant 1$, then (32) implies

$$|T^k p^j| \cong \gamma_j k^{g-1} |\lambda_j|^{k-g+1} \qquad (\text{as } k \to \infty) \tag{33}$$

where γ_j is the constant (independent of k):

$$\gamma_j = \frac{1}{(g-1)!} |(T - \lambda_j I)^{g-1} p^j| \tag{34}$$

Here we have used the asymptotic form for the binomial coefficient:

$$\binom{k}{g-1} = \frac{k(k-1) \ldots (k-g+2)}{(g-1)!} \cong \frac{k^{g-1}}{(g-1)!} \qquad (\text{as } k \to \infty) \tag{35}$$

Let $|\lambda_1| \geqslant \cdots \geqslant |\lambda_s|$. Let g be the largest grade of principal vectors p^j of maximum modulus $|\lambda_j| = |\lambda_1|$. Assume $|\lambda_1| > 0$. Then $T^k \sum p^j$ behaves, as $k \to \infty$, like a bounded vector times the scalar $k^{g-1} |\lambda_1|^k$. Define ν_e to be the average number of iterations needed to divide the error by the factor $e = 2.718 \ldots$. Then for large numbers r of repetitions of ν_e iterations, we should have the approximate equation

$$(r\nu_e)^{g-1} |\lambda_1|^{(r\nu_e)} \cong e^{-r}$$

Taking logarithms, we find

$$(g-1)(\log r + \log \nu_e) + (r\nu_e) \log |\lambda_1| \cong -r$$

Dividing by r and letting $r \to \infty$, we obtain

$$\nu_e \log |\lambda_1| = -1 \tag{36}$$

which yields $\nu_e = 1/\log (1/|\lambda_1|)$, as in (30).

Faster iterative methods are based on the choice of N to reduce $|\lambda_1|$. *Successive over-relaxation*, in a simple form, relies on the choice of the parameter $\omega > 1$ to reduce $|\lambda_1|$ for the scheme

$$v_i - u_i = \omega a_{ii}^{-1} (b_i - \sum_{j<i} a_{ij} v_j - \sum_{j>i} a_{ij} u_j) \qquad (i = 1, \ldots, n) \tag{37}$$

where $u = x^k$ and $v = x^{k+1}$. Such methods are studied in *Matrix Iterative Analysis* by R. S. Varga (Prentice-Hall, Inc., 1962).

PROBLEMS

1. Let A be an $n \times n$ Hermitian matrix, and assume all $a_{ii} > 0$. Let e^k be the kth unit vector. If a vector u is given, show (by calculus) that the unique value of the real parameter λ which minimizes $[A(u - \lambda e^k), (u - \lambda e^k)]$ is

$$\lambda = \frac{1}{a_{ii}} \sum_{j=1}^{n} a_{ij} u_j$$

2. Let A be an $n \times n$, nonsingular Hermitian matrix with all $a_{ii} > 0$. Let x and y be successive iterates in the Gauss-Seidel process for solving $Az = b$. Let u and v be the successive errors $u = x - z$, $v = y - z$. From the result of Problem 1, show that

$$(Av, v) \leqslant (Au, u)$$

with equality if $v = u = 0$. (Note that v is formed from u by a succession of n transformations of the form $u \to u - \lambda e^k$. Note also that $v = u$ implies $Au = 0$, which implies $u = 0$.)

3. Let A be an $n \times n$ nonsingular Hermitian matrix with all $a_{ii} > 0$. From the result of Problem 2, prove that the Gauss-Seidel method converges for the matrix A *only* if A is positive definite.

4. Generalize Theorem 1 for the successive over-relaxation scheme (37).

5.* Let

$$A = \begin{bmatrix} 3 & -1 \\ -1 & 2 \end{bmatrix}$$

For which real values of ω does the successive over-relaxation method (37) converge? For which value of ω is the rate of convergence maximized? Compare the maximum rate of convergence with the rate for the Gauss-Seidel method ($\omega = 1$). Graph the rate of convergence as a function of ω.

7.7 COMPUTATION OF EIGENVECTORS FROM KNOWN EIGENVALUES

Later we will discuss the computation of eigenvalues, but we hardly need to discuss the computation of eigenvectors. *If a simple eigenvalue is known, a corresponding eigenvector can be computed by solving a linear, inhomogeneous system of equations.*

EXAMPLE 1. Suppose that, for the matrix

$$A = \begin{bmatrix} 1 & 2 & 3 \\ 4 & 5 & 6 \\ 4 & 2 & 4 \end{bmatrix} \tag{1}$$

we have somehow computed an eigenvalue $\lambda = 1$. We wish to compute a corresponding eigenvector $x = \text{col}\,(x_1, x_2, x_3)$. At least one of the components x_i must be nonzero. We assume, say, $x_3 \neq 0$. If this highly probable assumption is correct, we may normalize the eigenvector x by requiring $x_3 = -1$. The equation $(A - \lambda I)x = 0$, with $\lambda = 1$, now takes the form

$$2x_2 + 3 = 0$$
$$4x_1 + 4x_2 + 6 = 0 \qquad (2)$$
$$4x_1 + 2x_2 + 3 = 0$$

Here we have three equations in two unknowns, x_1 and x_2. But *the last equation is redundant*, being the second equation minus the first. Therefore, we need only to satisfy the first two equations

$$2x_2 = -3, \qquad 4x_1 + 4x_2 = -6 \qquad (3)$$

This system has the unique solution $x_2 = -\frac{3}{2}$, $x_1 = 0$. Thus, we have computed the eigenvector $x = \text{col}\,(0, \frac{3}{2}, -1)$ belonging to the eigenvalue $\lambda = 1$.

In general, let A be an $n \times n$ matrix for which we have computed an eigenvalue. We wish to compute a corresponding eigenvector $x \neq 0$ satisfying the singular system

$$\sum_{j=1}^{n} (a_{ij} - \lambda \delta_{ij})x_j = 0 \qquad (i = 1, \ldots, n) \qquad (4)$$

Theorem 1. *Let* λ *be a* simple *eigenvalue of an* n $\times$ n *matrix* A. *Let* B_r *be the* (n − 1) $\times$ (n − 1) *matrix formed by omitting row r and column r from* $B = A - \lambda I$. *Then at least one of the matrices* $B_1, \ldots, B_n$ *is nonsingular.*

Proof. Let μ be a scalar variable. Let $\phi(\mu) = \det(A - \mu I)$. Since λ is a simple eigenvalue,

$$\phi(\lambda) = 0 \quad \text{and} \quad \phi'(\lambda) \neq 0 \qquad (5)$$

But, as we saw in Section 1.8, $\phi'(\mu)$ equals

$$\frac{d}{d\mu}\begin{vmatrix} a_{11} - \mu & a_{12} & \cdots & a_{1n} \\ a_{21} & a_{22} - \mu & \cdots & a_{2n} \\ \cdot & \cdot & \cdots & \cdot \\ a_{n1} & a_{n2} & \cdots & a_{nn} - \mu \end{vmatrix} = -\sum_{r=1}^{n} \det B_r \qquad \text{(when } \mu = \lambda) \qquad (6)$$

Therefore, at least one $\det B_r \neq 0$.

This result implies that the matrix $A - \lambda I$ has rank $n - 1$, and therefore that *all eigenvectors* x *belonging to the simple eigenvalue* λ *are scalar multiples* $x = \alpha x^0$ *of any one eigenvector* x^0.

Theorem 2. *Let* λ *be a simple eigenvalue of the* $n \times n$ *matrix* A. *In the notation of the last theorem, let* $\det B_q \neq 0$. *Then an eigenvector* x *can be computed by setting* $x_q = 1$ *and by solving the nonsingular system*

$$\sum_{\substack{j=1 \\ j \neq q}}^{n} (a_{ij} - \lambda \delta_{ij}) x_j = -a_{iq} \qquad (i = 1, \ldots, q-1, q+1, \ldots, n) \qquad (7)$$

Proof. The system (7) is nonsingular because its matrix is B_q, and $\det B_q \neq 0$. We will now show that the unique solution of (7) solves the extra equation

$$\sum_{\substack{j=1 \\ j \neq q}}^{n} a_{qj} x_j = -(a_{qq} - \lambda) \qquad (8)$$

Consider the singular matrix

$$\begin{bmatrix} a_{11} - \lambda & \cdots & a_{1q} & \cdots & a_{1n} \\ \cdot & \cdots & \cdot & \cdots & \cdot \\ a_{qq} & \cdots & a_{q1} - \lambda & \cdots & a_{qn} \\ \cdot & \cdots & \cdot & \cdots & \cdot \\ a_{n1} & \cdots & a_{nq} & \cdots & a_{nn} - \lambda \end{bmatrix} = A - \lambda I \qquad (9)$$

If we add x_j times column j to column q for all $j \neq q$, the result is a vector, v, with components $v_i = 0$ for all $i \neq q$; that is what (7) says. Expanding the determinant of the resulting matrix by column q, we find

$$v_q \det B_q = \det (A - \lambda I) = 0 \qquad (10)$$

where

$$v_q = a_{qq} - \lambda + \sum_{\substack{j=1 \\ j \neq q}}^{n} x_j a_{qj} \qquad (11)$$

Since $\det B_q \neq 0$, (10) implies $v_q = 0$; that is the extra equation (8). If we now define

$$x = \text{col}(x_1, \ldots, x_{q-1}, 1, x_{q+1}, \ldots, x_n) \qquad (12)$$

we have $(A - \lambda I)x = 0$, $x \neq 0$, as required.

If λ is a simple eigenvalue, the practical application of Theorem 2 requires only a little luck. We must choose q so that the B_q is nonsingular. By Theorem 1, *some* value q will succeed. Usually $\det B_q \neq 0$ for all q.

In practice, we first try $q = n$, as in Example 1. If $q = n$ fails, we try some $q \neq n$.

If λ is a multiple eigenvalue, the problem is more difficult. If $A - \lambda I$ has rank $r < n$, there are $\nu = n - r$ independent eigenvectors $x^1, \ldots, x^\nu$ corresponding to λ. In principle, the eigenvectors x^k can be found by first locating r independent columns of $A - \lambda I$. Let the *other* columns of $A - \lambda I$ be columns $j_1, \ldots, j_\nu$. Set

$$x_j^{(k)} = 1 \quad (\text{for } j = j_k) \qquad x_j^{(k)} = 0 \quad (\text{for all } j = j_\mu \neq j_k) \tag{13}$$

Now the equation $(A - \lambda I)x = 0$ can be rewritten as a nonsingular system of r equations in the r unknowns $x_j^{(k)}(j \neq j_1, \ldots, j_\nu)$.

In practice, the rank r of $A - \lambda I$ is usually unknown. If λ has multiplicity m, we can show only that $n - m \leqslant r \leqslant n - 1$. Further, the rank can seldom be computed numerically, since rounding error will produce nonzero values for certain determinants whose exact value is zero.

PROBLEMS

1. Let A be an $n \times n$ matrix, and let λ be an eigenvalue. If the rank of $A - \lambda I$ is r, why are there $n - r$ independent eigenvectors corresponding to λ? Can there be more than $n - r$ independent eigenvectors? (Use Theorem 5, Section 2.4).

2. For the matrix

$$A = \begin{bmatrix} 7 & 0 & 0 & 0 \\ 1 & 7 & 0 & 0 \\ 0 & 0 & 7 & 0 \\ 0 & 0 & 1 & 7 \end{bmatrix}$$

what is the multiplicity of the eigenvalue 7? What is the rank of $A - 7I$? What is the greatest number ν such that A has ν independent eigenvectors corresponding to the eigenvalue $\lambda = 7$? Calculate ν independent eigenvectors.

3. Calculate an eigenvector for the matrix

$$A = \begin{bmatrix} -1 & 2 & 3 \\ 4 & 3 & 6 \\ 7 & 8 & 7 \end{bmatrix}$$

corresponding to the eigenvalue $\lambda = -2$.

4. Calculate two linearly independent eigenvectors for the matrix

$$A = \begin{bmatrix} -1 & 2 & 3 \\ 1 & 0 & 3 \\ 1 & 2 & 1 \end{bmatrix}$$

corresponding to the eigenvalue $\lambda = -2$. Use formula (13) with $j_1 = 3$ and $j_2 = 1$. The eigenvectors will have the forms

$$x^{(1)} = \begin{bmatrix} 0 \\ \alpha \\ 1 \end{bmatrix}, \qquad x^{(2)} = \begin{bmatrix} 1 \\ \beta \\ 0 \end{bmatrix}$$

5. Let λ be an eigenvalue of multiplicity m for the $n \times n$ matrix A. Prove that

$$n - m \leqslant \text{rank } (A - \lambda I) \leqslant n - 1$$

(Use the method used to prove Theorem 1; here we have $\phi(\lambda) = \cdots = \phi^{(m-1)}(\lambda) = 0$, $\phi^{(m)}(\lambda) \neq 0$.)

6. In Problem 5, show that all the ranks r satisfying $n - m \leqslant r \leqslant n - 1$ can actually occur for certain matrices A. Illustrate all cases $r = 1, 2, 3$ when $n = 4$ and $m = 3$.

7.8 NUMERICAL INSTABILITY OF THE JORDAN CANONICAL FORM

In the preceding section we had an example of *numerical instability*. The problem was to compute the rank r of a singular matrix $B = A - \lambda I$. The integer r depends unstably on the data B. This is because an arbitrarily small perturbation of B produces a matrix B' whose rank r' may differ from r by a nonzero integer. Even if the data $B = (b_{ij})$ are stored with perfect precision, the method of computing rank by looking for the largest nonzero subdeterminant, is numerically unstable because an arbitrarily small error in the computation produces nonzero values for determinants whose true value is zero.

In general, if we wish to compute a quantity y from data x by some numerical method M, we may say that y depends unstably on x if small errors in the data x produce large errors in the computed quantity y even if the method M is executed with no rounding error. The method M is called numerically unstable if small rounding errors in the execution of M produce large errors in the computed value y even when the data are exact. *As a rule, one should not try to compute numerically unstable quantities, and one should not use numerically unstable methods.*

If A is an $n \times n$ matrix with multiple eigenvalues, quantities of great interest are the Jordan canonical form J and the associated matrix B of principal vectors (see Chapter 5). Unless A is known to be Hermitian or to have some other useful structure, *the quantities J and B depend unstably on A.*

EXAMPLE 1. If $\epsilon \neq 0$, and if T is nonsingular, the matrix

$$A = T \begin{bmatrix} 1 & 0 \\ \epsilon & 1 \end{bmatrix} T^{-1}$$

has the Jordan form

$$J = \begin{bmatrix} 1 & 0 \\ 1 & 1 \end{bmatrix}$$

But $\epsilon = 0$ yields the form $J = \text{diag}\,(1, 1)$.

EXAMPLE 2. If $\epsilon = 0$, the matrix

$$A_\epsilon = \begin{bmatrix} \epsilon & 0 \\ 1 & 0 \end{bmatrix}$$

has the Jordan form $J_0 = B_0^{-1}A_0B_0$, where

$$J_0 = \begin{bmatrix} 0 & 0 \\ 1 & 0 \end{bmatrix}, \qquad B_0 = \begin{bmatrix} 1 & 0 \\ 0 & 1 \end{bmatrix}$$

But if $\epsilon \neq 0$, we have $J_\epsilon = B_\epsilon^{-1}A_\epsilon B_\epsilon$, where

$$J_\epsilon = \begin{bmatrix} 0 & 0 \\ 0 & \epsilon \end{bmatrix}, \qquad B_\epsilon = \begin{bmatrix} 0 & \epsilon \\ 1 & 1 \end{bmatrix}$$

The matrices J_ϵ and B_ϵ do not approach J_0 and B_0 as $\epsilon \to 0$.

Sometimes a numerical method M is unstable even though the quantity to be computed, y, depends stably on the data, x. But if y depends unstably on x, every numerical method M will, as a rule, be unstable. The reason is that the method M prescribes certain computations: $u = f(x)$, $v = g(u, x)$, $\ldots, y = h(x, u, v \ldots)$. At the first stage, suppose that rounding error produces an inexact value u'. This value u' is exactly equal to $f(x')$ where x' is not exactly equal to x. Even if all later computations were exact, the computed value y' would be the exact value resulting from data $x' \neq x$. If the computed value depends unstably on the data, we must expect y' to be far from the true value y.

For this reason, all methods for computing the Jordan form are numerically unstable.

PROBLEMS

1.* Instead of saying that the quantity y depends *unstably* on the quantity x, why don't we use the familiar, precise mathematical term: *discontinuously*? (Do numbers x in a digital computer range continuously in intervals $a < x < b$?)

2. Suppose that we wish to compute $y = 3.1416x$. The quantity y depends stably on the data x. Let M be the numerical method of computing y

from x by the formula

$$y = 2^{50}x + 1.5708x - 2^{50}x + 1.5708x$$

Suppose that we are computing in single precision with 32 binary digits (bits) per word. Is the method M numerically stable?

3. Let a scalar y be computed from scalars $x_1, \ldots, x_n$ by the formula $y = f(x_1, \ldots, x_n)$. Suppose that the computation is executed with a small rounding error ϵ. If f is differentiable, give an approximate condition for data errors $\epsilon_1, \ldots, \epsilon_n$ to produce the same final error, ϵ. In other words, when do we have

$$f(x_1 + \epsilon_1, \ldots, x_n + \epsilon_n) = f(x_1, \ldots, x_n) + \epsilon$$

4.* Suppose that, for all ϵ in the range $0 < |\epsilon| < \epsilon_0$, the matrices $A(\epsilon)$ have a complete set of n independent unit eigenvectors $u^1(\epsilon), \ldots, u^n(\epsilon)$. Let $T(\epsilon)$ be the square matrix whose columns are $u^1(\epsilon), \ldots, u^n(\epsilon)$. Suppose that, for all positive $|\epsilon| < \epsilon_0$,

$$|\det T(\epsilon)| \geqslant \delta > 0$$

where δ is independent of ϵ. Suppose that $A(\epsilon) \to A$ as $\epsilon \to 0$. Prove that the limit, A, has a complete set of n independent unit eigenvectors $u^1, \ldots, u^n$. Conclude that A has a canonical diagonalization $T^{-1}AT = \Lambda$.

5.* Let $u^1, \ldots, u^n$ be unit vectors in E^n. We define a measure μ of independence by the formula

$$\mu = \min \| c_1 u^{(1)} + \cdots + c_n u^{(n)} \|$$

for all coefficients $c_1, \ldots, c_n$ normalized by the condition $\sum |c_j|^2 = 1$. By $\| \ \|$ we mean the Euclidean norm. Let T be the matrix whose columns are $u^1, \ldots, u^n$. Show that μ^2 is the least eigenvalue of T^*T. Conclude that

$$\mu \leqslant |\det T|^{1/n}$$

6. Let matrices $A(\epsilon) \to A$ as $\epsilon \to 0$. Suppose that, for $|\epsilon| \neq 0$, each matrix $A(\epsilon)$ has a complete set of independent unit eigenvectors $u^1(\epsilon), \ldots, u^n(\epsilon)$. From the results of the last two problems prove that the limit, A, has a complete set of independent unit eigenvectors $u^1, \ldots, u^n$ *unless* the sets $u^1(\epsilon), \ldots, u^n(\epsilon)$ become dependent, i.e., unless $\mu(\epsilon) \to 0$, where μ is the measure of independence defined in Problem 5.

7.* Using Hadamard's inequality (Section 6.6) show that the measure of independence μ defined in Problem 5 satisfies the inequality $0 \leqslant \mu \leqslant 1$, with $\mu = 1$ if and only if the unit vectors $u^1, \ldots, u^n$ are mutually orthogonal.

8. Let λ be a simple root of the equation

$$\phi(\lambda) \equiv \lambda^n + c_1 \lambda^{n-1} + \cdots + c_{n-1}\lambda + c_n = 0$$

How does λ vary if $c_1, \ldots, c_n$ are replaced by nearby values $c_1 + \epsilon_1$, $\ldots, c_n + \epsilon_n$? Does λ depend stably on the data $c_1, \ldots, c_n$ if $|\phi'(\lambda)|$ is small?

7.9 THE METHOD OF ITERATION FOR DOMINANT EIGENVALUES

In this section we shall present a method for computing the dominant eigenvalue or eigenvalues of an $n \times n$ matrix A. To take the most useful case, we shall assume that A is real. In scientific and engineering applications, we are typically interested in finding the real and the complex eigenvalues of a *real* matrix. Our analysis could readily be extended to matrices with complex components. In Section 7.10 we will show how to compute the smaller eigenvalues.

A real matrix A has a characteristic polynomial det $(\lambda I - A)$ with real coefficients. Therefore, the eigenvalues of A occur as real numbers or as complex-conjugate pairs, λ and $\bar{\lambda}$. For clarity, we shall suppose that the eigenvalues $\lambda_1, \lambda_2, \ldots, \lambda_n$ of A are distinct, so that A has n linearly independent eigenvectors $u^1, u^2, \ldots, u^n$. (Without difficulty the reader will be able to generalize this analysis, using either the Jordan form of A or an expansion in principal vectors, as in Section 7.6.)

Let $|\lambda_1| \geqslant |\lambda_2| \geqslant \cdots \geqslant |\lambda_n|$. The *dominant* eigenvalues are defined to be the eigenvalues of greatest absolute value. We shall consider only two cases.

Real case. Here we suppose that A has a single real eigenvalue λ_1 of maximum absolute value. We allow λ_1 to be either positive or negative. Thus,

$$\pm \lambda_1 = |\lambda_1| > |\lambda_2| \geqslant \cdots \geqslant |\lambda_n| \tag{1}$$

Complex case. Here we suppose that A has the complex-conjugate dominant eigenvalues

$$\lambda_1 = \alpha + i\beta, \qquad \lambda_2 = \alpha - i\beta \quad (\alpha \text{ and } \beta \text{ real}, \beta \neq 0)$$
$$|\lambda_1| = |\lambda_2| > |\lambda_3| \geqslant \cdots \geqslant |\lambda_n| \tag{2}$$

Other cases are possible but unusual, and we ignore them. For example, A could have the dominant eigenvalues $+1$ and -1. Or A could have the five dominant eigenvalues $\lambda_k = -7 \exp (2k\pi i/5)$ $(k = 1, \ldots, 5)$. Observe that, in both of these examples, the translation $\lambda_k \rightarrow \lambda_k + 1$, caused by adding 1 to each diagonal element of A, produces eigenvalues $\lambda_k + 1$ which fall into the real case (1) or the complex case (2).

In the real case (1), we pick an initial vector x^0 and form the iterates $x^1 = Ax^0$, $x^2 = Ax^1, \ldots$. If x^0 has the expansion

$$x^0 = \xi_1 u^1 + \xi_2 u^2 + \cdots + \xi_n u^n \tag{3}$$

then the iterate x^k has the expansion

$$x^k = A^k x^0 = \xi_1 \lambda_1^k u^1 + \xi_2 \lambda_2^k u^2 + \cdots + \xi_n \lambda_n^k u^n \tag{4}$$

$$= \lambda_1^k (\xi_1 u^1 + r^k) \tag{5}$$

where, since $|\lambda_\nu / \lambda_1| < 1$ for all $\nu \geqslant 2$,

$$r^k = \sum_{\nu=2}^{n} \xi_\nu \left(\frac{\lambda_\nu}{\lambda_1} \right)^k u^\nu \longrightarrow 0 \qquad (\text{as } k \to \infty) \tag{6}$$

We suppose that $\xi_1 \neq 0$. This supposition is almost surely correct if x^0 is picked in some bizarre way, e.g.,

$$x_j^0 = \left(1 + \frac{\pi}{100} \right)^{j-1} \qquad (j = 1, 2, \ldots, n) \tag{7}$$

Then for large k, as (5) shows,

$$x^{(k)} \cong \lambda_1^k \xi_1 u^{(1)} \qquad (\text{as } k \to \infty) \tag{8}$$

For large k, successive vectors are approximately multiples of each other, i.e., they are approximately eigenvectors:

$$x^{k+1} = A x^k \cong \lambda_1 x^k \qquad (\text{as } k \to \infty) \tag{9}$$

In the complex case (2), the iterates $x^k = A^k x^0$ do *not* approximate eigenvectors as $k \to \infty$.

EXAMPLE 1. Let

$$A = \begin{bmatrix} 1 & -1 \\ 1 & 1 \end{bmatrix}, \qquad x^0 = \begin{bmatrix} \gamma \\ \delta \end{bmatrix} \tag{10}$$

The eigenvalues are $\lambda_1 = 1 + i$, $\lambda_2 = 1 - i$. The iterates $x^0, x^1, \ldots$ are

$$\begin{bmatrix} \gamma \\ \delta \end{bmatrix} \begin{bmatrix} \gamma - \delta \\ \gamma + \delta \end{bmatrix} \begin{bmatrix} -2\delta \\ 2\gamma \end{bmatrix} \begin{bmatrix} -2\gamma - 2\delta \\ 2\gamma - 2\delta \end{bmatrix} \begin{bmatrix} -4\gamma \\ -4\delta \end{bmatrix} \cdots \tag{11}$$

The vector x^{k+1} is found by rotating x^k through $45°$ and multiplying the length by $\sqrt{2}$.

In general, let x^0 have an eigenvector expansion (3). Even though we are computing complex eigenvalues λ_1 and $\lambda_2 = \bar{\lambda}_1$, we will use only real numbers until the last step. We pick for x^0 a *real* vector such as the vector defined by (7). The iterate x^k has the eigenvector expansion (4). Let

$$\lambda_1 = \rho e^{i\theta}, \qquad \lambda_2 = \rho e^{-i\theta} \qquad (\rho > 0, \, 0 < \theta < \pi) \tag{12}$$

Since $\rho > |\lambda_\nu|$ for $\nu > 2$, the expansion (4) yields

$$x^k = \rho^k(\xi_1 e^{ik\theta}u^1 + \xi_2 e^{-ik\theta}u^2 + r^k) \tag{13}$$

where $r^k \to 0$ as $k \to \infty$. Since A and x^k are real, we may assume that $\xi_2 = \overline{\xi_1}$ and that the eigenvectors u^1 and u^2 are complex conjugates. *We assume that* $\xi_1 \neq 0$. Note that, for all k, since u^1 and u^2 are independent,

$$|\xi_1 e^{ik\theta}u^1 + \xi_2 e^{-ik\theta}u^2| \geqslant \min_{0 \leqslant \phi \leqslant \pi} |\xi_1 e^{i\phi}u^1 + \xi_2 e^{-i\phi}u^2| > 0$$

where $|y| \equiv \sum |y_i|$. Therefore, we have the asymptotic form

$$\begin{aligned} x^{(k)} &\cong \rho^k(\xi_1 e^{ik\theta}u^{(1)} + \xi_2 e^{-ik\theta}u^{(2)}) \\ &\cong \lambda_1^k \xi_1 u^{(1)} + \lambda_2^k \xi_2 u^{(2)} \qquad \text{(as } k \to \infty) \end{aligned} \tag{14}$$

In the complex case for large k, successive vectors x^k do not become multiples of each other. For large k, the vectors x^k lie approximately in the plane spanned by the independent eigenvectors u^1 and u^2. Therefore, *successive triples x^k, x^{k+1}, x^{k+2} are almost dependent*. Explicitly, if α and β are the real coefficients of the quadratic

$$(\lambda - \lambda_1)(\lambda - \lambda_2) = (\lambda - \lambda_1)(\lambda - \bar{\lambda}_1) = \lambda^2 + \alpha\lambda + \beta \tag{15}$$

then, for all k, $\lambda_j^{k+2} + \alpha\lambda_j^{k+1} + \beta\lambda_j^k = 0$ $(j = 1, 2)$, and hence

$$\begin{aligned} (\lambda_1^{k+2}\xi_1 u^1 + \lambda_2^{k+2}\xi_2 u^2) &+ \alpha(\lambda_1^{k+1}\xi_1 u^1 + \lambda_2^{k+1}\xi_2 u^2) \\ &+ \beta(\lambda_1^k \xi_1 u^1 + \lambda_2^k \xi_2 u^2) = 0 \end{aligned} \tag{16}$$

The asymptotic form (14) now yields the approximate equation

$$x^{(k+2)} + \alpha x^{(k+1)} + \beta x^{(k)} \cong 0 \qquad \text{(as } k \to \infty) \tag{17}$$

If we can find the coefficients of dependence α and β, we can compute λ_1 and λ_2 as the roots of the quadratic (15):

$$\lambda_1 = \tfrac{1}{2}(-\alpha + i\sqrt{4\beta - \alpha^2}), \qquad \lambda_2 = \bar{\lambda}_1 \tag{18}$$

Since λ_1 and λ_2 are complex, $\alpha^2 - 4\beta < 0$.

EXAMPLE 2. In Example 1, since $\lambda_1 = 1 + i$ and $\lambda_2 = 1 - i$ are the only eigenvalues, the iterates (11) satisfy

$$x^{k+2} - 2x^{k+1} + 2x^k = 0 \qquad \text{(for all } k) \tag{19}$$

Here $\alpha = -2$, $\beta = 2$, $(\lambda - \lambda_1)(\lambda - \lambda_2) = \lambda^2 - 2\lambda + 2$.

Computing procedure. In practice, we are given an $n \times n$ real matrix A; we assume that we have either the real case (1) or the complex case (2), *but we do not know which.* If we have the real case, we must compute λ_1; if we have the complex case, we must compute λ_1 and $\lambda_2 = \bar{\lambda}_1$.

Begin with the vector $x = x^0$ defined, say, by (7). Compute the first iterate $y = Ax$. Now make a least-squares fit of x to y, i.e., choose the real number λ to minimize

$$\| y - \lambda x \|^2 = (y - \lambda x, y - \lambda x) = \sum_{j=1}^{n} (y_j - \lambda x_j)^2 \tag{20}$$

Setting the derivative with respect to λ equal to zero, we find the value

$$\lambda = \frac{\sum_{j=1}^{n} x_j y_j}{\sum_{k=1}^{n} x_k^2} = \frac{(x, y)}{(x, x)}$$

Define a small tolerance $\epsilon > 0$, for example, $\epsilon = 10^{-5}$. If the quantities x, y, and λ satisfy

$$\| y - \lambda x \|^2 < \epsilon^2 \| y \|^2 \tag{21}$$

we conclude that we have the real case, and we assign the value λ to λ_1.

If the test (21) is failed, we compute the third iterate, $z = Ay$. Pick the real numbers α and β which minimize

$$\| z + \alpha y + \beta x \|^2 = \| z \|^2 + \alpha^2 \| y \|^2 + \beta^2 \| x \|^2 + 2\alpha(z, y) \\ + 2\beta(z, x) + 2\alpha\beta(y, x) \tag{22}$$

Calculus gives the necessary conditions

$$\| y \|^2 \alpha + (y, x)\beta + (z, y) = 0 \\ (y, x)\alpha + \| x \|^2 \beta + (z, x) = 0 \tag{23}$$

The optimal values α and β are found from (23) to be

$$\begin{bmatrix} \alpha \\ \beta \end{bmatrix} = \frac{-1}{\| x \|^2 \| y \|^2 - (y, x)^2} \begin{bmatrix} \| x \|^2 & -(y, x) \\ -(y, x) & \| y \|^2 \end{bmatrix} \begin{bmatrix} (z, y) \\ (z, x) \end{bmatrix} \tag{24}$$

If the quantities x, y, z, α, β satisfy

$$\| z + \alpha y + \beta x \| < \epsilon^2 \| z \|^2 \tag{25}$$

we conclude that we have the complex case, and we assign the root values (18) to λ_1 and λ_2.

Suppose that both the real test (21) and the complex test (25) are failed. Then we must iterate further. If we form the iterates $A^k x$ without some *scaling*, we may eventually obtain numbers too large or too small for the floating-point representation. The last computed iterate was $z = A^2x$. We scale z by dividing z by the component z_m of largest absolute value. We then define

$$\text{new vector } x = z_m^{-1}z \tag{26}$$

We now repeat the preceding process: We form $y = Ax$ and make the real test (21). If that test is failed, we form $z = Ay$ and make the complex test (25). If the complex test is also failed, we define a new vector x by (26), etc. If ϵ is not too small, one of the tests ultimately will be passed. Scaling does not affect the asymptotic equation for $x^k = x$, $x^{k+1} = y$, and $x^{k+2} = z$:

$$x^{k+1} \cong \lambda_1 x^k \quad \text{(real case)} \quad \text{or} \quad x^{k+2} + \alpha x^{k+1} + \beta x^k \cong 0 \quad \text{(complex case)}$$

because the equation is homogeneous. The sequence of scaled vectors $x; y, z; x, y, z; \ldots$ is simply

$$x^0, x^1, x^2; \sigma_1 x^2, \sigma_1 x^3, \sigma_1 x^4; \sigma_2 x^4, \sigma_2 x^5, \sigma_2 x^6; \ldots$$

where $\sigma_1, \sigma_2, \ldots$ are nonzero scalars.

The method of iteration suffers very little from rounding error. If a new x is slightly in error, we may simply regard this x as a new initial vector which is, no doubt, better than the previous initial vector. Rounding error affects the accuracy of the computed eigenvalues only in the last stage of the computation, when x is fitted to y, or when x and y are fitted to z.

The reader may have wondered why, if we are computing eigenvalues, we do not simply find the coefficients of the characteristic polynomial $\phi(\lambda)$ $= \det(\lambda I - A)$. Then the eigenvalues λ_j could be found by some numerical method for solving polynomial equations $\phi(\lambda) = 0$. Indeed, this is sometimes done. But unless an extremely efficient method such as that of Householder and Bauer (see Section 7.12) is used, there is a large rounding error from the extensive computations needed to obtain the n coefficients of $\phi(\lambda)$ from the n^2 components of A. Even for $n = 5$ or 6 the rounding error may be quite large.

Moreover, a root λ_j of $\phi(\lambda) = 0$ depends unstably on the coefficients if $|\phi'(\lambda_j)|$ is small. Infinitesimal variations $dc_1, \ldots, dc_n$ in the coefficients produce the variation $d\lambda$ according to the formula of calculus:

$$\frac{\partial \phi}{\partial \lambda} d\lambda + \frac{\partial \phi}{\partial c_1} dc_1 + \cdots + \frac{\partial \phi}{\partial c_n} dc_n = 0$$

Since $\phi \equiv \lambda^n + c_1 \lambda^{n-1} + \cdots + c_{n-1}\lambda + c_n$, we find

$$d\lambda = \frac{-1}{\phi'(\lambda_j)}[\lambda_j^{n-1}dc_1 + \cdots + \lambda_j dc_{n-1} + dc_n] \tag{27}$$

PROBLEMS

1. Show what happens when the method of iteration is applied to

$$A = \begin{bmatrix} 0 & 1 & 0 \\ 0 & 0 & 1 \\ -1 & -1 & -1 \end{bmatrix}, \qquad x^0 = \begin{bmatrix} \alpha \\ \beta \\ \gamma \end{bmatrix}$$

What are the coordinates of the vectors x^k for $k = 760, 761, 762, 763$?

2. Suppose that A has a simple eigenvalue λ_j which is known to be approximately equal to -1.83. Form the matrix $B = (A + 1.83I)^{-1}$, and apply the method of iteration to B. What is the dominant eigenvalue of B? How can you compute λ_j?

3. Suppose that the real matrix A has distinct eigenvalues. Suppose that two of the eigenvalues, λ_j and $\bar{\lambda}_j$, are known to be approximately equal to $1 \pm i$. Form the real matrix

$$B = (A^2 - 2A + 2I)^{-1}$$

How can the method of iteration be used to compute λ_j and $\bar{\lambda}_j$?

4. Let $|\lambda_1| > |\lambda_2| \geqslant \cdots \geqslant |\lambda_n|$. Define the rate of convergence to be the reciprocal of the asymptotic value v_e for the number of iterations needed to reduce the error by the factor $1/e$. Show that, for the method of iteration,

$$\text{rate of convergence} = \log \left| \frac{\lambda_1}{\lambda_2} \right|$$

5. Let A be a real, symmetric, positive-definite matrix with the eigenvalues $\lambda_1 > \lambda_2 > \cdots > \lambda_n$. Suppose that we have computed numerical values for λ_1 and for a corresponding unit eigenvector u^1. If $y \neq$ a multiple of u^1, form

$$x^0 = y - (y, u^1)u^1$$

The vector x^0 is nonzero and is (apart from rounding error) orthogonal to u^1. If there were no rounding error and if u^1 were exact, show that the method of iteration, applied to x^0, would produce the second eigenvalue, λ_2. Explain why rounding error causes the method of iteration, applied to x^0, to produce the dominant eigenvalue, λ_1, again.

6. In formula (24), the denominator

$$\|x\|^2 \|y\|^2 - (y, x)^2$$

equals zero if and only if the vectors x and y are dependent, as we saw in the proof of the Cauchy-Schwarz inequality. Why are the vectors x and y independent whenever formula (24) is applied in the method of iteration?

7. Let A be a real, symmetric matrix, with eigenvalues $\lambda_1 \geqslant \lambda_2 \geqslant \cdots \geqslant \lambda_n$.

Let λ be any number satisfying the test for a real eigenvalue:

$$\| Ax - \lambda x \|^2 < \epsilon^2 \| Ax \|^2$$

Prove that, for some eigenvalue λ_j,

$$|\lambda_j - \lambda| < \epsilon |\lambda_j|$$

Thus, ϵ represents an upper bound for the proportional error. (Expand x in terms of unit orthogonal eigenvectors $u^1, \ldots, u^n$.)

8.* Let A be an $n \times n$ matrix with independent unit eigenvectors $u^1, \ldots, u^n$. Let T be the matrix with columns $u^1, \ldots, u^n$. If

$$\| Ax - \lambda x \|^2 < \epsilon^2 \| Ax \|^2$$

prove that, for some eigenvalue λ_j,

$$|\lambda_j - \lambda| < \epsilon \| T \| \| T^{-1} \| |\lambda_j|$$

Use the inequality

$$\frac{1}{\| T \|} \leqslant \frac{\| Ty \|}{\| y \|} \leqslant \| T \|$$

7.10 REDUCTION TO OBTAIN THE SMALLER EIGENVALUES

In the last section we supposed that A was an $n \times n$ real matrix with real and complex eigenvalues $\lambda_1, \ldots, \lambda_n$. We showed how to compute either a dominant real eigenvalue, λ_1, satisfying

$$\pm \lambda_1 > |\lambda_2| \geqslant \cdots \geqslant |\lambda_n| \tag{1}$$

or a dominant complex-conjugate pair, $\lambda_1, \lambda_2 = \bar{\lambda}_1$, satisfying

$$|\lambda_1| = |\lambda_2| > |\lambda_3| \geqslant \cdots \geqslant |\lambda_n| \tag{2}$$

We will now show how to obtain from A *a reduced matrix* R *whose eigenvalues are the remaining eigenvalues of* A. The method of iteration for dominant eigenvalues, when applied to R, yields one or two smaller eigenvalues of A. The matrix R then can be reduced further to a matrix R', etc., until all the eigenvalues of the original matrix A have been computed.

In the real case (1) the method of iteration yielded quantities $\lambda = \lambda_1$, x, and $y = Ax$ satisfying

$$Ax = \lambda_1 x \qquad (x \neq 0) \tag{3}$$

apart from a negligible error. Suppose for the moment that

$$1 = x_1 = \max |x_i| \qquad (i = 1, \ldots, n) \tag{4}$$

Form the nonsingular $n \times n$ matrix

$$T = \begin{bmatrix} x_1 & 0 & 0 & \cdot & 0 \\ x_2 & 1 & 0 & \cdot & 0 \\ x_3 & 0 & 1 & \cdot & 0 \\ \cdot & \cdot & \cdot & \cdot & \cdot \\ x_n & 0 & 0 & \cdot & 1 \end{bmatrix} = [x e^2 e^3 \cdot e^n] \qquad (5)$$

We will show that

$$T^{-1}AT = \begin{bmatrix} \lambda_1 & * & * & \cdot & * \\ 0 & & & & \\ 0 & & & R & \\ \cdot & & & & \\ 0 & & & & \end{bmatrix} \qquad (6)$$

where the $(n-1) \times (n-1)$ matrix R has the required property

$$\det(\lambda I - R) = (\lambda - \lambda_2)(\lambda - \lambda_3) \ldots (\lambda - \lambda_n) \qquad (7)$$

The numbers * in the top row of (6) are irrelevant.

To prove (6), multiply (5) on the left by A. Since $Ax = \lambda_1 x$ and $Ae^j = a^j$, the jth column of A, we find

$$AT = [\lambda_1 x, a^2, a^3, \ldots, a^n] \qquad (8)$$

The matrix $B = T^{-1}AT$ satisfies the equation $TB = AT$. If the columns of B are $b^1, \ldots, b^n$, then the columns of TB are $Tb^1, \ldots, Tb^n$. By (8), the equation $TB = AT$ implies

$$Tb^1 = \lambda_1 x, \qquad Tb^2 = a^2, \ldots, Tb^n = a^n \qquad (9)$$

Since x is the first column of T, the solution of the equation $Tb^1 = \lambda_1 x$ is

$$b^1 = \lambda_1 e^1 = \text{col}(\lambda_1, 0, 0, \ldots, 0) \qquad (10)$$

Therefore, $B = T^{-1}AT$ has the form (6). The identity (7) follows by taking the characteristic determinants of the matrices on both sides of (6):

$$\det(\lambda I - T^{-1}AT) = \begin{bmatrix} \lambda - \lambda_1 & * & * & \cdot & * \\ 0 & & & & \\ 0 & & & \lambda I - R & \\ \cdot & & & & \\ 0 & & & & \end{bmatrix} \qquad (11)$$

Recalling the invariance (see Theorem 1, Section 4.2)

$$\det(\lambda I - T^{-1}AT) = \det(\lambda I - A) \tag{12}$$

we find from (11) the identity

$$(\lambda - \lambda_1)(\lambda - \lambda_2)\ldots(\lambda - \lambda_n) = (\lambda - \lambda_1)\det(\lambda I - R) \tag{13}$$

Division of both sides of (13) by $\lambda - \lambda_1$ yields the required result (7). Note that I in the expression $\lambda I - R$, is the identity of order $n - 1$.

To compute R, we verify that

$$T^{-1} = \begin{bmatrix} 1 & 0 & 0 & \cdot & 0 \\ -x_2 & 1 & 0 & \cdot & 0 \\ -x_3 & 0 & 1 & \cdot & 0 \\ \cdot & \cdot & \cdot & \cdot & \cdot \\ -x_n & 0 & 0 & \cdot & 1 \end{bmatrix} \tag{14}$$

Indeed, since $x_1 = 1$, the matrix (14) times the matrix (5) equals I. Since R comprises the elements $i, j \geqslant 2$ in the product $T^{-1}AT$, we have

$$R = XAY \tag{15}$$

where X consists of the rows $i \geqslant 2$ of T^{-1}, and Y consists of the columns $j \geqslant 2$ of T. Explicitly,

$$R = \begin{bmatrix} -x_2 & 1 & 0 & \cdot & 0 \\ -x_3 & 0 & 1 & \cdot & 0 \\ \cdot & \cdot & \cdot & \cdot & \cdot \\ -x_n & 0 & 0 & \cdot & 1 \end{bmatrix} A \begin{bmatrix} 0 & 0 & \cdot & 0 \\ 1 & 0 & \cdot & 0 \\ 0 & 1 & \cdot & 0 \\ \cdot & \cdot & \cdot & \cdot \\ 0 & 0 & \cdot & 1 \end{bmatrix} \tag{16}$$

Therefore,

$$R = \begin{bmatrix} -x_2 & 1 & 0 & \cdot & 0 \\ -x_3 & 0 & 1 & \cdot & 0 \\ \cdot & \cdot & \cdot & \cdot & \cdot \\ -x_n & 0 & 0 & \cdot & 1 \end{bmatrix} \begin{bmatrix} a_{12} & a_{13} & \cdot & a_{1n} \\ a_{22} & a_{23} & \cdot & a_{2n} \\ \cdot & \cdot & \cdot & \cdot \\ a_{n2} & a_{n3} & \cdot & a_{nn} \end{bmatrix} \tag{17}$$

which yields $R = (r_{ij})$ in the explicit form

$$r_{ij} = -x_{i+1}a_{1,j+1} + a_{i+1,j+1} \qquad (i,j = 1,\ldots,n-1) \tag{18}$$

Now we shall eliminate the assumption that $1 = x_1 = \max|x_i|$. This assumption was convenient because it insured that the matrix T, defined by (5), was nonsingular and because it produced no large numbers x_{i+1}

in the final formula (18). Given A, λ_1, and $x \neq 0$, we will find a new A and a new x satisfying $Ax = \lambda_1 x$ such that the new A has the same eigenvalues as the old A, and such that the new x does satisfy $1 = x_1 = \max |x_i|$. Let

$$|x_m| = \max |x_i| \qquad (i = 1, \ldots, n)$$
$$u = x_m^{-1} x \tag{19}$$

Since $x \neq 0$, we have $x_m \neq 0$. The vector u satisfies

$$Au = \lambda_1 u, \qquad 1 = u_m = \max |u_i| \quad (i = 1, \ldots, n) \tag{20}$$

Let P_{ij} be the matrix which permutes components i and j of a vector. For example, if $n = 3$,

$$P_{23} = \begin{bmatrix} 1 & 0 & 0 \\ 0 & 0 & 1 \\ 0 & 1 & 0 \end{bmatrix}, \qquad P_{23} \begin{bmatrix} z_1 \\ z_2 \\ z_3 \end{bmatrix} = \begin{bmatrix} z_1 \\ z_3 \\ z_2 \end{bmatrix}$$

P_{ij} is the matrix formed by interchanging rows i and j of the identity matrix. Note that

$$\cdot P_{ij} = P_{ji}, \qquad P_{ii} = I, \qquad P_{ij}^{-1} = P_{ij} \tag{21}$$

Note also that AP_{ij} is formed by interchanging *columns* i and j in A; $P_{ij}A$ is formed by interchanging *rows* i and j in A.

Referring to (20), we see that $v = P_{1m} u$ is a vector with maximal component $v_1 = 1$. Further,

$$(P_{1m}AP_{1m})(P_{1m}u) = \lambda_1(P_{1m}u) \tag{22}$$

But, by (21), $PAP = P^{-1}AP$, which has the same eigenvalues as A. Thus, we define

$$\text{new } A = P_{1m}AP_{1m}, \qquad \text{new } x = P_{1m}u = P_{1m}(x_m^{-1}x) \tag{23}$$

The new matrix A and the new vector x have all the required properties, including (4). Note that the new A is formed from A by interchanging rows 1 and m and interchanging columns 1 and m. The reduced matrix R is then computed directly from formula (18).

In the complex case (2), the method of iteration yielded real quantities α, β, x, $y = Ax$, and $z = Ay$ satisfying

$$z + \alpha y + \beta x = 0 \qquad (x \text{ and } y \text{ independent}) \tag{24}$$

We know that x and y are independent because in the testing procedure of the preceding section, the numbers α and β were computed only after the failure of an attempt to express y as a scalar multiple of $x \neq 0$. For the moment assume that x and y have the special forms

$$x = \begin{bmatrix} 1 \\ 0 \\ x_3 \\ \cdot \\ \cdot \\ \cdot \\ x_n \end{bmatrix}, \qquad y = \begin{bmatrix} 0 \\ 1 \\ y_3 \\ \cdot \\ \cdot \\ \cdot \\ y_n \end{bmatrix} \tag{25}$$

The coefficients α, β satisfy

$$\lambda^2 + \alpha\lambda + \beta = (\lambda - \lambda_1)(\lambda - \lambda_2) \tag{26}$$

We will find an $(n-2) \times (n-2)$ *matrix* R *whose eigenvalues are* $\lambda_3, \ldots, \lambda_n$.

Define the $n \times n$ matrix

$$T = [xye^3e^4 \ldots e^n] \tag{27}$$

Since $Ax = y$ and $Ay = z = -\beta x - \alpha y$,

$$AT = [y, -\beta x - \alpha y, a^3, \ldots, a^n] \tag{28}$$

The matrix $B = T^{-1}AT$ satisfies $TB = AT$. If $b^1, \ldots$ are the columns of B, then by (28)

$$Tb^1 = y, \qquad Tb^2 = -\beta x - \alpha y, \qquad Tb^3 = a^3, \ldots \tag{29}$$

By (27) we conclude that b^1 and b^2 have the forms

$$b^1 = \begin{bmatrix} 0 \\ 1 \\ 0 \\ \cdot \\ 0 \end{bmatrix}, \qquad b^2 = \begin{bmatrix} -\beta \\ -\alpha \\ 0 \\ \cdot \\ 0 \end{bmatrix} \tag{30}$$

Therefore, $B = T^{-1}AT$ has the form

$$B = \begin{bmatrix} 0 & -\beta & * & \cdots & * \\ 1 & -\alpha & * & \cdots & * \\ 0 & 0 & & & \\ \cdot & \cdot & & R & \\ 0 & 0 & & & \end{bmatrix} \tag{31}$$

The numbers $*$ are irrelevant. Because of the zeros below the 2×2 block in the upper-left corner,

$$\det (\lambda I - B) = \begin{vmatrix} \lambda & \beta \\ -1 & \lambda + \alpha \end{vmatrix} \det (\lambda I - R) \qquad (32)$$

Because B is similar to A, B has the same characteristic determinant. Therefore (32) implies

$$(\lambda - \lambda_1)(\lambda - \lambda_2)(\lambda - \lambda_3) \ldots (\lambda - \lambda_n) = (\lambda^2 + \alpha\lambda + \beta) \det (\lambda I - R) \qquad (33)$$

The identity $\lambda^2 + \alpha\lambda + \beta = (\lambda - \lambda_1)(\lambda - \lambda_2)$ now gives

$$\det (\lambda I - R) = (\lambda - \lambda_3) \ldots (\lambda - \lambda_n) \qquad (34)$$

To compute R, we verify that

$$T^{-1} = \begin{bmatrix} 1 & 0 & 0 & \cdot & 0 \\ 0 & 1 & 0 & \cdot & 0 \\ -x_3 & -y_3 & 1 & \cdot & 0 \\ \cdot & \cdot & \cdot & \cdot & \cdot \\ -x_n & -y_n & 0 & \cdot & 1 \end{bmatrix} \qquad (35)$$

Indeed, since x and y have the special forms (25), the matrix (35) times the matrix (27) equals I. Since R consists of the elements in rows $i \geqslant 3$ and columns $j \geqslant 3$ of the product $T^{-1}AT$, we have

$$R = XAY \qquad (36)$$

where X consists of the rows $i \geqslant 3$ of T^{-1}, and Y consists of the columns $j \geqslant 3$ of T. Explicitly,

$$R = \begin{bmatrix} -x_3 & -y_3 & 1 & \cdot & 0 \\ \cdot & \cdot & \cdot & \cdot & \cdot \\ -x_n & -y_n & 0 & \cdot & 1 \end{bmatrix} A \begin{bmatrix} 0 & \cdot & 0 \\ 0 & \cdot & 0 \\ 1 & \cdot & 0 \\ \cdot & \cdot & \cdot \\ 0 & \cdot & 1 \end{bmatrix} \qquad (37)$$

Therefore,

$$R = \begin{bmatrix} -x_3 & -y_3 & 1 & \cdot & 0 \\ \cdot & \cdot & \cdot & \cdot & \cdot \\ -x_n & -y_n & 0 & \cdot & 1 \end{bmatrix} \begin{bmatrix} a_{13} & a_{14} & \cdot & a_{1n} \\ \cdot & \cdot & \cdot & \cdot \\ a_{n3} & a_{n4} & \cdot & a_{nn} \end{bmatrix} \qquad (38)$$

which yields $R = (r_{ij})$ in the explicit form

$$r_{ij} = -x_{i+2}a_{1,j+2} - y_{i+2}a_{2,j+2} + a_{i+2,j+2} \qquad (i,j = 1,\ldots,n-2) \qquad (39)$$

Suppose now that x, $y = Ax$, and $z = Ay$ satisfy the dependence (24) but that x and y do *not* have the special form (25). Then x and y are independent vectors satisfying

$$A[xy] = [xy]\begin{bmatrix} 0 & -\beta \\ 1 & -\alpha \end{bmatrix} \qquad (40)$$

Here $[xy]$ represents the $n \times 2$ matrix with columns x and y. Let N and Q be nonsingular $n \times n$ and 2×2 matrices. By (40),

$$NAN^{-1}N[xy]Q = N[xy]Q \cdot Q^{-1}\begin{bmatrix} 0 & -\beta \\ 1 & -\alpha \end{bmatrix}Q \qquad (41)$$

Set

$$NAN^{-1} = A', \qquad N[xy]Q = [x'y'], \qquad Q^{-1}\begin{bmatrix} 0 & -\beta \\ 1 & -\alpha \end{bmatrix}Q = S \qquad (42)$$

Suppose further that the vectors x', y' have the special form

$$x' = \begin{bmatrix} 1 \\ 0 \\ * \\ \cdot \\ \cdot \\ \cdot \\ * \end{bmatrix}, \qquad y' = \begin{bmatrix} 0 \\ 1 \\ * \\ \cdot \\ \cdot \\ \cdot \\ * \end{bmatrix} \qquad (43)$$

In analogy to (27), let T' be the $n \times n$ matrix

$$T' = [x'y'e^3e^4 \ldots e^n] \qquad (44)$$

Equation (41) states that

$$A'[x'y'] = [x'y']S \qquad (45)$$

where the 2×2 matrix S is defined in (42). Note that

$$\det(\lambda I - S) = \det\left(\lambda I - \begin{bmatrix} 0 & -\beta \\ 1 & -\alpha \end{bmatrix}\right)$$
$$= \lambda^2 + \alpha\lambda + \beta = (\lambda - \lambda_1)(\lambda - \lambda_2) \qquad (46)$$

By analogy to (31), $B' = (T')^{-1}A'T'$ has the form

$$
B' = \begin{bmatrix}
\begin{matrix} S \end{matrix} & * & \cdots & * \\
 & * & \cdots & * \\
0 \quad 0 & & & \\
\cdot \quad \cdot & & R' & \\
0 \quad 0 & & &
\end{bmatrix}
\tag{47}
$$

Therefore,

$$
\det(\lambda I - B') = \det(\lambda I - S)\det(\lambda I - R')
$$
$$
= (\lambda - \lambda_1)(\lambda - \lambda_2)\det(\lambda I - R')
\tag{48}
$$

But B' is similar to A', which is similar to A. Therefore,

$$
\det(\lambda I - B') = \det(\lambda I - A) = (\lambda - \lambda_1)\ldots(\lambda - \lambda_n)
\tag{49}
$$

Dividing (48) by $(\lambda - \lambda_1)(\lambda - \lambda_2)$, we find

$$
(\lambda - \lambda_3)\ldots(\lambda - \lambda_n) = \det(\lambda I - R')
\tag{50}
$$

Therefore, R' is the required reduced matrix. By analogy to (39), we have the explicit form $R' = (r'_{ij})$, with

$$
r'_{ij} = -x'_{i+2}a'_{1,j+2} - y'_{i+2}a'_{2,j+2} + a'_{i+2,j+2} \qquad (i,j = 1,\ldots,n-2)
\tag{51}
$$

It remains only to find an $n \times n$ matrix N and a 2×2 matrix Q such that $N[xy]Q = [x'y']$, where x', y' have the form (43). Let

$$
|x_m| = \max|x_i| \qquad (i = 1,\ldots,n)
\tag{52}
$$

Define $Q_1 = x_m^{-1}I$. Define $N_1 = P_{1m}$, the matrix which permutes the first and mth components. Then we have the form

$$
N_1[xy]Q_1 = \begin{bmatrix}
1 & \eta \\
* & * \\
\cdot & \cdot \\
* & *
\end{bmatrix}
\tag{53}
$$

Let Q_2 be a 2×2 matrix which subtracts η times the first column from the second column:

$$
Q_2 = \begin{bmatrix} 1 & -\eta \\ 0 & 1 \end{bmatrix}
\tag{54}
$$

SEC. 7.10 NUMERICAL METHODS **249**

Then, by (53), we have the form

$$
N_1[xy]Q_1Q_2 = \begin{bmatrix} 1 & 0 \\ * & \zeta_2 \\ \cdot & \cdot \\ * & \zeta_n \end{bmatrix} \tag{55}
$$

Let $|\zeta_k| = \max |\zeta_i| \, (i \geqslant 2)$; this maximum is positive because the two columns (55) remain independent. Let $N_2 = P_{2k}$, and let N_3 divide row 2 by ζ_k. Then we have the form

$$
N_3N_2N_1[xy]Q_1Q_2 = \begin{bmatrix} 1 & 0 \\ \omega & 1 \\ * & * \\ \cdot & \cdot \\ * & * \end{bmatrix} \tag{56}
$$

Explicitly, $N_3 = \operatorname{diag}(1, \zeta_k^{-1}, 1, \ldots, 1)$. Let Q_3 subtract ω times column 2 from column 1:

$$
Q_3 = \begin{bmatrix} 1 & 0 \\ -\omega & 1 \end{bmatrix} \tag{57}
$$

Then we obtain x', y':

$$
N_3N_2N_1[xy]Q_1Q_2Q_3 = \begin{bmatrix} 1 & 0 \\ 0 & 1 \\ * & * \\ \cdot & \cdot \\ * & * \end{bmatrix} = [x'y'] \tag{58}
$$

There is no need to obtain $N = N_3N_2N_1$ and $Q = Q_1Q_2Q_3$ explicitly, but we must obtain $A' = NAN^{-1}$ explicitly to compute the reduced matrix R' from (51). We have

$$
\begin{aligned}
A' &= N_3N_2N_1AN_1^{-1}N_2^{-1}N_3^{-1} \\
&= \operatorname{diag}(1, \zeta_k^{-1}, 1, \ldots, 1) \, P_{2k}P_{1m}AP_{1m}P_{2k} \\
&\quad \cdot \operatorname{diag}(1, \zeta_k, 1, \ldots, 1)
\end{aligned} \tag{59}
$$

since $P_{ij}^{-1} = P_{ij}$. Formula (59) gives the following procedure. Begin with A. Interchange columns 1 and m. Interchange rows 1 and m. Interchange columns 2 and k. Interchange rows 2 and k. Divide row 2 by ζ_k. Multiply column 2 by ζ_k. The result is A'. Since the vectors x', y' were given by (58), we can now compute the reduced matrix from (51).

Although the analysis has been long, the explicit computations (58), (59), (51) are very brief. Therefore, double precision can be used with a negligible increase in computing time. In any case, rounding error is reduced by the choice of the maximal pivot-elements x_m and ζ_k.

PROBLEMS

1. Let

$$A = \begin{bmatrix} 2 & 8 & -6 \\ 1 & 3 & 0 \\ 5 & -3 & 2 \end{bmatrix}$$

This matrix has the simple eigenvalue $\lambda_1 = 4$, with the eigenvector $x = \text{col}\,(1, 1, 1)$. Find the 2×2 reduced matrix R.

2. Let

$$A = \begin{bmatrix} 5 & -10 & 3 \\ 2 & -1 & 0 \\ 4 & 10 & -4 \end{bmatrix}$$

This matrix has the simple eigenvalue $\lambda_1 = -1$, with the eigenvector $x = \text{col}\,(0, 3, 10)$. Find the 2×2 reduced matrix R.

3. Let

$$A = \begin{bmatrix} 0 & 1 & 0 \\ 0 & 0 & 1 \\ 15 & -17 & 7 \end{bmatrix}, \qquad x = \begin{bmatrix} 1 \\ 2 \\ 3 \end{bmatrix}$$

Verify that $A^2x - 4Ax + 5x = 0$. Compute two complex-conjugate eigenvalues. Using formula (51), compute the 1×1 reduced matrix R. First perform the transformations (58) and (59).

4. Let x and Ax be independent; let x, Ax, and A^2x be dependent:

$$A^2x + \alpha Ax + \beta x = 0$$

If $\lambda^2 + \alpha\lambda + \beta \equiv (\lambda - \lambda_1)(\lambda - \lambda_2)$, show that $(A - \lambda_2 I)x$ is an eigenvector belonging to λ_1.

5. Let

$$A = \begin{bmatrix} 0 & 1 & 0 & 0 \\ 0 & 0 & 1 & 0 \\ 0 & 0 & 0 & 1 \\ 1 & 1 & 0 & -1 \end{bmatrix}, \qquad x = \begin{bmatrix} 2 \\ -1 \\ -1 \\ 2 \end{bmatrix}$$

Verify that x, Ax, and A^2x are dependent. Compute two complex eigenvalues, and form the 2×2 reduced matrix, R. Then compute the other two eigenvalues of A.

7.11 EIGENVALUES AND EIGENVECTORS OF TRIDIAGONAL AND HESSENBERG MATRICES

Some methods for computing the eigenvalues of an $n \times n$ matrix A depend upon finding the coefficients c_j of the characteristic polynomial

$$\det (\lambda I - A) = \lambda^n + c_1 \lambda^{n-1} + c_2 \lambda^{n-2} + \cdots + c_n \qquad (1)$$

The eigenvalues are then found by some numerical method for computing the roots of polynomial equations.

In the method of Householder and Bauer, to be presented in the next section, given A, we construct a unitary matrix U such that the similar matrix U^*AU has the special form

$$U^*AU = \begin{bmatrix} h_{11} & \alpha_1 & 0 & 0 & \cdots & 0 \\ h_{21} & h_{22} & \alpha_2 & 0 & \cdots & 0 \\ \cdot & \cdot & \cdot & \cdot & \cdots & \cdot \\ h_{n1} & h_{n2} & h_{n3} & \cdot & \cdots & h_{nn} \end{bmatrix} = H \qquad (2)$$

This is the *Hessenberg form*, with

$$h_{ij} = 0 \qquad (\text{if } j \geqslant i + 2) \qquad (3)$$

In particular, if A is Hermitian, then H is Hermitian. *A Hermitian Hessenberg matrix* H *is tridiagonal, with* $h_{ij} = 0$ if $|i - j| \geqslant 2$.

The reduction (2) is useful if there is an easy way to find the coefficients of the characteristic polynomial of a Hessenberg matrix, since the identities $U^*AU = H$, $U^*U = I$ imply

$$\det (\lambda I - H) = \det (\lambda I - A) = \lambda^n + c_1 \lambda^{n-1} + \cdots + c_n \qquad (4)$$

The purpose of this section is to show how to find the coefficients c_j *of the characteristic polynomial of a Hessenberg matrix* H. As a by-product, we shall show how to find an eigenvector belonging to a known eigenvalue of H. We also will show, in the Hermitian case, that *the eigenvalues can be located in intervals* without any numerical evaluation of the roots of the characteristic equation.

Given $H = H_n$, construct the sequence of Hessenberg matrices

$$H_1 = [h_{11}], \qquad H_2 = \begin{bmatrix} h_{11} & \alpha_1 \\ h_{21} & h_{22} \end{bmatrix}, \qquad H_3 = \begin{bmatrix} h_{11} & \alpha_1 & 0 \\ h_{21} & h_{22} & \alpha_2 \\ h_{31} & h_{32} & h_{33} \end{bmatrix}, \ldots, H_n \qquad (5)$$

Let $\Delta_1 = \det H_1, \ldots, \Delta_n = \det H_n$. We will develop a recursion formula for these determinants.

EXAMPLE 1. For $n = 5$ we have

$$H = H_5 = \begin{bmatrix} h_{11} & \alpha_1 & 0 & 0 & 0 \\ h_{21} & h_{22} & \alpha_2 & 0 & 0 \\ h_{31} & h_{32} & h_{33} & \alpha_3 & 0 \\ h_{41} & h_{42} & h_{43} & h_{44} & \alpha_4 \\ h_{51} & h_{52} & h_{53} & h_{54} & h_{55} \end{bmatrix} \tag{6}$$

We shall expand $\Delta_5 = \det H_5$ by the last row.

$$\Delta_5 = h_{55} \begin{vmatrix} h_{11} & \alpha_1 & 0 & 0 \\ h_{21} & h_{22} & \alpha_2 & 0 \\ h_{31} & h_{32} & h_{33} & \alpha_3 \\ h_{41} & h_{42} & h_{43} & h_{44} \end{vmatrix} - h_{54} \begin{vmatrix} h_{11} & \alpha_1 & 0 & 0 \\ h_{21} & h_{22} & \alpha_2 & 0 \\ h_{31} & h_{32} & h_{33} & 0 \\ * & * & * & \alpha_4 \end{vmatrix}$$

$$+ h_{53} \begin{vmatrix} h_{11} & \alpha_1 & 0 & 0 \\ h_{21} & h_{22} & 0 & 0 \\ * & * & \alpha_3 & 0 \\ * & * & * & \alpha_4 \end{vmatrix} - h_{52} \begin{vmatrix} h_1 & 0 & 0 & 0 \\ * & \alpha_2 & 0 & 0 \\ * & * & \alpha_3 & 0 \\ * & * & * & \alpha_4 \end{vmatrix} + h_{51} \alpha_1 \alpha_2 \alpha_3 \alpha_4$$

Thus, if we define $\Delta_0 = 1$,

$$\Delta_5 = h_{55}\Delta_4 - h_{54}\alpha_4\Delta_3 + h_{53}\alpha_3\alpha_4\Delta_2 - h_{52}\alpha_2\alpha_3\alpha_4\Delta_1 + h_{51}\alpha_1\alpha_2\alpha_3\alpha_4\Delta_0$$
$$= h_{55}\Delta_4 + \sum_{\nu=1}^{4} (-)^{5-\nu} h_{5\nu}\alpha_\nu \ldots \alpha_4\Delta_{\nu-1}$$

In the general case, expanding $\Delta_n = \det H_n$ by the last row, we find

$$\Delta_n = h_{nn}\Delta_{n-1} + \sum_{\nu=1}^{n-1} (-)^{n-\nu} h_{n\nu}\alpha_\nu \ldots \alpha_{n-1}\Delta_{\nu-1} \tag{7}$$

To find the characteristic polynomial $\phi_n(\lambda) = \det (H_n - \lambda I)$, we only need to replace the diagonal elements $h_{\nu\nu}$ by $h_{\nu\nu} - \lambda$. Then (7) yields, for $n \geqslant 2$,

$$\phi_n(\lambda) = (h_{nn} - \lambda)\phi_{n-1}(\lambda) + \sum_{\nu=1}^{n-1} (-)^{n-\nu} h_{n\nu}\alpha_\nu \ldots \alpha_{n-1}\phi_{\nu-1}(\lambda) \tag{8}$$

where $\phi_0(\lambda) = 1$ and $\phi_1(\lambda) = h_{11} - \lambda$. *This is a formula for computing, successively, $\phi_2(\lambda), \phi_3(\lambda), \ldots$* If H_n is tridiagonal, (8) takes the simpler form

$$\phi_n(\lambda) = (h_{nn} - \lambda)\phi_{n-1}(\lambda) - h_{n, n-1}\alpha_{n-1}\phi_{n-2}(\lambda) \tag{9}$$

Next we shall show that, *if* λ *is an eigenvalue of* H_n, *an eigenvector* $x = \text{col}\,(x_1, \ldots, x_n)$ *is given by*

$$x_n = \phi_{n-1}(\lambda), \qquad x_\nu = (-)^{n-\nu}\alpha_\nu \ldots \alpha_{n-1}\phi_{\nu-1}(\lambda) \qquad (\nu = 1, \ldots, n-1)$$
$$(10)$$

provided that at least one of these numbers x_i *is nonzero. Since* $x_1 = \pm\alpha_1$ $\cdots \alpha_{n-1}$, we have at least $x_1 \neq 0$ if all $\alpha_\nu \neq 0$.

To show that (10) provides an eigenvector, we must show that, if $\phi_n(\lambda) = 0$, then

$$(H_n - \lambda I)x = 0 \qquad (11)$$

If $y = (H_n - \lambda I)x$, then

$$y_n = (h_{nn} - \lambda)x_n + \sum_{\nu=1}^{n-1} h_{n\nu}x_\nu$$
$$= (h_{nn} - \lambda)\phi_{n-1}(\lambda) + \sum_{\nu=1}^{n-1} h_{n\nu}(-)^{n-\nu}\alpha_\nu \ldots \alpha_{n-1}\phi_{\nu-1}(\lambda)$$

which equals $\phi_n(\lambda) = 0$, by (8). For $k < n$ we have

$$y_k = (h_{kk} - \lambda)x_k + \sum_{\nu=1}^{k-1} h_{k\nu}x_\nu + \alpha_k x_{k+1}$$
$$= (h_{kk} - \lambda)(-)^{n-k}\alpha_k \ldots \alpha_{n-1}\phi_{k-1}(\lambda)$$
$$+ \sum_{\nu=1}^{k-1} h_{k\nu}(-)^{n-\nu}\alpha_\nu \ldots \alpha_{n-1}\phi_{\nu-1}(\lambda) + (-)^{n-k-1}\alpha_k \ldots \alpha_{n-1}\phi_k(\lambda) \qquad (12)$$
$$= (-)^{n-k}\alpha_k \ldots \alpha_{n-1}[(h_{kk} - \lambda)\phi_{k-1}(\lambda) + \sum_{\nu=1}^{k-1} h_{k\nu}(-)^{k-\nu}\alpha_\nu \cdot$$
$$\cdots \alpha_{k-1}\phi_{\nu-1}(\lambda) - \phi_k(\lambda)]$$

But this expression equals 0, as we see by replacing n by k in the recursion formula (8).

If H *is Hermitian, with all* $\alpha_j \neq 0$, *we will show how the eigenvalues can be located in intervals.* Since $h_{j,j+1} = \bar{h}_{j+1,j} = \alpha_j$, the polynomials $\phi_0(\lambda)$, $\ldots, \phi_n(\lambda)$ defined by (9) satisfy

$$\phi_j(\lambda) = (h_{jj} - \lambda)\phi_{j-1}(\lambda) - |\alpha_{j-1}|^2\phi_{j-2}(\lambda) \qquad (j \geqslant 2)$$
$$\phi_0(\lambda) = 1, \qquad \phi_1(\lambda) = h_{11} - \lambda \qquad (13)$$

Let $a < \lambda < b$ be a given interval. We suppose that neither a nor b is a zero of any of the polynomials $\phi_j(\lambda)$. *We will count the number of zeros of* $\phi_n(\lambda)$ *in the interval* (a, b). Note the following properties:

(i) $\phi_0(\lambda) \neq 0$ *in* (a, b). [In fact, $\phi_0(\lambda) \equiv 1$.]

(ii) *If* $\phi_{j-1}(\lambda_0) = 0$, *then* $\phi_j(\lambda_0)$ *and* $\phi_{j-2}(\lambda_0)$ *are nonzero and of opposite signs.*

Proof. By (13), if either adjacent polynomial, ϕ_j or ϕ_{j-2}, is zero, the other one must also be zero. But then ϕ_{j-1} and ϕ_{j-2} have a common zero, and the recursion formula shows that $\phi_{j-3}(\lambda_0) = 0$, etc. Finally, we could conclude $\phi_0(\lambda_0) = 0$, which is impossible. Therefore, $\phi_{j-1}(\lambda_0) = 0$ implies both $\phi_j(\lambda_0) \neq 0$ and $\phi_{j-2}(\lambda_0) \neq 0$. By (13),

$$\phi_j(\lambda_0) = -|\alpha_{j-1}|^2 \phi_{j-2}(\lambda_0)$$

Therefore, $\phi_j(\lambda_0)$ and $\phi_{j-2}(\lambda_0)$ have opposite signs.

(iii) *As λ passes through a zero of $\phi_n(\lambda)$, the quotient $\phi_n(\lambda)/\phi_{n-1}(\lambda)$ changes from positive to negative.*

Proof: By (ii), the adjacent polynomials ϕ_n and ϕ_{n-1} cannot have a common zero. By the inclusion principle (Section 6.4), the zeros μ_j of $\phi_{n-1}(\lambda) = \det(H_{n-1} - \lambda I)$ separate the zeros λ_j of $\phi_n(\lambda) = \det(H_n - \lambda I)$:

$$\lambda_1 > \mu_1 > \lambda_2 > \cdots > \lambda_{n-1} > \mu_{n-1} > \lambda_n$$

Furthermore,

$$\frac{\phi_n(\lambda)}{\phi_{n-1}(\lambda)} \simeq \frac{(-)^n \lambda^n}{(-)^{n-1} \lambda^{n-1}} = -\lambda < 0 \quad (\text{as } \lambda \to +\infty)$$

Therefore, $\phi_n(\lambda)/\phi_{n-1}(\lambda)$ changes sign exactly once, at the pole $\lambda = \mu_j$, between consecutive zeros λ_{j+1}, λ_j; and we have Fig. 7.6 as a picture of the algebraic signs of ϕ_n/ϕ_{n-1}. We see that the sign changes from $+$ to $-$ as λ crosses each λ_j.

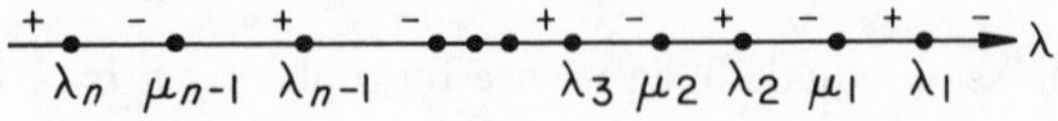

Figure 7.6

Sequences of polynomials $\phi_0(\lambda), \ldots, \phi_n(\lambda)$ with properties (i), (ii), (iii) are called *Sturm sequences*. They have this remarkable property:

Theorem 1. *Let $\phi_0(\lambda), \ldots, \phi_n(\lambda)$ be a Sturm sequence on the interval (a, b). Let $\sigma(\lambda)$ be the number of sign changes in the ordered array of numbers $\phi_0(\lambda), \ldots, \phi_n(\lambda)$. Then the number of zeros of the function ϕ_n in the interval (a, b) equals $\sigma(b) - \sigma(a)$.*

EXAMPLE. Let

$$H_3 = \begin{bmatrix} 1 & -2 & 0 \\ -2 & 1 & 4 \\ 0 & 4 & 5 \end{bmatrix}, \quad H_2 = \begin{bmatrix} 1 & -2 \\ -2 & 1 \end{bmatrix}, \quad H_1 = [1]$$

If $\phi_0(\lambda) = 1$ and $\phi_\nu(\lambda) = \det(H_\nu - \lambda I)$ for $\nu \geqslant 1$, then

$$\phi_0 = 1, \qquad \phi_1(\lambda) = 1 - \lambda, \qquad \phi_2(\lambda) = \lambda^2 - 2\lambda - 3$$
$$\phi_3(\lambda) = -\lambda^3 + 7\lambda^2 + 9\lambda - 31$$

For $\lambda = 0$ we have the signs

$$\phi_0, \phi_1, \phi_2, \phi_3 = +\ +\ -\ - \qquad \text{(one sign change)}$$

Hence, $\sigma(0) = 1$. For $\lambda = 10$ we have the signs

$$\phi_0, \phi_1, \phi_2, \phi_3 = +\ -\ +\ - \qquad \text{(three sign changes)}$$

Hence, $\sigma(10) = 3$. The number of zeros of $\phi_3(\lambda)$ in the interval $(0, 10)$ is, therefore, $\sigma(10) - \sigma(0) = 3 - 1 = 2$.

Proof of Sturm's Theorem. The function $\sigma(\lambda)$ can change only when λ passes through a zero of one of the functions $\phi_j(\lambda)$. By property (i), $\phi_0(\lambda)$ never changes sign in (a, b). If $1 \leqslant j \leqslant n - 1$, consider the triple

$$\phi_{j-1}(\lambda), \phi_j(\lambda), \phi_{j+1}(\lambda) \tag{14}$$

If $\phi_j(\lambda_0) = 0$, property (ii) states that $\phi_{j-1}(\lambda_0)$ and $\phi_{j+1}(\lambda_0)$ have opposite signs. Therefore, the triple (14) yields exactly one sign change for *all* λ in the neighborhood of λ_0. Assume $\phi_n(\lambda_0) \neq 0$. Then $\sigma(\lambda)$ cannot change as λ crosses λ_0.

If λ crosses a zero λ_ν of $\phi_n(\lambda)$, property (iii) states that the signs of

$$\phi_{n-1}(\lambda), \phi_n(\lambda)$$

change from $+\ +$ to $+\ -$, or $-\ -$ to $+\ +$. Therefore, exactly one sign change is added in the sequence of ordered values $\phi_0(\lambda), \ldots, \phi_{n-1}(\lambda), \phi_n(\lambda)$. In other words, $\sigma(\lambda)$ increases by 1. In summary, $\sigma(\lambda)$ increases by 1 each time λ crosses a zero of $\phi_n(\lambda)$; otherwise, $\sigma(\lambda)$ remains constant. Therefore, $\sigma(b) - \sigma(a)$ is the total number of zeros of $\phi_n(\lambda)$ in the interval (a, b).

In practice, Sturm's theorem can be used with Gershgorin's theorem (Section 6.8). For tridiagonal $H = H^*$, we know from Gershgorin's theorem that every eigenvalue of H satisfies one of the inequalities

$$|\lambda - h_{jj}| \leqslant |h_{j, j-1}| + |h_{j, j+1}| \qquad (j = 1, \ldots, n) \tag{15}$$

where $h_{01} = h_{n, n+1} = 0$. The union of the possibly-overlapping intervals (15) is a set of disjoint intervals

$$(a_1, b_1), \ldots, (a_k, b_k) \tag{16}$$

These intervals can be subdivided, and Sturm's theorem can be applied quickly to each of the resulting subintervals $(a_{i\alpha}, b_{i\alpha})$.

When Sturm's theorem is used numerically to locate the eigenvalues of tridiagonal $H = H^*$, the coefficients of the characteristic polynomials $\phi_j(\lambda)$ should *not* be computed. Instead, the recursion formula (13) should be used *directly* to evaluate successively the numbers $\phi_0(\lambda), \ldots, \phi_n(\lambda)$ and hence the integer $\sigma(\lambda)$.

In the proof of Sturm's theorem, we assumed that

$$\phi_j(a) \neq 0, \qquad \phi_j(b) \neq 0 \quad (j = 1, \ldots, n) \tag{17}$$

We can show that *it was only necessary to assume*

$$\phi_n(a) \neq 0, \qquad \phi_n(b) \neq 0 \tag{18}$$

If (18) is true but (17) is false, then for all sufficiently small $\epsilon > 0$ we have

$$\phi_j(a + \epsilon) \neq 0, \qquad \phi_j(b - \epsilon) \neq 0 \quad (j = 1, \ldots, n) \tag{19}$$

By what we have already proved, the number of zeros of $\phi_n(\lambda)$ in $(a + \epsilon, b - \epsilon)$ is $\sigma(b - \epsilon) - \sigma(a + \epsilon)$. But

$$\sigma(a) = \sigma(a + \epsilon) \quad \text{and} \quad \sigma(b) = \sigma(b - \epsilon) \tag{20}$$

because $\phi_n(\lambda)$ has no zeros for $a \leqslant x \leqslant a + \epsilon$ or $b - \epsilon \leqslant x \leqslant b$. Thus, the number of zeros of $\phi_n(\lambda)$ in (a, b) equals the number of zeros of $\phi_n(\lambda)$ in $(a + \epsilon, b - \epsilon)$, which equals $\sigma(b) - \sigma(a)$.

For a precise computation of the eigenvalues, Newton's method should be used after the eigenvalues have been separated and approximated by the theorems of Gershgorin and Sturm. Newton's method for computing the real roots of an equation $\phi(\lambda) = 0$ is discussed in texts on numerical analysis. This method converges extremely rapidly if the first approximation is fairly accurate.

PROBLEMS

1. Using the recurrence formula (8), evaluate $\det(H - \lambda I)$ for the $n \times n$ Hessenberg matrix

$$H_n = \begin{bmatrix} 0 & 1 & 0 & \cdots & 0 \\ 0 & 0 & 1 & \cdots & 0 \\ \cdot & \cdot & \cdot & \cdots & \cdot \\ 0 & 0 & 0 & \cdots & 1 \\ -c_n & -c_{n-1} & -c_{n-2} & \cdots & -c_1 \end{bmatrix}$$

2. Evaluate successively

$$\Delta_1 = 1, \qquad \Delta_2 = \begin{vmatrix} 1 & 1 \\ 2 & 1 \end{vmatrix}, \qquad \Delta_3 = \begin{vmatrix} 1 & 1 & 0 \\ 2 & 1 & 1 \\ 3 & 2 & 1 \end{vmatrix}, \ldots, \Delta_5 = \begin{vmatrix} 1 & 1 & 0 & 0 & 0 \\ 2 & 1 & 1 & 0 & 0 \\ 3 & 2 & 1 & 1 & 0 \\ 4 & 3 & 2 & 1 & 1 \\ 5 & 4 & 3 & 2 & 1 \end{vmatrix}$$

3.* Let

$$f(x) = c_1 x - c_2 x^2 + c_3 x^3 - c_4 x^4 + \cdots \qquad (|x| < \epsilon)$$

Define $\Delta_0 = 1$, $\Delta_1 = c_1$,

$$\Delta_n = \begin{bmatrix} c_1 & 1 & 0 & \cdots & 0 & 0 \\ c_2 & c_1 & 1 & \cdots & 0 & 0 \\ \cdot & \cdot & \cdot & \cdots & \cdot & \cdot \\ c_{n-1} & c_{n-2} & c_{n-3} & \cdots & c_1 & 1 \\ c_n & c_{n-1} & c_{n-2} & \cdots & c_2 & c_1 \end{bmatrix} \qquad (n \geqslant 2)$$

Prove that

$$\Delta_0 + \Delta_1 x + \Delta_2 x^2 + \cdots = \frac{1}{1 - f(x)}$$

[Show that (7) implies $\sum_1^\infty \Delta_n x^n \equiv f(x) \sum_0^\infty \Delta_n x^n$.] If $c_n = n$, as in Problem 2, evaluate Δ_n for all n.

4. Using formula (10), calculate an eigenvector for the matrix

$$\begin{bmatrix} 1 & 1 & 0 \\ 2 & 1 & 1 \\ 3 & 2 & 1 \end{bmatrix}$$

belonging to the eigenvalue $\lambda = 0$.

5. Let H be a Hessenberg matrix, as in formula (2). Show that H is similar to a Hessenberg matrix H' with $\alpha_j' = 1$ if $\alpha_j \neq 0$, $\alpha_j' = 0$ if $\alpha_j = 0$. (Form $H' = \Lambda H \Lambda^{-1}$, where Λ is a suitable diagonal matrix.)

6. Let

$$A = \begin{bmatrix} 2 & -1 & 0 & 0 & 0 \\ -1 & 2 & -1 & 0 & 0 \\ 0 & -1 & 2 & -1 & 0 \\ 0 & 0 & -1 & 2 & -1 \\ 0 & 0 & 0 & -1 & 2 \end{bmatrix}$$

Let $\phi_0(\lambda) = 1, \phi_1(\lambda) = 2 - \lambda, \ldots, \phi_5(\lambda) = \det(A - \lambda I)$. Using the recursion formula (13), calculate numerical values for the $\phi_j(\lambda)$ for $\lambda = 0$ and for $\lambda = 4$. How many eigenvalues of A lie between 0 and 4?

7.* Let H_n be the $n \times n$ matrix

$$H_n = \begin{bmatrix} 2 & -1 & 0 & \cdots & 0 & 0 \\ -1 & 2 & -1 & \cdots & 0 & 0 \\ \cdot & \cdot & \cdot & \cdots & \cdot & \cdot \\ 0 & 0 & 0 & \cdots & -1 & 2 \end{bmatrix}$$

(The matrix A in the last problem is H_5.) Let $\phi_0(\lambda) = 1$ and, for $n \geqslant 1$, let $\phi_n(\lambda) = \det(H_n - \lambda I)$. Making the change of variable $\lambda = 2 - 2 \cos \theta$, prove that

$$\phi_n(\lambda) = \frac{\sin(n+1)\theta}{\sin \theta}$$

Hence find all the eigenvalues of H_n. [Use the recursion formula (13).]

7.12 THE METHOD OF HOUSEHOLDER AND BAUER

Let A be a real, symmetric $n \times n$ matrix. We will show how A can be reduced to tridiagonal form by $n - 2$ real, unitary similarity-transformations. For $n = 5$ the process is illustrated as follows:

$$
\begin{array}{l}
\text{x x x x x} \\
\text{x x x x x} \\
\text{x x x x x} \quad \longrightarrow \\
\text{x x x x x} \\
\text{x x x x x}
\end{array}
\quad
\begin{array}{l}
\text{x x 0 0 0} \\
\text{x x x x x} \\
\text{0 x x x x} \quad \longrightarrow \\
\text{0 x x x x} \\
\text{0 x x x x}
\end{array}
\quad
\begin{array}{l}
\text{x x 0 0 0} \\
\text{x x x 0 0} \\
\text{0 x x x x} \quad \longrightarrow \\
\text{0 0 x x x} \\
\text{0 0 x x x}
\end{array}
\quad
\begin{array}{l}
\text{x x 0 0 0} \\
\text{x x x 0 0} \\
\text{0 x x x 0} \\
\text{0 0 x x x} \\
\text{0 0 0 x x}
\end{array}
\quad (1)
$$

From the tridiagonal form, the characteristic polynomial can be found by the recursion formula (9) of the preceding section, or the eigenvalues can be located in intervals by Sturm's theorem (Theorem 1, Section 7.11).

If A is real but not symmetric, the method will produce zeros in the upper right corner but not in the lower left corner. For $n = 5$, the process would appear as follows:

$$
\begin{array}{l}
\text{x x x x x} \\
\text{x x x x x} \\
\text{x x x x x} \quad \longrightarrow \\
\text{x x x x x} \\
\text{x x x x x}
\end{array}
\quad
\begin{array}{l}
\text{x x 0 0 0} \\
\text{x x x x x} \\
\text{x x x x x} \quad \longrightarrow \\
\text{x x x x x} \\
\text{x x x x x}
\end{array}
\quad
\begin{array}{l}
\text{x x 0 0 0} \\
\text{x x x 0 0} \\
\text{x x x x x} \quad \longrightarrow \\
\text{x x x x x} \\
\text{x x x x x}
\end{array}
\quad
\begin{array}{l}
\text{x x 0 0 0} \\
\text{x x x 0 0} \\
\text{x x x x 0} \\
\text{x x x x x} \\
\text{x x x x x}
\end{array}
\quad (2)
$$

The final matrix is in the Hessenberg form, and the characteristic polynomial can be found by the recursion formula (8) of the last section. If A is complex, the method is modified in the obvious way, by replacing transposes x^T by their complex conjugates x^*.

In the real, symmetric case, the first transformation $A \rightarrow B = U^T A U$ is required to produce a matrix of the form

$$B = \begin{bmatrix} b_{11} & b_{12} & 0 & \cdots & 0 \\ b_{21} & b_{22} & b_{23} & \cdots & b_{2n} \\ 0 & b_{32} & b_{33} & \cdots & b_{3n} \\ \cdot & \cdot & \cdot & \cdots & \cdot \\ 0 & b_{n2} & b_{n3} & \cdots & b_{nn} \end{bmatrix} \qquad (b_{1k} = b_{k1} = 0 \text{ for } k \geqslant 3) \qquad (3)$$

If all a_{1k} already $= 0$ $(k \geqslant 3)$, we set $B = A$. Otherwise, we will use a matrix of the form

$$U = I - 2uu^T \qquad \text{(with } u^T u = 1\text{)} \qquad (4)$$

Explicitly, if the real column-vector u has components u_i, then $U = (\delta_{ij} - 2u_i u_j)$. Since we require u to have unit length, U is unitary.

$$U^T U = (I - 2uu^T)(I - 2uu^T) = I - 4uu^T + 4u(u^T u)u^T = I \qquad (5)$$

U is also real and symmetric: $U^T = U$. The requirements

$$b_{13} = 0, \ldots, b_{1n} = 0, \qquad u^T u = 1 \qquad (6)$$

place $n - 1$ constraints on the n-component vector u. Since there is one degree of freedom, *we set $u_1 = 0$*. Note that $b_{1k} = 0$ *implies* $b_{k1} = 0$, since B is symmetric.

The first row of $B = UAU$ is the first row of UA times U. Since $u_1 = 0$, the first row of $U = I - 2uu^T$ is just $(1, 0, \ldots, 0)$. Therefore, the first row of UA is just the first row of A. Hence, the first row of B is

$$b^T \equiv [b_{11}b_{12}b_{13} \ldots b_{1n}] = [a_{11}a_{12}a_{13} \ldots a_{1n}] \, U \equiv a^T U \qquad (7)$$

Since $U = I - 2uu^T$, we have $a^T U = a^T - 2(a^T u)u^T$, or

$$b_{11} = a_{11}, \qquad b_{1j} = a_{1j} - 2(a^T u)u_j \quad (j = 2, \ldots, n) \qquad (8)$$

The unknowns $u_2, \ldots, u_n$ must solve the $n - 1$ equations

$$a_{1j} - 2(a^T u)u_j = 0 \qquad (j = 3, \ldots, n) \qquad (9)$$

$$u_2^2 + \cdots + u_n^2 = 1 \qquad (10)$$

To solve these equations, we observe that the rows a^T and $b^T = a^T U$ must have equal lengths: $b^T b = a^T U U^T a = a^T a$. Thus, we require

$$b_{11}^2 + b_{12}^2 = a_{11}^2 + a_{12}^2 + a_{13}^2 + \cdots + a_{1n}^2 \qquad (11)$$

By (8), $b_{11} = a_{11}$. Then (11) takes the form

$$b_{12}^2 = a_{12}^2 + a_{13}^2 + \cdots + a_{1n}^2 \equiv \alpha^2 \tag{12}$$

If $\alpha = (a_{12}^2 + \cdots + a_{1n}^2)^{1/2} > 0$, equations (8) and (12) yield

$$b_{12} = a_{12} - 2(a^T u)u_2 = \pm \alpha \tag{13}$$

We now multiply (13) by u_2, (9) by u_j $(j = 3, \ldots, n)$, and add to obtain

$$\sum_{k=2}^n [a_{1k} - 2(a^T u)u_k]u_k = \pm \alpha u_2$$

or

$$a^T u - 2(a^T u)(u^T u) = \pm \alpha u_2$$

or, since we require $u^T u = 1$,

$$a^T u = \pm \alpha u_2 \tag{14}$$

This is a relationship between the unknown inner product $a^T u$ and the unknown component u_2. Using (14) in the identity (13) for b_{12}, we find

$$b_{12} = a_{12} \pm 2\alpha u_2^2 = \pm \alpha \tag{15}$$

We have $\alpha > 0$ because at least one $a_{1k} \neq 0$ $(k \geqslant 3)$. Therefore, (15) has the positive solution

$$\boxed{u_2 = \left[\frac{1}{2}\left(1 \pm \frac{a_{12}}{\alpha}\right) \right]^{1/2}} \qquad \text{with } \alpha = \left(\sum_{k=2}^n a_{1k}^2 \right)^{1/2} \tag{16}$$

We choose the sign $\pm$ *so that* $\pm a_{12} \geqslant 0$. Since $\alpha > |a_{12}|$, we have $1/\sqrt{2} \leqslant u_2 < 1$. Having computed u_2, we compute $u_3, \ldots, u_n$ from (9) and (14).

$$u_j = [2(a^T u)]^{-1}a_{1j}$$

$$\boxed{u_j = [\pm 2\alpha u_2]^{-1}a_{1j} \qquad (j = 3, \ldots, n)} \tag{17}$$

Exercise. *If* $\pm$ *is chosen so that* $\pm a_{12} \geqslant 0$, *and if we define*

$$\alpha \equiv (a_{12}^2 + \cdots + a_{1n}^2)^{1/2} \quad \text{and} \quad a^T u \equiv a_{12}u_2 + \cdots + a_{1n}u_n \tag{18}$$

verify directly that the numbers $u_2, \ldots, u_n$ *defined by* (16) *and* (17), *solve the required equations* (9) *and* (10).

We now transform A into $B = UAU$, with $b_{1k} = b_{k1} = 0$ for $k \geqslant 3$. If $n > 3$, we wish next to transform B into a matrix $C = VBV$ with

$$c_{1k} = c_{k1} = 0 \ (k \geqslant 3) \quad and \quad c_{2r} = c_{r2} = 0 \quad (r \geqslant 4) \tag{19}$$

We shall require $V^T V = I$ and $V = V^T$.

Observe the matrix B in (3). We can partition B as follows:

$$B = \begin{bmatrix} b_{11} & b_{12} & 0 & \cdots & 0 \\ b_{21} & & & & \\ 0 & & & & \\ \cdot & & A' & & \\ 0 & & & & \end{bmatrix} \tag{20}$$

where A' is the $(n-1) \times (n-1)$ matrix (b_{ij}) $(i,j \geqslant 2)$. By analogy to (16) and (17), we can reduce A' to the form

$$B' = \begin{matrix} \text{x} & \text{x} & 0 & \cdots & 0 \\ \text{x} & \text{x} & \text{x} & \cdots & \text{x} \\ 0 & \text{x} & \text{x} & \cdots & \text{x} \\ \cdot & \cdot & \cdot & \cdots & \cdot \\ 0 & \text{x} & \text{x} & \cdots & \text{x} \end{matrix} \tag{21}$$

by a transformation $B' = U'A'U'$, where

$$U' = I' - 2u'(u')^T = (\delta_{ij} - 2u_i'u_j') \quad (i,j = 1, \ldots, n-1) \tag{22}$$

If A' has not already the form (21), we simply define

$$\alpha' = [(a_{12}')^2 + \cdots + (a_{1,n-1}')^2]^{1/2} > 0$$

and define, in analogy to (16) and (17),

$$u_2' = \left[\frac{1}{2} \left(1 \pm \frac{a_{12}'}{\alpha'} \right) \right]^{1/2}, \qquad u_1' = 0$$
$$u_j' = [\pm 2\alpha' u_2']^{-1} a_{1j}' \qquad (j = 3, \ldots, n-1) \tag{23}$$

The sign $\pm$ is chosen to make $\pm a_{12}' \geqslant 0$.

We now assert that *the required matrix* V *has the form*

$$V = \begin{bmatrix} 1 & 0 & \cdots & 0 \\ 0 & & & \\ \cdot & & & \\ \cdot & & U' & \\ \cdot & & & \\ 0 & & & \end{bmatrix} \tag{24}$$

Proof: Since $u_1' = 0$, the matrix V has the form

$$V = \begin{bmatrix} 1 & 0 & 0 & \cdots & 0 \\ 0 & 1 & 0 & \cdots & 0 \\ 0 & 0 & x & \cdots & x \\ \cdot & \cdot & \cdot & \cdots & \cdot \\ 0 & 0 & x & \cdots & x \end{bmatrix} \qquad (25)$$

The first row of VBV is the first row of V times BV. Since the first row of V is $(1, 0, \ldots, 0)$, the first row of VBV is just the first row of B times V, or

$$[b_{11}\, b_{12}\, 0 \ldots 0]V = [b_{11}\, b_{12}\, 0 \ldots 0] \qquad (26)$$

Here we have used the form (25) for V. Thus, *the first row and*, by symmetry, *the first column are unaffected.* The partitoned form (24) now shows that

$$VBV = \begin{bmatrix} b_{11} & b_{12} & 0 & \cdots & 0 \\ b_{21} & & & & \\ 0 & & & & \\ \cdot & & U'A'U' & & \\ 0 & & & & \end{bmatrix} \qquad (27)$$

But $U'A'U' = B'$ of the form (21). Therefore, $VBV = C$ of the required form

$$C = \begin{bmatrix} x & x & 0 & 0 & \cdots & 0 \\ x & x & x & 0 & \cdots & 0 \\ 0 & x & & & & \\ 0 & 0 & & & & \\ \cdot & \cdot & & A'' & & \\ 0 & 0 & & & & \end{bmatrix} \qquad (28)$$

where A'' is an $(n - 2) \times (n - 2)$ symmetric matrix.

We note parenthetically that V in (24) has the form

$$V = I - 2vv^T \qquad (29)$$

where v is the unit vector col $(0, 0, u_2', \ldots, u_{n-1}')$.

The process now continues. Let U'' be the $(n - 2) \times (n - 2)$ matrix of the form $I'' - 2u''(u'')^T$ which reduces A'' to the form

$$U''A''U'' = \begin{bmatrix} x & x & 0 & \cdots & 0 \\ x & x & x & \cdots & x \\ 0 & x & x & \cdots & x \\ \cdot & \cdot & \cdot & \cdot & \cdot & \cdot \\ 0 & x & x & \cdots & x \end{bmatrix} \tag{30}$$

We then define

$$W = \begin{bmatrix} 1 & 0 & 0 & \cdots & 0 \\ 0 & 1 & 0 & \cdots & 0 \\ 0 & 0 & & & \\ \cdot & \cdot & & U'' & \\ 0 & 0 & & & \end{bmatrix} = I - 2 \begin{bmatrix} 0 \\ 0 \\ 0 \\ u_2'' \\ \cdot \\ u_{n-2}'' \end{bmatrix} [0, 0, 0, u_2'', \cdots, u_{n-2}''] \tag{31}$$

Since $u_1'' = 0$, this matrix has the form

$$W = \begin{bmatrix} 1 & 0 & 0 & 0 & \cdots & 0 \\ 0 & 1 & 0 & 0 & \cdots & 0 \\ 0 & 0 & 1 & 0 & \cdots & 0 \\ 0 & 0 & 0 & & & \\ \cdot & \cdot & \cdot & & X & \\ 0 & 0 & 0 & & & \end{bmatrix} \tag{32}$$

Therefore, as (28) shows, the first two rows and the first two columns are unaffected by the transformation $C \rightarrow WCW$. Therefore,

$$WCW = \begin{bmatrix} x & x & 0 & 0 & \cdots & 0 \\ x & x & x & 0 & \cdots & 0 \\ 0 & x & & & & \\ 0 & 0 & & & & \\ \cdot & \cdot & U''A''U'' & & \\ 0 & 0 & & & & \end{bmatrix} = \begin{bmatrix} x & x & 0 & 0 & \cdots & 0 \\ x & x & x & 0 & 0 & \cdots & 0 \\ 0 & x & x & x & 0 & \cdots & 0 \\ 0 & 0 & x & & & \\ 0 & 0 & 0 & & & \\ \cdot & \cdot & \cdot & & A''' & \\ 0 & 0 & 0 & & & \end{bmatrix} \tag{33}$$

After k reductions we obtain a symmetric $n \times n$ matrix, say $Z = (z_{ij})$, with

$$z_{ij} = 0 \quad (\text{if } i \leqslant k \text{ and } j \geqslant i + 2)$$
$$z_{ij} = 0 \quad (\text{if } j \leqslant k \text{ and } i \geqslant j + 2) \tag{34}$$

We call $A^{(k)}$ the *lower-right part*.

$$A^{(k)} = (z_{ij}) \qquad (i, j = k+1, \ldots, n) \tag{35}$$

If $k < n - 2$, we will reduce Z further. If at least one of the numbers $a_{13}^{(k)}, \ldots, a_{1,n-k}^{(k)}$ is nonzero, we form $u_2^{(k)}, \ldots, u_{n-k}^{(k)}$ from (16) and (17), replacing A by $A^{(k)}$, and n by $n - k$. Setting $u_1^{(k)} = 0$, we have the form

$$U^{(k)} A^{(k)} U^{(k)} = \begin{bmatrix} \mathrm{x} & \mathrm{x} & 0 & \cdots & 0 \\ \mathrm{x} & & & & \\ 0 & & & & \\ \cdot & & A^{(k+1)} & & \\ 0 & & & & \end{bmatrix} \tag{36}$$

where

$$U^{(k)} = (\delta_{ij} - 2u_i^{(k)} u_j^{(k)}) \qquad (i, j = 1, \ldots, n - k) \tag{37}$$

If we define the $n \times n$ matrix

$$M = I - 2 \begin{bmatrix} 0 \\ \cdot \\ \cdot \\ \cdot \\ 0 \\ u_2^{(k)} \\ \cdot \\ \cdot \\ \cdot \\ u_{n-k}^{(k)} \end{bmatrix} [0, \ldots, 0, u_2^{(k)}, \ldots, u_{n-k}^{(k)}] \tag{38}$$

we must show that the first k rows and the first k columns of Z are unaffected by the transformation $Z \to MZM = Z'$. Now

$$z_{ij}' = \sum_{\alpha=1}^{n} \sum_{\beta=1}^{n} m_{i\alpha} z_{\alpha\beta} m_{\beta j}$$

Let $i \leqslant k$. Then, by (38), $m_{i\alpha} = \delta_{i\alpha}$ and

$$z_{ij}' = \sum_{\beta=1}^{n} z_{i\beta} m_{\beta j} \qquad (\text{if } i \leqslant k) \tag{39}$$

By (34), $z_{i\beta} = 0$ if $\beta \geqslant i + 2$. Therefore, (39) yields

$$z_{ij}' = \sum_{\beta=1}^{i+1} z_{i\beta} m_{\beta j} \qquad (\text{if } i \leqslant k) \tag{40}$$

But (38) shows that

$$m_{\beta j} = \delta_{\beta j} \qquad (\text{if } \beta \leqslant k + 1) \tag{41}$$

Then (40) implies $z'_{ij} = z_{ij}$ if $i \leqslant k$. By symmetry, we also have $z'_{ij} = z_{ij}$ if $j \leqslant k$.

Finally, we must show that $Z' = MZM$ implies

$$U^{(k)} A^{(k)} U^{(k)} = (z'_{ij}) \qquad (i, j = k + 1, \ldots, n) \tag{42}$$

Now the form (38) shows that

$$\begin{aligned} m_{i\alpha} &= 0 \qquad (\text{if } i \geqslant k + 1 \quad \text{and} \quad \alpha \leqslant k) \\ m_{\beta j} &= 0 \qquad (\text{if } j \geqslant k + 1 \quad \text{and} \quad \beta \leqslant k) \end{aligned} \tag{43}$$

Therefore,

$$z'_{ij} = \sum_{\alpha = k+1}^{n} \sum_{\beta = k+1}^{n} m_{i\alpha} z_{\alpha\beta} m_{\beta j} \qquad (\text{if } i, j \geqslant k + 1) \tag{44}$$

But (44) is equivalent to (42), since

$$U^{(k)} = (m_{ij}) \quad \text{and} \quad A^{(k)} = (z_{ij}) \qquad (i, j = k + 1, \ldots, n) \tag{45}$$

COMPUTING ALGORITHM

The preceding three paragraphs give a rigorous justification of the method. In practice, the matrix M in (38) is not formed explicitly, nor is the matrix $U^{(k)}$.

At each stage $k = 0, 1, \ldots, n - 3$ our task is to replace the $(n - k) \times (n - k)$ matrix $A^{(k)}$ by the matrix

$$U^{(k)} A^{(k)} U^{(k)} = \begin{bmatrix} \theta & \phi & 0 \cdots 0 \\ \phi & & \\ 0 & & \\ \cdot & & A^{(k+1)} \\ 0 & & \end{bmatrix} \tag{46}$$

The number θ is unchanged $= a_{11}^{(k)}$. If, by chance,

$$a_{13}^{(k)} = \cdots = a_{1,n-k}^{(k)} = 0 \tag{47}$$

then no computation is performed at stage k, since $A^{(k)}$ already has the form of the right-hand side of (46). Otherwise, *we do compute the numbers* $u_2^{(k)}, \ldots, u_{n-k}^{(k)}$ by (16) and (17), replacing A by $A^{(k)}$, and n by $n - k$.

Dropping the superscript k, we observe that

$$UAU = (I - 2uu^T)A(I - 2uu^T)$$
$$= A - 2uu^T A - 2Auu^T + 4uu^T uu^T \tag{48}$$

Define the quadratic form

$$\beta = u^T A u \tag{49}$$

Compute $Au = b$, i.e., *compute*

$$b_i^{(k)} = b_i = \sum_{j=2}^{n-k} a_{ij}^{(k)} u_j^{(k)} \qquad (i = 1, \ldots, n-k) \tag{50}$$

By (48), the i,j-component of $U^{(k)} A^{(k)} U^{(k)}$ is

$$a_{ij}^{(k)} - 2u_i^{(k)} b_j - 2b_i u_j^{(k)} + 4\beta u_i^{(k)} u_j^{(k)} \tag{51}$$

Replace $a_{12}^{(k)}$ *by*

$$\phi = a_{12}^{(k)} - 2b_1 u_2^{(k)} \tag{52}$$

Replace $a_{13}^{(k)}, \ldots, a_{1n}^{(k)}$ *by* $0, \ldots, 0$. *For* $2 \leqslant i \leqslant j \leqslant n - k$ *replace* $a_{ij}^{(k)}$ *by the following equivalent of* (51):

$$a_{ij}^{(k)} + u_i c_j + c_i u_j \qquad (2 \leqslant i \leqslant j \leqslant n - k) \tag{53}$$

where

$$c_i = 2(\beta u_i - b_i) \qquad (i = 2, \ldots, n - k)$$

The components with $i > j$ *are now formed by symmetry.*

COUNT OF OPERATIONS

We will count the number of multiplications and the number of square roots. At stage $k = 0, 1, \ldots, n - 3$, the calculations

$$\alpha = \alpha^{(k)} = \left[\sum_{j=2}^{n-k} (a_{1j}^{(k)})^2 \right]^{1/2}$$

$$u_2^{(k)} = \left[\frac{1}{2} \left(1 \pm \frac{a_{12}^{(k)}}{\alpha} \right) \right]^{1/2} \tag{16'}$$

$$u_j^{(k)} = [\pm 2\alpha u_2^{(k)}]^{-1} a_{1j}^{(k)} \qquad (j = 3, \ldots, n - k) \tag{17'}$$

require 2 square roots and approximately $2(n - k)$ multiplications. To form b in (50) requires $(n - k)(n - k - 1)$ multiplications. The calculation of c requires $n - k - 1$ multiplications. The calculations (53) require

$$\sum_{i=2}^{n-k} \sum_{j=i}^{n-k} 2 = 2 \sum_{i=2}^{n-k} (n - k - i + 1) = 2 \sum_{m=1}^{n-k-1} m$$

which is equal to $(n - k)(n - k - 1)$ multiplications. In summary, at stage k there are

2 square roots and about $2(n - k)(n - k - 1)$ multiplications   (54)

Summing for $k = 0, \ldots, n - 3$, we find a total of

$$2(n - 2) \text{ square roots and about } \frac{2n^3}{3} \text{ multiplications} \qquad (55)$$

Thus, there are very few multiplications. After all, just to square an $n \times n$ matrix requires n^3 multiplications. Since the number of multiplications is small, it will usually be economically feasible to use double precision.

PROBLEMS

1. Reduce the matrix

$$\begin{bmatrix} 1 & 2 & 3 \\ 2 & 4 & 5 \\ 3 & 5 & 6 \end{bmatrix}$$

to tridiagonal form by the method of Householder and Bauer.

2. Reduce the matrix

$$\begin{bmatrix} 1 & 2 & 3 \\ 4 & 5 & 6 \\ 7 & 8 & 9 \end{bmatrix}$$

to Hessenberg form by the method of Householder and Bauer.

3.* Reduce the matrix

$$\begin{bmatrix} 0 & 1 & 2 & 3 \\ 1 & 4 & 5 & 6 \\ 2 & 5 & 7 & 8 \\ 3 & 6 & 8 & 9 \end{bmatrix}$$

to tridiagonal form by the method of Householder and Bauer.

4.* According to formula (55), the H-B reduction of an $n \times n$ symmetric matrix requires "about" $2n^3/3$ multiplications. What is the exact number of multiplications?

5. If A is real but not symmetric, and if A is to be reduced to Hessenberg form by the H-B method, how should formulas (50)–(53) be modified?

6. If a real matrix A is reduced to a tridiagonal or Hessenberg matrix X by the H-B method, show that $\sum \sum a_{ij}^2 = \sum \sum x_{ij}^2$. (This identity can be used as a check of rounding error.)

7.13 NUMERICAL IDENTIFICATION OF STABLE MATRICES

In the theory of automatic control, in circuit theory, and in many other contexts the following problem arises: *Given an* n $\times$ n *matrix* A, *determine whether all of its eigenvalues lie in the left half-plane* Re $\lambda < 0$. The matrix A is called *stable* if all of its eigenvalues lie in the left half-plane. The importance of this concept is shown by the following theorem:

Theorem 1. *An* n $\times$ n *matrix* A *is stable if and only if all solutions* x(t) *of the differential equation*

$$\frac{dx(t)}{dt} = Ax(t) \tag{1}$$

tend to zero as t $\longrightarrow \infty$.

Proof. Suppose that A has an eigenvalue λ with Re $\lambda \geqslant 0$. If c is an associated eigenvector, then the solution

$$x(t) = e^{\lambda t}c$$

does not tend to zero as $t \longrightarrow \infty$ because $e^{\lambda t} \nrightarrow 0$.

Suppose, instead, that A is stable. Let $\lambda_1, \ldots, \lambda_s$ be the different eigenvalues of A, with multiplicities $m_1, \ldots, m_s$. In formula (17) of Section 5.1, we showed that every component $x_v(t)$ of every solution $x(t)$ of the differential equation $dx/dt = Ax$ is a linear combination of polynomials in t times exponential functions exp $\lambda_i t$. Since all λ_i have negative real parts, every such expression tends to zero as $t \longrightarrow \infty$. This completes the proof.

One way to show that a matrix is stable is to compute all its eigenvalues and to observe that they have negative real parts. But the actual computation of the eigenvalues is not necessary. By results of *Routh and Hurwitz*, it is only necessary to compute the coefficients c_i of the characteristic polynomial

$$\det (\lambda I - A) = \lambda^n + c_1\lambda^{n-1} + c_2\lambda^{n-2} + \cdots + c_n \tag{2}$$

Assume that A is real, and hence that the c_i are real. Form the fraction

$$R_1(\lambda) = \frac{\lambda^n + c_2\lambda^{n-2} + c_4\lambda^{n-4} + \cdots}{c_1\lambda^{n-1} + c_3\lambda^{n-3} + \cdots} \tag{3}$$

If $c_1 \neq 0$, this fraction can be rewritten in the form

$$R_1(\lambda) = \alpha_1\lambda + \frac{1}{R_2(\lambda)} \tag{4}$$

where $\alpha_1 = 1/c_1$ and

$$R_2(\lambda) = \frac{c_1\lambda^{n-1} + c_3\lambda^{n-3} + \cdots}{d_0\lambda^{n-2} + d_2\lambda^{n-4} + \cdots} \tag{5}$$

with

$$d_k = c_{k+2} - \alpha_1 c_{k+3} \qquad (k = 0, 2, \ldots) \tag{6}$$

Similarly, we write

$$R_2(\lambda) = \alpha_2\lambda + \frac{1}{R_3(\lambda)}$$

and so on until we obtain the full continued fraction

$$R_1(\lambda) = \alpha_1\lambda + \cfrac{1}{\alpha_2\lambda + \cfrac{1}{\alpha_3\lambda + \cfrac{}{\ddots + \cfrac{1}{\alpha_n\lambda}}}} \tag{7}$$

Theorem 2. *The zeros of the polynomial* $\lambda^n + c_1\lambda^{n-1} + \ldots + c_0$ *all lie in the left half-plane if and only if the coefficients* α_i *in the continued fraction* (7) *are all positive.*

EXAMPLE 1. Consider the polynomial

$$\lambda^3 + 3\lambda^2 + 7\lambda + 5 \tag{8}$$

We have

$$R_1(\lambda) = \frac{\lambda^3 + 7\lambda}{3\lambda^2 + 5}$$

$$= \frac{1}{3}\lambda + \frac{1}{R_2(\lambda)}$$

with

$$R_2(\lambda) = \frac{3\lambda^2 + 5}{(16/3)\lambda}$$

$$= \frac{9}{16}\lambda + \frac{1}{(16/15)\lambda}$$

The full continued fraction is

$$R_1(\lambda) = \frac{1}{3}\lambda + \cfrac{1}{(9/16)\lambda + 1/(16/15)\lambda}$$

Here

$$\alpha_1 = \frac{1}{3}, \qquad \alpha_2 = \frac{9}{16}, \qquad \alpha_3 = \frac{16}{15}$$

Since all α_i are positive, Routh's theorem states that the zeros λ_ν of the polynomial (8) are in the left half-plane. In fact, the zeros are

$$\lambda_1 = -1, \qquad \lambda_2 = -1 + 2i, \qquad \lambda_3 = -1 - 2i$$

We will not prove Routh's theorem, which is not a theorem about matrices, but a theorem about polynomials. A proof and a thorough discussion appear in E. A. Guillemin's book, *The Mathematics of Circuit Analysis* (John Wiley and Sons, Inc., 1949) pp. 395–407. *If the* n × n *matrix* A *is real, and if* n *is small, Routh's theorem provides a practical criterion for the stability of the matrix* A. But if n is large, Routh's theorem is less useful because it is hard to compute accurately the coefficients of the characteristic polynomial. If the coefficients c_i are very inaccurate, there is no use in applying Routh's theorem to the wrong polynomial.

A second criterion, which applies directly to the matrix A, and which does not require that A be real, is due to *Lyapunov*.

Theorem 3. *The* n × n *matrix* A *is stable if and only if there is a positive definite Hermitian matrix* P *solving the equation*

$$PA + A^*P = -I \tag{9}$$

If n is large, this theorem is hard to use numerically. The system (9) presents a large number, $n(n + 1)/2$, of linear equations for the unknown components p_{ij} ($1 \leqslant i \leqslant j \leqslant n$). One must then verify that P is positive definite by the determinant criterion (see Section 6.5)

$$p_{11} > 0, \qquad \begin{vmatrix} p_{11} & p_{12} \\ p_{21} & p_{22} \end{vmatrix} > 0, \ldots, \det P > 0 \tag{10}$$

Because Lyapunov's theorem has great theoretical interest, we shall give the proof.

Proof. First assuming $PA + A^*P = -I$, we shall prove that A is stable. By Theorem 1, it will be sufficient to show that every solution of the differential equation $dx/dt = Ax$ tends to zero as $t \to \infty$. We have, for the solution $x(t)$,

$$\frac{d}{dt}(Px, x) = \left(P\frac{dx}{dt}, x\right) + \left(Px, \frac{dx}{dt}\right)$$

$$= (PAx, x) + (Px, Ax) \tag{11}$$

$$= ((PA + A^*P)x, x) = -(x, x)$$

Since P is positive definite, there is a number $\rho > 0$ for which

$$\rho(Pz, z) \leqslant (z, z) \qquad \text{(for all } z) \tag{12}$$

Then (11) yields

$$\frac{d}{dt}(Px, x) \leqslant -\rho(Px, x) \tag{13}$$

Therefore,

$$\frac{d}{dt}\left[e^{\rho t}(Px, x)\right] \leqslant 0 \tag{14}$$

If $x(0) = b$, we conclude that $e^{\rho t}(Px, x) \leqslant (Pb, b)$ for $t \geqslant 0$, and hence

$$(Px, x) \leqslant e^{-\rho t}(Pb, b) \to 0 \qquad \text{(as } t \to \infty) \tag{15}$$

But $(z, z) \leqslant \sigma(Pz, z)$ for some $\sigma > 0$. Therefore,

$$(x, x) \leqslant \sigma(Px, x) \to 0 \qquad \text{(as } t \to \infty) \tag{16}$$

which shows that $x \to 0$ as $t \to \infty$.

Conversely, supposing that A is stable, we shall construct the positive-definite matrix P solving $PA + A^*P = -I$. Let the $n \times n$ matrix $X(t)$ solve

$$\frac{dX}{dt} = A^*X, \qquad X(0) = I \tag{17}$$

As in the proof of Theorem 1, we know that every component of the matrix $X(t)$ is a linear combination of polynomials in t (possibly constants) times exponential functions $\exp \bar{\lambda}_v t$, where $\operatorname{Re} \bar{\lambda}_v = \operatorname{Re} \lambda_v < 0$. We bear in mind that the adjoint matrix A^* has the eigenvalues $\bar{\lambda}_v$ if A has the eigenvalues λ_v. Taking adjoints in (17), we find

$$\frac{dX^*}{dt} = X^*A, \qquad X^*(0) = I \tag{18}$$

Now the product $X(t)X^*(t)$ satisfies

$$\frac{d}{dt}(XX^*) = \frac{dX}{dt}X^* + X\frac{dX^*}{dt}$$
$$= A^*(XX^*) + (XX^*)A \tag{19}$$

Define the integral

$$P = \int_0^\infty X(t)X^*(t)\,dt \tag{20}$$

This integral converges because every component of the integrand has the form

$$\sum_{\nu=1}^n x_{i\nu}(t)\bar{x}_{j\nu}(t) \tag{21}$$

which is a linear combination of polynomials in t times decaying exponential functions. By integrating equation (19) from $t = 0$ to $t = \infty$, we find

$$-I = A^*P + PA \tag{22}$$

The left-hand side, $-I$, appears because XX^* equals I when $t = 0$ and equals zero when $t = \infty$. The matrix P is positive definite because the quadratic form belonging to a vector $z \neq 0$ equals

$$z^*Pz = \int_0^\infty z^*X(t)X^*(t)z\,dt = \int_0^\infty \| X^*(t)z \|^2\,dt > 0 \tag{23}$$

This completes the proof.

Lyapunov's theorem shows that, if a matrix A *is stable, then there is a family of ellipsoidal surfaces* (Pz, z) = const *relative to which every solution of* dx/dt = Ax *is constantly moving inward. In fact,* (11) *shows that*

$$\frac{d}{dt}(Px(t), x(t)) < 0 \qquad (\text{unless } x(t) \equiv 0) \tag{24}$$

A PRACTICAL NUMERICAL CRITERION

Let us suppose that A is an $n \times n$ matrix, not necessarily real, with n large. We will give a criterion for the stability of A which

(a) does not require explicit computation of the eigenvalues;
(b) does not require explicit computation of the coefficients of the characteristic polynomial; and
(c) does not require the solution of systems of N linear equations with $N \gg n$.

If A has eigenvalues $\lambda_1, \ldots, \lambda_n$, and if τ is any positive number, the numbers

$$\mu_j = \frac{\lambda_j + \tau}{\lambda_j - \tau} \qquad (j = 1, \ldots, n) \tag{25}$$

all lie in the unit circle $|\mu| < 1$ if and only if all the numbers λ_j lie in the left half-plane. This is evident from Figure 7.7.

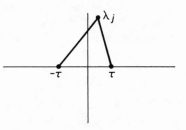

Figure 7.7

The absolute value $|\mu_j|$ equals the distance of λ_j from $-\tau$ divided by the distance of λ_j from τ. In the figure $\mathrm{Re}\,\lambda_j > 0$; therefore $|\mu_j| > 1$.

The numbers μ_j are the eigenvalues of the n $\times$ n *matrix*

$$B = (A - \tau I)^{-1}(A + \tau I) \tag{26}$$

unless $\tau =$ some λ_j. Proof:

$$
\begin{aligned}
\det(\lambda I - B) &= \det[\lambda I - (A - \tau I)^{-1}(A + \tau I)] \\
&= \det\{(\tau I - A)^{-1}[\lambda(\tau I - A) + (A + \tau I)]\} \\
&= [\det(\tau I - A)]^{-1}\det\left\{(\lambda - 1)\left[\frac{\tau(\lambda + 1)}{\lambda - 1}I - A\right]\right\} \\
&= \left[\prod_{j=1}^{n}(\tau - \lambda_j)\right]^{-1}(\lambda - 1)^n \prod_{j=1}^{n}\left(\frac{\tau(\lambda + 1)}{\lambda - 1} - \lambda_j\right) \\
&= \prod_{j=1}^{n}\left(\lambda - \frac{\lambda_j + \tau}{\lambda_j - \tau}\right) = \prod_{j=1}^{n}(\lambda - \mu_j)
\end{aligned}
$$

Assume that $\tau > 0$ has been chosen. The problem now is to determine whether all the eigenvalues μ_j of the matrix B lie inside the unit circle $|\mu| < 1$. By Theorem 3 in Section 4.9, all $|\mu_j| < 1$ if and only if

$$\lim_{k \to \infty} B^k = 0 \tag{27}$$

In principle, we could form the powers B^k, but we prefer not to do so because each multiplication of two $n \times n$ matrices requires n^3 scalar multiplications.

We prefer to form the iterates $B^k x^{(0)} = x^{(k)}$, where $x^{(0)}$ is some initial vector. As the vectors $x^{(0)}, x^{(1)}, x^{(2)}, \ldots$ are computed, we look at the successive lengths squared:

$$\sum_{\nu=1}^{n}|x_\nu^{(0)}|^2, \; \sum_{\nu=1}^{n}|x_\nu^{(1)}|^2, \; \ldots \tag{28}$$

If these numbers appear to be tending to zero, we infer that A is stable; if these numbers appear to be tending to infinity, we infer that A is unstable; if the numbers $\| x^{(k)} \|^2$ appear to be tending neither to 0 nor to ∞, we infer that A is stable or unstable by a very small margin. We will justify this procedure in Theorem 4.

If A is a stable *normal* matrix—e.g., a stable Hermitian matrix—the numbers (28) will form a monotone decreasing sequence. We see this from the expansion

$$x^{(0)} = \sum_{j=1}^{n} c_j u^j$$

of $x^{(0)}$ in the unit orthogonal eigenvectors u^j of A. The vectors u^j are also eigenvectors of B. Then

$$x^{(k)} = B^k x^{(0)} = \sum_{j=1}^{n} c_j \mu_j^k u^{(j)}$$

$$\sum_{\nu=1}^{n} | x_\nu^{(k)} |^2 = \sum_{j=1}^{n} | c_j |^2 | \mu_j |^{2k} \qquad (k = 0, 1, \ldots)$$

where all $| \mu_j | < 1$. If A is not a normal matrix, the sequence (28) will not usually be monotone.

How large should the number $\tau > 0$ be chosen? If τ is too small or too large, all of the eigenvalues

$$\mu_j = \frac{\lambda_j + \tau}{\lambda_j - \tau}$$

of B are near ± 1. If any λ_j has $\operatorname{Re} \lambda_j > 0$, we would like the modulus $| \mu_j |$ to be as large as possible. We assert that, if $\operatorname{Re} \lambda > 0$, then

$$\max_{\tau > 0} \left| \frac{\lambda + \tau}{\lambda - \tau} \right| \text{ is achieved when } \tau = | \lambda | \tag{29}$$

Proof. If $\lambda = \rho e^{i\theta}$, with $| \theta | < \pi/2$, we must show that

$$\left| \frac{\rho e^{i\theta} + \tau}{\rho e^{i\theta} - \tau} \right|^2 \leqslant \left| \frac{\rho e^{i\theta} + \rho}{\rho e^{i\theta} - \rho} \right|^2$$

This is true if

$$\frac{\rho^2 + 2\rho\tau \cos \theta + \tau^2}{\rho^2 - 2\rho\tau \cos \theta + \tau^2} \leqslant \frac{1 + \cos \theta}{1 - \cos \theta}$$

or if

$$0 \leqslant (2 \cos \theta)(\rho^2 - 2\rho\tau + \tau^2)$$

which is true, with equality only if $\tau = \rho$. If A is given, a reasonable first guess for the modulus, ρ, of an eigenvalue is

$$\tau = \frac{1}{n} \sum_{i=1}^{n} \sum_{j=1}^{n} |a_{ij}| \tag{30}$$

We find this value by summing

$$\left| \sum_{j=1}^{n} a_{ij}x_j \right| = |\lambda|\,|x_i| \qquad (i = 1, \ldots, n)$$

for $i = 1, \ldots, n$, and by falsely replacing all a_{ij} by $|a_{ij}|$ and all x_i by 1. *The number τ defined by (30) is of the right general size.*

Lemma. *Let* B *be an* n × n *matrix. Let* p *be a principal vector of grade* g ⩾ 1 *belonging to the eigenvalue* μ. *Then for large* k *we have the asymptotic forms*

$$B^k p = k^{g-1}\mu^{k-g+1}v + r^{(k)} \tag{31}$$

where v *is an eigenvector belonging to* μ *and where the remainder* $r^{(k)}$ *equals* 0 *if* g = 1 *or equals*

$$r^{(k)} = O(k^{g-2}|\mu|^k) \qquad (if\ g \geqslant 2) \tag{32}$$

Proof. By the notation (32) we mean that, for some constant $\gamma > 0$,

$$\| r^{(k)} \| \leqslant \gamma k^{g-2}|\mu|^k$$

If $g = 1$, then p is an eigenvector, $p = v$, and $r^{(k)} = 0$ in (31). If $g \geqslant 2$, we have for $k \geqslant g - 1$

$$B^k p = (B - \mu I + \mu I)^k p \tag{33}$$
$$= \mu^k p + k\mu^{k-1}(B - \mu I)p + \cdots +$$
$$\frac{k(k-1)\ldots(k-g+2)}{(g-1)!}\mu^{k-g+1}(B - \mu I)^{g-1}p$$

In the expansion by the binomial theorem, we have

$$(B - \mu I)^v p = 0 \qquad (if\ v \geqslant g)$$

for the principal vector p. The vector

$$v = \frac{1}{(g-1)!}(B - \mu I)^{g-1}p \neq 0$$

is an eigenvector because p has grade g. Since g is fixed as $k \rightarrow \infty$, we have

$$k(k-1) \ldots (k-g+2)\mu^{k-g+1} = k^{g-1}\mu^{k-g+1} + \mathrm{O}(k^{g-2}|\mu|^k) \quad (34)$$

For the other terms in (33) we have $r \leqslant g-2$ in the formula

$$\mu^{k-r}\frac{k(k-1) \ldots (k-r+1)}{r!}(B-\mu I)^r p = \mathrm{O}(k^{g-2}|\mu|^k) \quad (35)$$

The last three formulas yield the required asymptotic form (31).

In the following theorem, we shall use the phrase "with probability one," and we wish now to define the sense in which this phrase will be used. Consider an arbitrary nonzero n-component vector x. Let B be an $n \times n$ matrix with the different eigenvalues $\mu_1, \ldots, \mu_s$ with multiplicities $m_1, \ldots, m_s$, where $\sum m_i = n$. As we showed in Section 5.2, the vector x has a unique expansion

$$x = p^{(1)} + p^{(2)} + \cdots + p^{(s)} \quad (36)$$

in principal vectors $p^{(j)}$ belonging to the eigenvalues μ_j. In the last paragraph of Section 5.3 we concluded that the space of principal vectors $p^{(j)}$ has dimension m_j. Let Z_j be the linear space of vectors x for which $p^{(j)} = 0$ in the representation (36). Then the dimension of Z_j is $n - m_j < n$. Thus, Z_j has n-dimensional measure zero. The set Z of vectors x for which at least one $p^{(j)} = 0$ in the expansion (36), is the union

$$Z = Z_1 \cup Z_2 \cup \cdots \cup Z_s$$

of the sets Z_j, all of which have measure zero. Therefore, Z has measure zero. In this sense we say that, *with probability one*, all of the principal vectors $p^{(j)}$ are nonzero in the expansion (36) of a random vector x.

Theorem 4. *Let* B *be an* $n \times n$ *matrix. Let* $x = x^{(0)}$ *be a random vector. Let*

$$x^{(1)} = Bx^{(0)}, \qquad x^{(2)} = Bx^{(1)}, \qquad x^{(3)} = Bx^{(2)}, \ldots$$

Let $\mu_1, \mu_2, \ldots$ *be the eigenvalues of* B

Case 1. *If all* $|\mu_j| < 1$, *then* $x^{(k)} \rightarrow 0$ *as* $k \rightarrow \infty$.

Case 2. *If all* $|\mu_j| \leqslant 1$, *and if at least one* $|\mu_j| = 1$, *then with probability one the sequence* $x^{(k)}$ *does not tend to zero.*

Case 3. *If at least one* $|\mu_j| > 1$, *then with probability one* $\| x^{(k)} \| \rightarrow \infty$ *as* $k \rightarrow \infty$.

Proof. In Case 1 we know that $B^k \to O$ as $k \to \infty$, and therefore

$$x^{(k)} = B^k x \longrightarrow 0 \qquad (\text{as } k \to \infty)$$

Let $\mu_1, \ldots, \mu_s$ be the different eigenvalues of B, with multiplicities $m_1, \ldots, m_s$. Let

$$|\mu_1| = \cdots = |\mu_r| > |\mu_{r+1}| \geqslant \cdots \geqslant |\mu_s| \tag{37}$$

where $\sum m_i = n$ and $1 \leqslant r \leqslant s$. Form the expansion (36) of x as a sum $\sum p^{(j)}$ of principal vectors of B. With probability one *all* $p^{(j)} \neq 0$. In other words, with probability one every $p^{(j)}$ in the expansion $x = \sum p^{(j)}$ has grade $g_j \geqslant 1$. Then, by the preceding lemma,

$$\begin{aligned} x^{(k)} = B^k x &= \sum_{j=1}^{s} B^k p^{(j)} \\ &= \sum_{j=1}^{s} [k^{g_j-1} \mu_j^k v^{(j)} + O(k^{g_j-2} |\mu_j|^k)] \end{aligned} \tag{38}$$

where $v^{(1)}, \ldots, v^{(s)}$ are eigenvectors corresponding to $\mu_1, \ldots, \mu_s$. Let

$$g = \max (g_1, g_2, \ldots, g_r) \tag{39}$$

Let J be the set of integers j such that $1 \leqslant j \leqslant r$ and such that $g_j = g$. Then (38) yields

$$x^{(k)} = \sum_{j \in J} k^{g-1} \mu_j^k v^{(j)} + o(k^{g-1} \rho^k) \tag{40}$$

where $\rho = |\mu_1| = \cdots = |\mu_r|$. By the notation $o(k^{g-1}\rho^k)$ we mean any function of k such that

$$|o(k^{g-1}\rho^k)| \leqslant \epsilon_k k^{g-1} \rho^k \qquad (\text{where } \epsilon_k \to 0) \tag{41}$$

For all $j \in J$ we have $|\mu_j| = \rho$. Let

$$\mu_j = \rho e^{i\theta_j} \qquad (\text{for } j \in J) \tag{42}$$

where the angles θ_j are distinct numbers in the interval $0 \leqslant \theta < 2\pi$. In Cases 2 and 3 we assume $\rho \geqslant 1$. From (40) we have

$$x^{(k)} = k^{g-1} \rho^k \{ \sum_{j \in J} e^{ik\theta_j} v^{(j)} + o(1) \} \tag{43}$$

Eigenvectors $v^{(j)}$ belonging to different eigenvalues μ_j are linearly independent. Therefore, the minimum length

$$\delta = \min \| \sum_{j \in J} \alpha_j v^{(j)} \| \qquad (\text{for all } |\alpha_j| = 1) \tag{44}$$

is a positive number $\delta > 0$. Letting $\alpha_j = \exp(ik\theta_j)$ in (43), we find

$$\| x^{(k)} \| \geqslant k^{g-1}\rho^k[\delta - o(1)] \qquad \text{(as } k \to \infty)$$
$$\| x^{(k)} \| \geqslant k^{g-1}\rho^k(\tfrac{1}{2}\delta) \qquad \text{(for sufficiently large } k) \tag{45}$$

In Case 2 we have $\rho = 1$, and $\| x^{(k)} \| \to \infty$ if $g > 1$. If $g = 1$ and $\rho = 1$, then (43) shows that $x^{(k)}$ remains bounded but (45) shows that $x^{(k)}$ does not tend to zero. In Case 3 we have $\rho > 1$, and (45) shows that $\| x^{(k)} \| \to \infty$.

PROBLEMS

1. Let A be an $n \times n$ matrix. Let $\phi(\lambda)$ and $\psi(\lambda)$ be polynomials with real or complex coefficients. Suppose that $\psi(\lambda_j) \neq 0$ for all eigenvalues λ_j of A. Prove that the $n \times n$ matrix $\psi(A)$ has an inverse. Then prove that the eigenvalues of the matrix $[\psi(A)]^{-1}\phi(A)$ are $\mu_j = \phi(\lambda_j)/\psi(\lambda_j)$ $(j = 1, \dots, n)$. (First prove the result for triangular matrices T. Then use the canonical triangularization $A = UTU^*$.)

2. Find the Lyapunov ellipses $(Px, x) = \text{const}$ for the stable matrix

$$A = \begin{bmatrix} 1 & 8 \\ 2 & -3 \end{bmatrix}$$

3. Let A be any stable $n \times n$ matrix and let Q be any $n \times n$ positive-definite Hermitian matrix. Show that there is a positive-definite matrix P solving the equation $-Q = A^*P + PA$.

4. Let A be any stable $n \times n$ matrix. Let C be an arbitrary $n \times n$ matrix. Show that the equation $-C = A^*M + MA$ has a solution M. Since *every* equation $-C = A^*M + MA$ has a solution, M, deduce that the particular equation $-I = A^*P + PA$ has a *unique* solution, P.

5. Let $\lambda^3 + c_1\lambda^2 + c_2\lambda + c_3$ have real coefficients. According to the Routh-Hurwitz criterion, what inequalities are necessary and sufficient for the zeros of the polynomial to have negative real parts?

6. For the stable matrix A in Problem 2, compute the number τ in formula (30). Compute the matrix B in formula (26). What are the eigenvalues of B?

7. Let

$$A = \begin{bmatrix} -4 & 5 \\ -1 & 2 \end{bmatrix}$$

Compute the number τ and the matrix B. For which vectors x do the iterates $B^k x$ tend, in length, to infinity as $k \to \infty$? What is the probability, for a random vector x, that $\| B^k x \| \to \infty$ as $k \to \infty$?

7.14 ACCURATE UNITARY REDUCTION TO TRIANGULAR FORM

In the QR method of computing eigenvalues, we shall need an accurate way of reducing an $n \times n$ matrix A to a right-triangular matrix R by transformation

$$UA = R \tag{1}$$

Here we assume that A, U, and R are real or complex matrices, with

$$U^*U = I, \qquad r_{ij} = 0 \quad (\text{for } i > j) \tag{2}$$

In principle, we could perform this transformation by the Gram-Schmidt process described in Section 4.5. If the columns $a^1, \ldots, a^n$ of A were independent, we could form unit vectors $v^1, \ldots, v^n$ such that a^k would be a linear combination of $v^1, \ldots, v^k$.

$$a^k = r_{1k}v^1 + r_{2k}v^2 + \cdots + r_{kk}v^k \qquad (k = 1, \ldots, n) \tag{3}$$

In other words,

$$[a^1, \ldots, a^n] = [v^1, \ldots, v^n] \begin{bmatrix} r_{11} & r_{12} & \cdot & r_{1n} \\ 0 & r_{22} & \cdot & r_{2n} \\ 0 & 0 & \cdot & r_{3n} \\ \cdot & \cdot & \cdot & \cdot \\ 0 & 0 & \cdot & r_{nn} \end{bmatrix}$$

or

$$A = VR$$

Then we could take $U = V^*$ in (1). Unfortunately, the Gram-Schmidt process has been found to be highly inaccurate in digital computation. This inaccuracy is demonstrated in J. H. Wilkinson's book.[2]

In this section, we shall show how to perform the reduction $UA = R$ by a sequence of reflections

$$U_{n-1} \ldots U_2 U_1 A = R \tag{4}$$

where each U_j has the form $I - 2ww^*$, or where $U_j = I$. Here w is a unit vector depending on j. The matrices U_j are both unitary and Hermitian:

$$U_j^*U_j = I \quad \text{and} \quad U_j^* = U_j \tag{5}$$

[2] J. H. Wilkinson, *Rounding Errors in Algebraic Processes*. Englewood Cliffs, N.J.: Prentice-Hall, Inc., 1963, pp. 86–91.

The matrix U_j will produce zeros below the diagonal in column j; and U_j will not disturb the zeros which shall already have been produced in columns $1, \ldots, j - 1$. Thus, if $n = 4$,

$$U_1 A = \begin{bmatrix} x & x & x & x \\ 0 & x & x & x \\ 0 & x & x & x \\ 0 & x & x & x \end{bmatrix}$$

$$U_2 U_1 A = \begin{bmatrix} x & x & x & x \\ 0 & x & x & x \\ 0 & 0 & x & x \\ 0 & 0 & x & x \end{bmatrix}$$

$$U_3 U_2 U_1 A = \begin{bmatrix} x & x & x & x \\ 0 & x & x & x \\ 0 & 0 & x & x \\ 0 & 0 & 0 & x \end{bmatrix} = R$$

Let $A_1 = A$, and for $j > 1$ let

$$A_j = U_{j-1} \ldots U_1 A$$

Assume that A_j has zeros below the diagonal in columns $1, \ldots, j - 1$. Let the jth column of A_k have the form

$$c = \mathrm{col}\,(c_1, \ldots, c_j, c_{j+1}, \ldots, c_n) \tag{6}$$

Let

$$\beta = |c_{j+1}|^2 + \cdots + |c_n|^2 \tag{7}$$

If $\beta = 0$, then A_j already has zeros below the diagonal in column j, and we set $U_j = I$.

If $\beta > 0$, we look for U_j in the form

$$U_j = I - 2ww^* \tag{8}$$

We shall have

$$U_j c = c - 2w(w^*c) \tag{9}$$

For this vector to have zeros in components $j + 1, \ldots, n$, we must have $w_{j+1}, \ldots, w_n$ proportional to $c_{j+1}, \ldots, c_n$, since $2(w^*c)$ is simply a scalar.

Thus, we look for w in the form

$$w = \lambda \begin{bmatrix} 0 \\ \cdot \\ \cdot \\ \cdot \\ 0 \\ \mu \\ c_{j+1} \\ \cdot \\ \cdot \\ \cdot \\ c_n \end{bmatrix} \Bigg\} j \tag{10}$$

Then

$$2w^*c = 2\bar{\lambda}(\bar{\mu}c_j + \beta)$$

and U_jc will have zeros in components $j+1, \ldots, n$ if

$$2|\lambda|^2 (\bar{\mu}c_j + \beta) = 1 \tag{11}$$

For w to be a unit vector, we must have

$$|\lambda|^2 (|\mu|^2 + \beta) = 1 \tag{12}$$

Elimination of $|\lambda|^2$ from (11) and (12) gives

$$|\mu|^2 - 2c_j\bar{\mu} - \beta = 0 \tag{13}$$

If $c_j = |c_j| \exp(i\gamma_j)$, we will look for μ in the form $\mu = |\mu| \exp(i\gamma_j)$. Then (13) becomes

$$|\mu|^2 - 2|c_j||\mu| - \beta = 0$$

which has the positive solution

$$|\mu| = |c_j| + \sqrt{|c_j|^2 + \beta}$$

Then

$$\boxed{\mu = (|c_j| + \sqrt{|c_j|^2 + \beta})e^{i \arg c_j}} \tag{14}$$

Now (11) yields

$$2|\lambda|^2 = (|\mu||c_j| + \beta)^{-1}$$

and hence

$$2ww^* = (|\,\mu\,|\,|\,c_j\,| + \beta)^{-1} \begin{bmatrix} 0 \\ \cdot \\ \cdot \\ \cdot \\ 0 \\ \mu \\ c_{j+1} \\ \cdot \\ \cdot \\ \cdot \\ c_n \end{bmatrix} [0, \ldots, 0, \bar{\mu}, \bar{c}_{j+1}, \ldots, \bar{c}_n] \qquad (15)$$

Then $U_j = I - 2ww^*$.

We must show, finally, that multiplication by U_j does not disturb the zeros below the diagonal in columns $1, \ldots, j-1$. If z is any of the first $j-1$ columns of A_j, then $z_j = z_{j+1} = \cdots = z_n = 0$. Therefore,

$$\underbrace{[0, \ldots, 0, \bar{\mu}, \bar{c}_{j+1}, \ldots, \bar{c}_n]}_{j}z = 0$$

Now (15) shows that the first $j-1$ columns of A_j are not changed in the multiplication $U_j A_j$.

We also observe that, since $2ww^*$ has zeros in rows $1, \ldots, j-1$, the first $j-1$ rows of A_j are, likewise, not changed in the multiplication $U_j A_j$.

To perform the multiplication $U_j A_j$, we do *not* first form the matrix U_j. If x is the kth column of A_j $(k \geqslant j)$, then the kth column of the product $U_j A_j$ is

$$x = \frac{1}{|\,\mu c_j\,| + \beta} \begin{bmatrix} 0 \\ \cdot \\ \cdot \\ \cdot \\ 0 \\ \mu \\ c_{j+1} \\ \cdot \\ \cdot \\ \cdot \\ c_n \end{bmatrix} (\bar{\mu}x_j + \sum_{k=j+1}^{n} \bar{c}_k x_k) \qquad (16)$$

In real Euclidian space, the matrix $I - 2ww^*$ represents the easily-visualized geometric transformation in Figure 7.8. Through the origin there is a plane, π, to which w is a unit normal. The vector $(w^*x)w$ is the

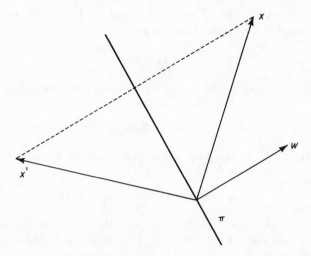

Figure 7.8

projection of x in the direction of w. If we subtract twice this projection from x, we obtain the vector

$$x' = x - 2(w^*x)w = (I - 2ww^*)x$$

which is the *reflection* of x through the plane π.

PROBLEMS

1. Let $\alpha, \beta, \gamma, \delta$ be real. Let

$$A = \begin{bmatrix} e^{i\alpha} & e^{i\beta} \\ e^{i\gamma} & e^{i\delta} \end{bmatrix}$$

Reduce A to right-triangular form by a transformation $(I - 2ww^*)A = R$.

2. Using the method described in this section, reduce the matrix

$$A = \begin{bmatrix} -3 & 1 & 1 \\ 0 & 1 & 2 \\ 4 & 1 & 3 \end{bmatrix}$$

to right-triangular form.

7.15 THE QR METHOD FOR COMPUTING EIGENVALUES

In this section we will present an introduction to the method of Francis and Kublanovskaya, known as the QR method. We wish to compute the eigenvalues of an $n \times n$ real or complex matrix A. By the method of the preceding section, we factor A in the form

$$A = Q_1 R_1 \tag{1}$$

where $Q_1 Q_1^* = I$ and where R_1 is right-triangular. Setting $A = A_1$, we now form

$$A_2 = R_1 Q_1 \tag{2}$$

We now factor A_2 in the form $A_2 = Q_2 R_2$, and we form $A_3 = R_2 Q_2$. In general,

$$\text{if } A_s = Q_s R_s, \qquad \text{then } A_{s+1} \equiv R_s Q_s \tag{3}$$

Under certain conditions on A, *as* s $\rightarrow \infty$ *the matrix* A_s *becomes a right-triangular matrix with the eigenvalues of* A *on the diagonal.* We will prove this convergence in the simplest case; we shall assume that A has eigenvalues with distinct moduli:

$$|\lambda_1| > |\lambda_2| > \cdots > |\lambda_n| > 0 \tag{4}$$

This proof and more general proofs have been given by Wilkinson.[3]

First, we discuss the transition from A_s to A_{s+1}. By the method of the preceding section, we can find unitary, Hermitian matrices $U_1, \ldots, U_{n-1}$, depending on s, such that

$$U_{n-1} \ldots U_2 U_1 A_s = R_s \tag{5}$$

Thus, $A_s = Q_s R_s$, where $Q_s = U_1 \ldots U_{n-1}$. Then

$$A_{s+1} = R_s U_1 U_2 \ldots U_{n-1} \tag{6}$$

The matrix Q_s is never computed explicitly, nor are the matrices U_j. We know that each U_j has the form

$$U_j = I \quad \text{or} \quad U_j = I - \zeta_j q^{(j)} q^{(j)*} \tag{7}$$

as in formula (15) of the preceding section. We do compute the scalars and vectors ζ_j and $q^{(j)}$, and by means of them we compute successively

$$U_1 A_s, U_2 U_1 A_s, \ldots, U_{n-1} \ldots U_1 A_s = R_s$$

Then we compute successively

$$R_s U_1, R_s U_1 U_2, \ldots, R_s U_1 \ldots U_{n-1} = A_{s+1} \tag{8}$$

[3] J. H. Wilkinson, "Convergence of the LR, QR, and related algorithms," *The Computer Journal*, vol. 8 (1965), 77–84.

Every product $X(I - \zeta qq^*)$ occurring in (8) is computed as $X - \zeta yq^*$, where $y = Xq$.

We shall now study the *uniqueness* and the *continuity* of QR factorizations.

Lemma 1. *Let A be a nonsingular matrix with two* QR *factorizations*

$$A = Q_1 R_1 = Q_2 R_2 \tag{9}$$

where the Q's *are unitary and the* R's *are right-triangular. Then there is a diagonal matrix of the form*

$$E = \text{diag}\,(e^{i\theta_1}, \ldots, e^{i\theta_n}) \tag{10}$$

such that

$$Q_2 = Q_1 E^* \quad \text{and} \quad R_2 = E R_1 \tag{11}$$

Proof. First suppose that $Q = R$, where

$$Q^*Q = I, \qquad r_{ii} > 0, \qquad r_{ij} = 0 \quad (\text{for } i > j) \tag{12}$$

Then $I = Q^*Q = R^*R$. The first row of R^*R is

$$r_{11}(r_{11}, r_{12}, \ldots, r_{1n})$$

Therefore,

$$r_{11} = 1, \qquad r_{12} = 0, \ldots, \qquad r_{1n} = 0 \tag{13}$$

Since $r_{12} = 0$, the second row of R^*R is

$$r_{22}(0, r_{22}, r_{23}, \ldots, r_{2n})$$

Therefore,

$$r_{22} = 1, \qquad r_{23} = 0, \ldots, \qquad r_{2n} = 0$$

Continuing in this way, we verify that $r_{ij} = \delta_{ij}\,(i, j = 1, \ldots, n)$. Therefore, $Q = R = I$.

If $A = Q_1 R_1 = Q_2 R_2$, where A is nonsingular, then R_1^{-1} exists and

$$Q_2^* Q_1 = R_2 R_1^{-1} \tag{14}$$

If the diagonal elements of the right-triangular matrix $R_2 R_1^{-1}$ have arguments $\theta_1, \ldots, \theta_n$, and if E is defined by (10), then the matrices

$$Q \equiv Q_2^* Q_1 E^*, \qquad R \equiv R_2 R_1^{-1} E^*$$

satisfy the conditions (12), and $Q = R$. Therefore, $Q = R = I$, and the identities $Q_2 = Q_1 E^*$, $R_2 = E R_1$ follow.

Lemma 2. *Let* $A_k \to I$ *as* $k \to \infty$. *Let* $A_k = Q_k R_k$, *where* Q_k *is unitary, and where* R_k *is right-triangular with positive-diagonal elements. Then* $Q_k \to I$ *and* $R_k \to I$ *as* $k \to \infty$.

Proof. We have

$$R_k^* R_k = A_k^* A_k \longrightarrow I \qquad (\text{as } k \to \infty)$$

Let $r_{ij}(k)$ be the i, j component of R_k. The first row of $R_k^* R_k$ is

$$r_{11}(k)[r_{11}(k), r_{12}(k), \ldots, r_{1n}(k)]$$

Hence,

$$r_{11}(k) \longrightarrow 1, \qquad r_{12}(k) \longrightarrow 0, \ldots, r_{1n}(k) \longrightarrow 0 \qquad (15)$$

The second row of $R_k^* R_k$ is

$$\bar{r}_{12}(k) \cdot (\text{first row of } R_k) + r_{22}(k) \cdot [0, r_{22}(k), r_{23}(k), \ldots, r_{2n}(k)]$$

Using the first result (15), we conclude that

$$r_{22}(k) \longrightarrow 1, \qquad r_{23}(k) \longrightarrow 0, \ldots, r_{2n}(k) \longrightarrow 0 \qquad (16)$$

Continuing by successive rows in this way, we conclude that $R_k \to I$ as $k \to \infty$. The explicit form of the inverse $R_k^{-1} = (\det)^{-1} \cdot (\text{cofactor matrix})^T$ now shows that $R_k^{-1} \to I$, and hence also $Q_k = A_k R_k^{-1} \to I$ as $k \to \infty$.

Lemma 3. *If* $Q_1, Q_2, \ldots$ *are unitary, and if* $R_1, R_2, \ldots$ *are right-triangular, and if*

$$A_1 = Q_1 R_1, \qquad A_s = R_{s-1} Q_{s-1} = Q_s R_s \quad (s > 1) \qquad (17)$$

then, for s = 2, 3, \ldots,

$$A_1^s = Q_1 Q_2 \ldots Q_s R_s \ldots R_2 R_1 \qquad (18)$$

and

$$A_s = (Q_1 \ldots Q_{s-1})^* A_1 (Q_1 \ldots Q_{s-1}) \qquad (19)$$

Proof. The identities (17) imply that

$$R_1 Q_1 Q_2 \ldots Q_s = Q_2 R_2 Q_2 \ldots Q_s = \cdots = Q_2 Q_3 \ldots Q_{s+1} R_{s+1}$$

Therefore, if (18) is true for any s, we have

$$A_1^{s+1} = Q_1 R_1 Q_1 \ldots Q_s R_s \ldots R_1 = Q_1 Q_2 \ldots Q_{s+1} R_{s+1} R_s \ldots R_1$$

Since (18) is true for $s = 1$, it is true for all s.

Formula (19) also follows by induction from (17), since

$$A_s = R_{s-1}Q_{s-1} = Q^*_{s-1}(Q_{s-1}R_{s-1})Q_{s-1} = Q^*_{s-1}A_{s-1}Q_{s-1}$$

Theorem 1. *Let* A_1 *be an* n × n *matrix with eigenvalues* λ_j *such that* $|\lambda_1| > |\lambda_2| > \cdots > |\lambda_n| > 0$. *Let* A_1 *have a canonical diagonalization*

$$A_1 = XDX^{-1} \tag{20}$$

where $D = \text{diag}\,(\lambda_1, \ldots, \lambda_n)$. *Assume that all of the* n *principal minors of the matrix* $Y = X^{-1}$ *are nonsingular:*

$$y_{11} \neq 0, \quad \begin{vmatrix} y_{11} & y_{12} \\ y_{21} & y_{22} \end{vmatrix} \neq 0, \ldots, \det Y \neq 0 \tag{21}$$

Let matrices $A_2, A_3, \ldots$ *be formed by the* QR *method* (17). *Then there is a sequence of diagonal matrices* $E_1, E_2, \ldots$ *of the form* (10) *such that*

$$E^*_s A_{s+1} E_s \longrightarrow R_X D R_X^{-1} \quad (\text{as } s \to \infty) \tag{22}$$

where the matrix R_X *is right-triangular.*

In this sense, A_s tends to a right-triangular matrix with the eigenvalues of A, in order, appearing on the main diagonal.

Proof. As we proved in Section 7.3, the condition (21) is necessary and sufficient for the matrix $Y = X^{-1}$ to have a decomposition $Y = L_Y R_Y$, where L_Y is left-triangular, where R_Y is right-triangular, and where L_Y has 1's on the main diagonal. Then

$$D^s X^{-1} = D^s Y = D^s L_Y R_Y$$

But

$$D^s L_Y D^{-s} \longrightarrow I \quad (\text{as } s \to \infty) \tag{23}$$

since the elements above the diagonal are zero, while the elements on the diagonal are 1's, and the elements below the diagonal satisfy

$$\lambda_i^s l_{ij} \lambda_j^{-s} \longrightarrow 0 \quad (\text{as } s \to \infty) \quad (i > j) \tag{24}$$

Let X have the factorization $X = Q_X R_X$, where Q_X is unitary and R_X is right-triangular. Then

$$\begin{aligned} A_1^s &= XD^s Y \\ &= Q_X R_X D^s L_Y R_Y \\ &= Q_X R_X (D^s L_Y D^{-s}) D^s R_Y \\ &= Q_X J_s \cdot R_X D^s R_Y \end{aligned} \tag{25}$$

where

$$J_s = R_X(D^s L_Y D^{-s}) R_X^{-1} \longrightarrow I \qquad (\text{as } s \to \infty)$$

Since $J_s \to I$ as $s \to \infty$, J_s has a QR factorization

$$J_s = \hat{Q}_s \hat{R}_s \qquad (\text{with } \hat{Q}_s \to I \quad \text{and} \quad \hat{R}_s \to I) \tag{26}$$

where $\hat{Q}_s$ is unitary and $\hat{R}_s$ is right-triangular; that follows from Lemma 2. Then A_1^s has the QR decomposition

$$A_1^s = (Q_X \hat{Q}_s)(\hat{R}_s R_X D^s R_Y) \tag{27}$$

But Lemma 3 gives the QR decomposition

$$A_1^s = (Q_1 \ldots Q_s)(R_s \ldots R_1)$$

Now Lemma 1 states that there is a matrix E_s of the form (10) such that

$$Q_1 \ldots Q_s = Q_X \hat{Q}_s E_s^* \tag{28}$$

Now the identity (19) for A_s yields

$$A_{s+1} = (Q_1 \ldots Q_s)^* A_1 (Q_1 \ldots Q_s)$$
$$= E_s \hat{Q}_s^* Q_X^* A_1 Q_X \hat{Q}_s E_s^*$$

But

$$A_1 = XDX^{-1} = Q_X R_X D R_X^{-1} Q_X^*$$

Therefore,

$$A_{s+1} = E_s \hat{Q}_s^* R_X D R_X^{-1} \hat{Q}_s E_s^*$$

and

$$E_s^* A_{s+1} E_s \longrightarrow R_X D R_X^{-1} \qquad (\text{as } s \to \infty) \tag{29}$$

This is the justification of the QR method in the simplest case. It is possible to remove the restriction that X^{-1} have nonsingular principal minors. It is even possible to remove the restriction that the eigenvalues of A have distinct moduli. If the moduli are not distinct, the matrices A_s tend to block-right-triangular matrices, where each $m \times m$ block centered on the diagonal is an $m \times m$ matrix whose m eigenvalues are eigenvalues of equal moduli belonging to A. The theory underlying this method is surprisingly difficult.

The idea for the QR method came, no doubt, from an older method due to Rutishauser:

$$A_1 = L_1 R_1, \qquad A_s = R_{s-1} L_{s-1} = L_s R_s \quad (s = 2, 3, \ldots) \qquad (30)$$

where $L_1, L_2, \ldots$ are left-triangular and $R_1, R_2, \ldots$ are right-triangular.

PROBLEMS

In the following problems, assume that all matrices L are left-triangular matrices with 1's on the main diagonal, and that all matrices R are right-triangular matrices.

1. If $A = L_1 R_1 = L_2 R_2$, and if A is nonsingular, prove that $L_1 = L_2$ and $R_1 = R_2$.

2. If $A_k = L_k R_k \to I$ as $k \to \infty$, prove that $L_k \to I$ and $R_k \to I$.

3. If A_1 is a nonsingular matrix, and if

$$A_1 = L_1 R_1, \qquad A_s = R_{s-1} L_{s-1} = L_s R_s \quad (s = 2, 3, \ldots)$$

prove that

$$A_1^s = L_1 \ldots L_s R_s \ldots R_1$$
$$A_{s+1} = (L_1 \ldots L_s)^{-1} A_1 (L_1 \ldots L_s)$$

4.* Let A_1 satisfy the conditions of Theorem 1. Assume that matrices $A_2, A_3, \ldots$ can be formed as in the last problem. Show that, as $s \to \infty$, A_s tends to a right-triangular matrix whose diagonal elements are the eigenvalues of A_1.

INDEX